"*My Baby Can Dance* is one of the most hopeful books yet on the treatment of ASD. The success of the approach — as beautifully told in a series of personal accounts by families and RDI Certified Consultants — lies in taking a whole systems orientation in which all family members become committed participants. Coupled with the ability of RDI to harness the inherently creative power of open family communication, what emerges is an intense drama of love, patience, and a deepening appreciation of the humanity we all share."

—**Alan Fogel**, author of *Developing Through Relationships*

"Families that include a child with autism or Asperger's likely will connect with the 12 families chronicled in a new book by Steven Gutstein, a nationally respected expert on autism who wrote *Autism/Aspergers: Solving the Relationship Puzzle*, published six years ago. The new book, *My Baby Can Dance*, tells stories of how the dozen families were changed by their experiences and learned to handle the challenges of having a child with autism."

—**Ellen Tomson**, Pioneer Press

"RDI is a philosophy of treatment which focuses not on symptoms but on relationships. It emphasizes personal strengths, and not just weaknesses. And it empowers families to work with their children with confidence, using ingenious approaches under the guidance of well-trained consultants. I especially like RDI because it is based on sound principles of social communication development. My Baby Can Dance is a book for all parents and therapists who wish to learn more about RDI. Eleven families and their consultants tell us, in diary form, of their ongoing everyday experiences using RDI: their anguish, hopes, triumphs, set-backs, and occasional break-through. The stories are poignant, but the parents seem buoyed with hope that the road-map they have been given for working with their child will lead to his or her having a better life. Every parent of a newly diagnosed child with autism should read this book."

—**Peter E. Tanguay, M.D.**
Ackerly Endowed Professor of Child and Adolescent Psychiatry (Emeritus)
University of Louisville, Louisville, Kentucky

"The stories that unfold in *My Baby Can Dance* are testament to the magic of what can be accomplished with the a set of deceptively simple ingredients: patience, tenacity, common sense and a sense of respect and curiosity about how our children with autism think, learn and experience the world. The families who share their experiences in *My Baby Can Dance* show us that RDI®, whose very core ingredient is love, can for some children be powerful and wondrously effective. Family-based and non-invasive, RDI's gentle and sensible approach is one that should be considered first, rather than after other treatments or therapies have failed."

—**Ellen Notbohm**
author of *Ten Things Every Child with Autism Wishes You Knew*

My Baby Can Dance

Also by Steve Gutstein

Autism Apsergers: Solving the Relationship Puzzle (2000)

Can My Baby Learn to Dance? Friendship Development in Adolescents with Asperger's Syndrome. In Willey, H. *Asperger's Syndrome in Adolescence* (2003)

Going to the Heart of Autism: The Relationship Development Intervention® Program - DVD (2004)

Relationship Development Intervention with Children, Adolescents and Adults: Social and Emotional Development Activities for Asperger Syndrome, Autism, PDD and NLD (2002)

Relationship Development Intervention with Young Children: Social and Emotional Development Activities for Asperger Syndrome, Autism, PDD and NLD (2002)

My Baby Can Dance

Stories of Autism, Asperger's and Success through the Relationship Development Intervention® (RDI®) Program

Introduction by Steven E. Gutstein

Edited by Steven E. Gutstein, Hannah R. Gutstein and Carlotta Baird

Connections Center Publishing
Houston, Texas USA

For information on ordering from Connections Center Publishing, please contact us by phone 713.838.1362, fax 713.838.1447 or email baird@rdiconnect.com

www.rdiconnect.com

Library of Congress Control Number: 2006920754

ISBN 0-9777186-0-3

Established in 1995 and led by Drs. Steven Gutstein and Rachelle Sheely, the Connections Center is the primary development, training and education center for the Relationship Development Intervention® (RDI®) Program to families and professional worldwide. RDI is a family-based remediation program for individuals with Autism Spectrum Disorder. More information about RDI is available at www.rdiconnect.com.

Table of Contents

We would like to thank all of the families and professionals who wrote about the realities of their lives in the hope that it would inspire others who may have lost faith in their own dreams. More meaningful than a story that ends with 'happily ever after' is the recognition of how far you have come and the miracle of who you are today.

Introduction

by Steven E. Gutstein, Ph.D.

These are the stories of 12 families, each with a child on the autism spectrum. Their accounts do not describe breakthroughs and cures. Rather they are the chronicles of small miracles. These parents want the real thing for their son or daughter; a good job, independent living and intimate friendships. And then they want to reach even further; they want to look forward to being grandparents and believe that their son or daughter will someday make a great husband, wife, father or mother. They continue to believe in the power of family.

When this book was initially conceived, it was envisioned as a beginning step for parents considering the RDI® treatment program for autism spectrum disorders. I wanted a book that would reveal the true texture of everyday family life with a child on the autism spectrum. But, what I slowly realized as I read the book was that these stories transcend autism. They are stories for those struggling with any disability and handicap, searching for inspiration.

The boys and girls within these chapters are a diverse group. They range from pre-school to high school ages and attend private schools, public schools and home schools. Some have been speaking since they were infants, and some are just starting to talk. They are children with superior IQ's and others that have severe learning disabilities. Some have gentle easy-going temperaments, while others have been a challenge since day one. They are from a variety of cultures, ethnic groups and geographic regions of North America.

Despite their diversity they are united by their experience. Before the age of two, they all found the world an incomprehensible and terrifying place. They retreated from change, novelty and challenge. They lost the desire to explore and discover and continually broaden their world. They lost all but the most basic ways of emotionally connecting with those around them. They did the best they could to make sense of the perceived chaos around them. To avoid change, they created never-changing, safe "micro-environments" where they could stare at spinning fans or watch trains go round and round and feel safe in the predictable world of sameness. They asked the same questions over and over, not because they forgot the answers, but because of the comfort of knowing that each time they would receive a familiar response and be comforted that the world was, at least for a moment, a predictable place.

They are also united in their basic humanity. No matter how they are depicted in the media, they are not aliens from another planet. They are not some other species. They are our children; our flesh and blood and as such are born with the same basic desires and motivations that make our species unique from all others. They are born with the desire to grow and discover. They are born with the drive to seek out challenges. And, most importantly, they are born with the powerful need to be emotionally and socially connected to others. For each of these children, the neurological disorder that is ASD (Autism Spectrum Disorder) led to the abandonment of these basic human motivations. That is the tragedy they share.

Now they share something else. They are all becoming less afraid of exploring their worlds. They are learning to enjoy change and novelty and not be threatened by it. They are learning that the world can be a place where they can feel competent, despite the constant variations and unexpected events that characterize daily life. They are all connected to their family's daily emotional life. They strive to share their experiences with others in every setting and look forward to expanding their universe and surmounting new challenges.

Parents along with their children are regaining a feeling of competence. Parenting a child with ASD is like being a blind captain of a sailboat with a blind crew. It doesn't matter how good a captain you are. If you cannot see the impact of your actions on the direction of the boat, if you cannot observe the currents and waves, if you cannot monitor the conditions of your sails, your craft will inevitably founder.

The goal of the Relationship Development Intervention® Program (RDI)* is to return parents to their natural role as captains of the developmental ship. And like many captains, there are officers-in-training, future captains on board, who must be prepared to some day assume command of their own vessel. But, none of this is possible if a family member is forgotten or left behind.

The husbands and wives depicted in these chapters have recognized the need to strengthen their intimacy and go on regular dates. They have learned to leave their sense of desperation behind and through their mutual support; determine that they will reach their goals in a pace that best fits all family members. Similarly, non-autistic siblings are provided with the time and devotion they need as individuals, as well as the experience of achieving a real relationship with their ASD sibling; a relationship that is a two-way-street and where genuine respect and enjoyment takes the place of pity and compassion. Fathers, who have largely been orphaned in the autism community, are equally involved as mothers. They experience the feeling of being valued for the essential moments of guidance and support that they can uniquely offer.

This all comes about under the guidance of a consultant. And our consultants are as unique as the children they work with. They range in age from "twenty-something's" to grandparents. Some come to training with over 30 years of experience in the field. Others have just completed college. Currently we have three husband-wife and two mother-daughter consultant teams who are constructing their RDI® Certified Consultant careers as a joint family effort. Consultants come from all over the globe, from Japan and Australia to Canada and Mexico. They have been trained in every discipline. They are physicians, psychologists, speech pathologists, occupational and physical therapists and applied behavior analysts. Several come from occupations that are completely removed from autism. A number are parents of a child on the spectrum who, excited by the gains they themselves made with their children, determined that they would devote their lives to bringing this hope to others.

They have several things in common. They chose to make financial and personal sacrifices to train as an RDI® Program Certified Consultant; a process that typically takes almost two years. They recognize that they are part of a developing, worldwide community united in the belief that people with ASD deserve a second chance to obtain a quality of life*. Most importantly to me, they all went against the grain and took a courageous leap into the unknown.

For those unfamiliar with our approach, you will learn that RDI is not a cookbook method, but rather an ongoing developing process, anchored by a set of ideas, clear goals and frameworks for reaching those goals. The techniques of RDI are and will remain a work in progress, while the idea of finding a way for each child with ASD to grow into an adult possessing the abilities to have a full quality of life will not change. Central in RDI is the belief that every individual with ASD, regardless of their age, strengths or weaknesses, deserves the opportunity for a second chance at mastering the foundational abilities that are essential building blocks of later competence.

I have long viewed autism as the loss of ability to engage in the numerous, constantly evolving dances that form the basis of human relationships. Infants and parents begin their simple but elegant dances at birth. By three months of age, infants are synchronizing their attention and sounds with parents. By 6 months they are active participants in early infant games like peek-a-boo. By 18 months they have become full-fledged partners in coordinating their actions with familiar adults. The dances of social relationship have their own critical value, but the special dances between parents serving as both guides and participants and their children, playing the role of the apprentice, learning to perceive meaning through the eyes of the adult guide, have a second unique function. They form the crucible for development of the mind*.

1

Feel Like I Got My Baby Back

by Carmen Gendel, LCSW & Dana and Barry Craven

Things Never Go Exactly as Planned
Introduction

It is an old adage that things don't always go exactly as you plan. In fact, it's a very rare occasion that they do. I was thinking about this as I knocked on Dana and Barry's door for a long planned meeting to talk about their son Jason. I was apprehensive about how the meeting would go. When Dana opened the door, I immediately sensed something was not right. She wasn't quite herself and she softly told me, "I want to tell our story. It's a good story but, you know, sometimes things happen."

"Jason is in a wheelchair today, because he fell," Dana revealed and as I recovered from my shock, Dana explained what happened shortly after our RDI® session the previous week. Apparently he fell the way children fall every day; this particular fall resulted in a severely fractured thighbone and required more than just a cast to heal. Jason's thigh needed surgery, a metal plate, and a healing period that would require him to lay prone and not place any pressure on his leg for at least four weeks.

Imagine those restrictions for any running and bouncing 5 year old boy and then imagine them for a 5 year old boy with Autism Spectrum Disorder*

(ASD) who can't describe his needs, his pain and his fears. Dana and Barry were already enormously stressed by Jason and their older son David, who also has autism. Could this be the last straw on their proverbial back?

As I entered the home, Jason was busy coloring while sitting in his wheelchair. When I approached, he looked up and gave me the big smile I've become used to, coupled this time with a brief flash of confusion, perhaps expressing, "You don't expect me to go bouncing around with you as usual today, do you?" He shifted his gaze over to his mom, who assured him I was just there for a visit with her. Dana and I chose a place to sit and talk; where we could be in easy visual range of Jason and his older brother.

We began talking amidst a flurry of activity, constantly shifting attention between both boys, while telling, remembering and embracing Jason's story. And, though things often don't go exactly as planned, during our conversations, I would hear the painful and rewarding story of how Dana and Barry lost and then got their baby back.

The Second Baby will be the Easy One
Jason's First Year

Jason is Dana and Barry's second child. His older brother, David, was diagnosed with autism when Dana was six months pregnant with Jason. Naturally, both Dana and Barry were devastated by David's diagnosis. They allowed themselves a brief period of immobilization before proceeding down a road filled with therapists, doctors, diet consultants, biomedical interventions and medications. Further complicating the situation, were Dana's concerns about the effects of this stress on her unborn child and what his or her life would be like having a sibling with autism.

David was a very difficult baby and as he was not easily consoled, sleep was hard to come by for both parents. "His energy was endless; he was constant motion. I remember wondering how all this would effect a new baby." Dana said, "What was supposed to be a very joyful time of anticipation was peppered with worry. My mother, who was my constant support and a soft place to land, reassured Barry and me that our second baby would be the easy one. I always remembered those words."

We Knew Waiting Rooms
Mom and Dad's Early Recollections - Dana

I prayed that Jason would be my easy baby; he'll love to sleep and to be held. Within days of Jason's birth, it was clear this was not to be.

Jason cried in the hospital and could not be consoled. He seemed in perpetual distress. He could not fall asleep. He was fussy, irritable and experienced stomach problems. I don't remember him being happy and content in that first year. We tried everything to calm him down. We'd turn the water on in the shower and bath or push him in the stroller back and forth. I would put him in a front carrier and walk with him for what seemed like hours. Sometimes these efforts worked, but usually not.

We were running ragged, back and forth between two children who were incredibly needy, crying, fussy, never sleeping and never on a schedule. Jason would wake up at least every hour and would need to be rocked or placed in a stroller to fall back asleep.

In those early months, Jason would scream in pain and after a while he was diagnosed with acid reflux. We got medication for that, which helped a little bit, but I think our primary and never-ending mission was to help Jason calm down.

No one in the house was on a schedule. From the very beginning, we were trying to get the boys regulated and wishing one of them, at least, could fall asleep by himself. Though we loved him endlessly, we thought Jason must feel miserable almost all the time. What else could explain all the crying?

When Jason finally would fall asleep, we would breathe a sigh of relief, but then he would be up again 20 minutes or, at most, an hour later. During the day, it was hard to get him to nap. This was especially difficult because we were on David's therapy circuit during the day and this prevented Jason from having extended quiet times.

From the time he was 2 weeks old, in the middle of winter, Jason was being schlepped. If I was lucky, Jason would fall asleep in the car - if I was having the luckiest day of my life, I could place him in the stroller and he would continue to sleep while David was in therapy. Otherwise, I would spend the hour trying to soothe him. Jason was more likely to remain calm in the stroller while I pushed him back and forth endlessly. It could make for a very long hour. I knew many, many waiting rooms too well and Barry and I began to realize we were living a life very different from the one we had both imagined and planned.

Lightning Doesn't Strike Twice
Developmental Vigilance - Dana

I clearly remember the first time I voiced my concerns that Jason may have autism to our pediatrician. He said, "Lightning doesn't strike twice." For obvious reasons, we were vigilant to autism. The possibility Jason could develop autism was on our minds from day one. But he presented differently from David; he wasn't as active and I thought he'd be okay. There was also so much going on during Jason's first year, there wasn't a lot of time to think or reflect on things. We just lived life minute to minute.

Jason did reach all of his physical milestones, but he didn't babble. He had the social smile, but it came later than most babies and we didn't see it all that often. In retrospect, we were just trying to get through the day. We had so little sleep; I don't think we could think straight. It was a full time job to just keep them both calm. We were just trying to get through it all.

I did try to get Jason engaged in playful interactions. Sometimes we would get something going, but just for a second or two. As a mother and a father, you want to engage your babies in those little games of tickle, peek-a-boo, this little piggy and how big is baby? We tried all those things and hundreds more, but neither of our babies could respond.

I didn't know why my attempts to engage Jason weren't working. Was it his stomach? Was he tired? Was he hungry? I do remember once, when he was 3 or 4 months old, he smiled at me when I came near him in the stroller and I thought for a minute, "Oh, he's okay!" Then his gaze would avert and there was nothing I could do to get it back. It was heartbreaking to realize only a minute later that he wasn't okay. I think it was that feeling that led me to share my concerns with the kids' pediatrician. The pediatrician assured us that Jason was developing normally and that some children are simply fussy babies.

Neither of the children made noises aside from screaming, crying and fussing. Barry and I tried so many things. We kept holding them, tickling them, talking and singing to them, playing little games. We just persevered and I think that helped over time to make Jason and David feel more secure somehow. We supported each other through the difficult times of limited response from both the boys.

People would tell us to let them cry, but we just couldn't. We knew we had to hold on and in our hearts we knew they had to find their comfort in us. We were their parents. I think we did the right thing. I now know we did.

I Couldn't Shake the Feeling
The Therapist's Observations - Carmen

As Dana says this, David is sitting sweetly in her lap and Jason is glancing frequently at her from his wheelchair. To see this small success is simultaneously heartbreaking and wonderful.

I have worked with children with autism and their families for 23 years. I have had parents, especially mothers, share their worries about siblings born subsequent to having an older child diagnosed with autism. There is almost never a sense of total relaxation in the first two years of the new baby's life.

I knew Jason's family because his brother David received Speech and Language services in our clinic. And, though not my client, Dana's outgoing and sweet personality made her a very welcome presence in the office. She was and continues to be an inspiration to all the parents who share waiting room time with her. Everyone in the office anxiously waited for the call to cancel David's appointment because of the new baby's birth. When it finally came, it was just two short weeks until Dana was back, bringing David to his speech session with Jason in tow.

Jason was and is a beautiful boy. More often than not, he would come into the office in his stroller, with Dana pushing him back and forth during his brother's therapy hour. Though you could never tell from Dana, I remembered thinking Jason wasn't an easy-going baby. I thought of him as an "egg-shell" baby, one who caused you to tread very carefully, so as to not upset him. I recall thinking I hadn't observed Jason engaging in back and forth babbling, cooing, or smiling like most babies. I dismissed it as limited observation and yet…I couldn't really shake the feeling that something was wrong with this beautiful little boy.

I Guess We Knew It
Diagnosis - Dana

We did fear that he had autism, but then I had these shreds of hope. I almost hoped that it was something I had done. Maybe the stress of having a sibling with autism had somehow affected him and our ability to parent. I hoped that maybe it was me, because then we could do something about it. So there I was talking myself in and out of autism. I don't think it was denial, I knew it was something, but I was hoping it was emotional and not neurological.

By his first birthday, Jason was a much calmer baby. He was content to sit alone. He didn't have the hyperactivity of his brother, but he didn't seek us out either. He didn't engage in those early baby games and wasn't babbling. Remarkably, he was a quiet toddler.

We sought the advice of a developmental social worker. She did not give him a formal diagnosis, but she did feel he had developmental delays. She recommended that we begin speech therapy, which we did. Both the speech therapist and our family therapist, who later became our RDI® Consultant recommended that we have Jason evaluated for autism.

Jason was formally diagnosed at 19 months. When we were in the office and got the diagnosis, our reaction was much more reserved than with David. I thought, "Okay, I guess we knew it." We were prepared in some way.

Carmen

At the time of Jason's diagnosis, I was working with Dana and Barry on parenting strategies for the boys. The family was ready to move out of crisis mode and get their life back.

They wanted to create a life for their boys that had some routine to it. They wanted to start having normal expectations of their children including: having a regular and reasonable bedtime, eating a meal at the table, toilet training, and walking hand in hand to the car. If they could do these tasks, they figured there would be plenty of time and reason for joy and laughter. Looking back we were steering right towards RDI, but we didn't know it at the time. It was during this period Barry and Dana asked me if I thought Jason had autism and I shared similar suspicions.

Jason was 12 months old when we began family therapy and I had never had the professional opportunity to observe a child this young. While he didn't present with the overtly stereotyped autistic behaviors of his brother, the jumping, flapping and squeals of delight and frustration, Jason presented with behaviors that I know now represent the core deficits* of autism. For example, he didn't gaze at his parents' faces, initiate interactions or imitate. He also didn't orient to his mother's voice or approach either parent face to face. He would approach both from the side or climb on their backs.

Because of their ongoing struggles with David, I wanted to believe there might be some other explanation for this. Like the pediatrician, I was hoping lightning wouldn't strike twice.

If You Think Something Will Help…
The Therapy Maze - Dana

Unfortunately, we were all too familiar with therapy by the time it was recommended that Jason receives speech therapy. We began work with David's speech therapist. In between, we did a whole lot of things for both the boys and I'm sure as I list these, I'm leaving something out. We did the gluten casein free diet, but we didn't stay on it long. Jason was losing weight and we didn't feel it was working. He has been on vitamins and supplements. We have done some biomedical interventions and they seemed to help some of his digestive issues. I think it's made both boys healthier. We tried Secretin and a brief trial of Prozac.

Jason also did Hippo therapy, therapeutic horseback riding, until the program moved too far for us to travel. He received early interventions including developmental therapy and small group therapy. We've had our floors replaced with a more natural product and we had a special sauna installed. That's Barry's little project. If you think something will help, you feel you need to try.

Surprisingly enough, there are two rather common interventions we've never done with Jason. He's never had Occupational Therapy or Applied Behavioral Analysis (ABA). David received a great deal of individual therapy, including occupational therapy, but with Jason I guess we just didn't have time before we started RDI.

What I Thought was True about Autism
My Clinical Journey - Carmen

I'm a social worker because I'm lousy in math and science. It's no joke. I wanted to be a physical therapist but a heavy dose of math and sciences with no less than a B average was required. After I earned a C in chemistry in my first semester, it was time to shift gears. I finally graduated with a MSW, but more importantly spent my 2nd year of social work school in a wonderful clinical internship that gave me the opportunity to work with children with autism.

What I lacked in understanding of the disorder (autism was discussed as a single chapter in graduate school), I made up for with sheer energy and willingness to learn from experience along with a handful of inspiring professionals and the true experts in the field, parents. I took as much as I could from that internship and when the opportunity came to work individually with a youngster with autism, I grabbed it. That was in 1982.

I did home-based therapy, working as a developmental therapist. I benefited from the guidance of many talented clinicians, but occasionally I felt misplaced by what I thought was true about autism. Early on I believed the only goal was to treat the symptoms. At times, for example, I would take my index and middle finger and point to my eyes and say, "Look at me." And, I talked a lot!

I taught turn taking and many other social skills*. But, I also had plain old fun; squirting shaving cream all over a mirror, spontaneously throwing on coats and running outside to make a snowman, swinging kids in a parachute until we both laughed so hard we were crying. I knew everything important happened from the neck up, so I tried to emphasize that, as much as possible, in every session. I knew connections were important and I knew that the way to fight rigidity was to keep the kids guessing.

Yet, I still felt I was falling short. If I didn't recognize it at the time, my clients would find ways to tell me. I had been working with a particular teenager since he was 4 years old. By any standards it was a successful treatment. He was fully included at school without an assistant. He made honor roll. He went away to overnight camp. He was able to advocate for himself where his autism was concerned. And, most importantly, he enjoyed the company of classmates and teachers and people liked him.

But, I remember during one session he told me he didn't have a best friend. He was sad about that and didn't have the slightest clue what to do about it. And, I didn't either.

I had more stories like that than felt right. Here I was, 20 years in the field and I knew enough to know something was missing. I knew what I was doing wasn't good enough. That's a tough place to be in as a clinician, but sometimes, when you don't have a plan, one gets handed to you.

In my case a colleague told me about a book, *Solving the Relationship Puzzle*, by Dr. Steven Gutstein. I read it and honestly I said, "Duh!" It just made so much sense and I wondered why I didn't see it before. That same colleague called again and said there would be a 4-day training program with Dr. Gutstein at the Connections Center in Houston. He couldn't go, but he thought I should.

Houston? August? Why not?
Carmen

What made good sense about RDI before the training made even more sense during and after. It was clear to me that RDI was quality clinical intervention for children with autism and their families. I knew that autism affected the entire family system and I knew that children in individual therapy with me were not generalizing progress. RDI addressed what was missing in intervention for children with autism. It empowered parents and gave them the tools they needed to help their children remediate* autism. It was like getting a new pair of glasses. I returned to my family and individual practice ready to embark on this journey.

For me, I wouldn't be starting over, but rather starting from where I was. I already knew it was about relationships; I was working with families and now I had a road map to share. The first family I wanted to share it with was Jason's.

A Leap of Faith
From Family Therapy to RDI

Barry, Dana and I had been working in family therapy. Both parents asked if I would work with the boys individually. At that time, I was working with many children with autism on social skill development using individual therapy. Barry and Dana thought it was time to add a social component to their children's therapy.

This request came at the same time I had been introduced to RDI and I asked Dana and Barry if we could hold off any decision about individual therapy for the boys until I returned from my training in Houston. In our first family session after Houston, I proposed that we start RDI with Jason. They agreed. I also wanted Dana and Barry to agree to one more thing, which was to act as my supervision family*. That meant Dr. Sheely, Clinical Director of the Connections Center, would review our sessions and Dana and Barry would have to make a 6-month commitment to a therapy they had never heard of. Talk about a leap of faith.

Dana and Barry

We don't really remember having any concerns. We had a trusting relationship with Carmen and that seemed enough. We were also excited to be part of a therapy that included us. Up to that point so much of what went on with both boys happened behind closed doors with feedback that didn't easily translate to our lives. All we ever wanted was to parent both boys in a way that would help them reach their potential. We were willing to take this road because simply, it made sense and we trusted our guide.

Carmen

I don't like to fail. I was asking to take along a family who had been through a lot in the last 4 years. They had tried a lot of therapies and had more than their share of disappointment. It seemed right, but would I be able to do it?

I had watched both live and taped RDI® interventions at the Connections Center. It was beautiful work. It was inspiring to watch skilled clinicians guide families. I was accustomed to providing direct service, doing the intervention. Could I shift that orientation and become the guide Barry and Dana needed? I had no concerns about the commitment of Dana and Barry, or their ability to learn, if only I could figure out how to teach.

RDI is a program where everyone learns to be an apprentice*. I had to put myself back in the role of supervisee, a true apprenticeship, a role I hadn't experienced since graduate school. While Dana and Barry trusted me, I had only met Dr.Sheely during the 4-day training in Houston. My impression was a very positive one and I remember telling a fellow trainee, "She's like butter on toast." Dr. Sheely has a way of saying things that allow even challenging comments to sink in.

Even so, after I sent our first tape in and saw Dr. Sheely's e-mail on my computer, my anxieties caused 20 minutes to pass before I hit the read button. And, there it was in writing, butter on toast. I had made mistakes, but I got enough right to make this "not a bad first tape" according to Dr. Sheely. Mostly I remember thinking, "I can do this. I can let myself be guided and it will feel okay." I was building trust in the process and the accompanying sigh of relief felt good.

Dana

We learned to look forward to our RDI® sessions as another opportunity to learn, to see things differently. Carmen was giving us positive feedback and we began feeling empowered. It was exciting to see Jason respond to us. That was the best feedback of all and was a very novel experience for us. We were so programmed to respond to him. We were actually planning things very deliberately to meet just one objective, face-to-face gaze to intensify joy.

We quickly learned to not do all the work. Our first big breakthrough was the realization that we were doing too much. Before RDI, we would do this little piggy and Jason certainly enjoyed it. Of course we'd do it all the way through and if he laughed we'd do it again and again. When we started doing less, stopping midway, not starting up right away, Jason began to wiggle his toes, raise his leg and even get the 'p' sound out. He became more of a social partner in our little plays. It was a wonderful beginning for all of us.

We learned a lot about Jason and about ourselves. That's a process that hasn't stopped. For example, there are times when we need our consultant to leave chants and songs on our answering machine, so we can hear it while we're doing it at home. We give each other hand-over-hand assistance with some of the activities, especially ones that require hands and legs doing different things. And, help each other co-ordinate moves, which may have explained my dread of the dance sequence in high school. Together we helped and supported each other and shared a laugh or two at each other's expense.

Carmen

So it went; Dr. Sheely guided me, I guided Dana and Barry and they guided Jason. Now, 2 ½ years later, I guide new consultants in our clinic, Dana and Barry guide new RDI® families and Jason continues to enjoy his role as apprentice and inspires us all. And, we're all still learning and growing.

Starting at the Very Beginning
Running the RDI Marathon - Carmen

Dr. Gutstein says that doing RDI is like running a marathon. He's right. Jason and his family have been diligently running the RDI® marathon for 2½ years, since Jason was 2 years 10 months old. It's not the superhuman pace of an elite runner churning out 4 minute miles. Because, we jog a little and walk a lot, it's closer to a 30 minute mile. That's the pace Jason needs. That's the course that is working.

When Jason began RDI he had the use of a few single words. He did not use mommy, daddy, or his own name. He would respond to playful interactions with both his parents, but he did not initiate or work to sustain them. During these interactions there was little evidence of facial gazing. He did not seem to understand or use gestures. Too much language seemed to produce increased stress. He was content to play alone for long periods of time. Using the Relationship Development Assessment™ (RDA™)*, it was clear that Jason had not mastered any of the RDI® objectives that would typically occur in the first year of life. He could not make use of that glorious parent interaction. So, we had to start our marathon at the very beginning.

Perhaps the best way to see our developmental milestones is to take you through our RDI® journal. These are actual entries from our notes that span our work over the last 2½ years. It illustrates how important communication is as we all work together to best meet Jason's needs. We had amazing firsts and disheartening setbacks; even the most-conditioned runner can experience a cramp when they least expect it.

December 19, 2002 - Carmen

We need to be vigilant about face-to-face engagement. Jason tends to approach from behind, and this needs to be directed to the front so he can fully engage in playful activities with his parents. It's not that he doesn't come to his parent, but he climbs on their backs.

Dana and Barry would joke that Jason was like a monkey, always preferring to climb on their backs. It was through RDI that we recognized this as more problematic. By doing so, he was missing out on the opportunity to get information from their faces. With Dr. Sheely's guidance, we set up activities that encouraged Jason to approach either parent face-to-face. Initially I needed to guide Jason with a slight physical touch on his back to accomplish this, but eventually he became increasingly more comfortable and confident with this approach and took off toward mom or dad on his own, face-to-face.

Remember airplane? You pick up the child with your legs and fly them in the air. Jason really enjoyed this activity. We started by putting both coaches fairly close together. One would pick Jason up and let him fly for a little bit, then set him down and guide him to his other parent. Up he'd go again. Slowly we moved further apart and removed away physical guidance. We watched as Jason successfully navigated back and forth between two coaches* with growing confidence and pleasure. These initial activities can take the place of workouts in the gym, an added benefit.

January 20, 2003 - Dana

Jason was very distracted by other objects in our basement. It was very difficult for him to engage. His grandpa was the second coach and Jason seemed to respond positively, but then he became very distracted. He tried to leave the room several times and our attempts to get him interested did not work well. Find Me, (a simple hide and seek game) didn't work at all. Jason was more interested in the furniture behind me. Everything I did to entice him to look for me was unsuccessful.

This would be the leg cramp during our marathon I was referring to. It is difficult to reproduce the distraction free environment of the clinic at home -especially in the beginning of work. Small things like grandpa as the coach, which should be positive, can become more of an obstacle than one might imagine. For Jason such a simple shift as having grandpa instead of mom or dad early in his experience with relationships seems to have provided too much uncertainty. In RDI we try to make sure that periods of uncertainty are productive, just the right amount to challenge and be successful, not so much as to cause distress.

We looked at ways to create a more suitable environment -back to less is more. Things needed to be removed from the space. Actual activity time or lab time* might need to be shorter at home but with more frequency; perhaps 10-15 minutes, 4-6 times a day. We also needed to accept the possibility that initially things might go better in the office. But we were slowly moving toward the milepost where that would not necessarily be true.

Both parents did incorporate communication changes as a lifestyle* shift: always orienting to Jason when they spoke, aware of face-to-face orientation at all possible times, and taking unexpected actions toward Jason. For example, a quick tickle when they walked past him, a little dance, an unexpected sound.

One day, as Dana was watering and spraying the plants with Jason nearby, she gave him a little spray of water. He was delighted. He quickly got up and followed her around as she watered the plants waiting for another surprise splash. Now he regularly joins mom as she takes care of the plants and has started doing some of the watering himself.

March 14, 2003 - Dana

Jason approached me after dinner. He took my hand, led me to Barry, took Barry's hand and brought us both to the couch, looked at each of us and said 'swing'. We were so excited! Jason initiated this and thought of a way to get us all together. I think we have positive persistence.

It is exciting when a child begins to take ownership of RDI. Here Jason is initiating a game he learned at the hands of his parents. It is a beautiful example of him moving from his thoughts to action and getting a wonderful payoff. For both Barry and Dana, it was the beginning of seeing Jason as an active social partner.

March 24, 2003 - Dana and Barry

Jason shows the most emotion sharing during swing and boom. He loves this. He has such a sense and look of anticipation and joy on his face. He also shifts his gaze between us a lot as if he wants to make sure he isn't missing anything by not looking at both of us. He likes using the stool for walk and swing to mom with chairs. He quickly repeats the sequence over and over with a lot of enthusiasm. I think he feels a sense of competence because he can use the stool to easily get on the chair by himself.

No fancy equipment was needed here. No "look at me" and no direct teaching. (Direct teaching actually provides the child with instruction. In RDI, we become the guides, inviting the child to learn by watching and doing.) Using a few chairs, Jason simply walks on the chairs to get to mom or dad who will then swing him in their arms when he arrives.

The chairs add an element of productive uncertainty*; the right amount of the unknown to cause Jason to seek out his parents to resolve that uncertainty. This made Jason extremely vigilant to his parents. Initially, one coach is the silent guide assuring that Jason will experience success. Once he feels competent in his ability to act as a social partner that feeling drives his desire to repeatedly engage in this simple game with great joy. I often hear, "Nothing motivates my child." Competence is a great motivator.

April 8, 2003 - Dr. Sheely

Today, he applauded the two of you, shifted gaze and maintained the play within the framework you established for him. Dana has become so good at using hesitation to engage him and in general giving him the time he needs to practice repair*.*

In the taped segment Dr. Sheely is referring to, Jason is on a pile of beanbags and mom and I are holding our hands out, making funny noises. Jason comes toward us and we pick him up joyfully and throw him back in the pile. Shortly afterwards, Jason again comes out. There are times, however, when it takes quite a bit of restraint to not assist him in navigating the beanbags and returning to us. But, had we done that, we would have communicated to Jason that he couldn't do this task on his own - that his best wasn't good enough.

This was the fuel that kept us going. Just as competence motivates children, it motivates adults. It was clear in talking with Barry and Dana that in those first few years of Jason's life, they felt very little they did was good enough. They questioned their core parenting abilities. With RDI they began to feel more capable.

We all had to realize another very important RDI® lesson; less can absolutely be more. Often as a therapist, I know I did more than I needed to, thinking that if I didn't lead the child wouldn't follow. With this entry we begin to see the payoff for doing less, hesitating and giving a child the time he needs to figure things out and then act.

If expediency was the goal, no child would ever tie his own shoes; parents would rush in to do it. We allow our children to struggle and even fail in order to reach the greater goal; healthy independence. We guide and then trust that it is time to let go. Dana and Barry were learning to do this dance with Jason as they helped him learn to tie relationships together.

May 9, 2003 - Barry

We can see a lot of differences in Jason lately. He is initiating a lot more interactions with us and working hard to keep them going, but the bigger difference is that he has been interacting and playing with extended family members and friends who he ignored or withdrew from before. He cried when his uncle left the house the other day. I have got to say it made his uncle feel good. Previously he didn't even seem aware of him. Jason also kept interactions going with his older cousins several times this week. They all felt so good that they were getting responses from him. Everyone in the family who saw him this week is so happy with the difference and we are thrilled.

They say that you know you've made a change when other people notice. RDI is the epitome of family work and here you can see how it is impacting the entire system. It doesn't mean we aren't going to cramp up from time to time, but we're all building a very positive episodic memory* of competence. Episodic memory is what we all use to plan for the present and guide us in the future. We remember not just the rough patch, but what we did to get through it - the old, been there, done that. This will hold us during the trying times.

May 9, 2003 - Carmen

We had two major language firsts! Jason said 'Jason swing' at the beginning of our session and used 'mommy' during drumming! Not just a first in session, but first ever. Jason initiated foot play and swing and stays engaged as we hesitate and become more passive. Jason moves easily between 2 coaches for fly. Nice facial gazing for jump.

In RDI, facial gazing is the child's efforts to take in the entire face of the parent to receive information, to soothe, to share joyful interactions. This is the foundation block of social relationships. It is what infants in typical development spend thousands of hours doing. It is what we are now seeing Jason do.

We are still struggling more than I'd expect for stand and fall and walk and fall. I want to try elevation and see if it improves referencing (using facial expression to resolve uncertainty). Jason needs to seek out mom's face to determine the relative safety of the situation. He has such an easy time referencing* when his body is grounded and seems to lose some of that ability in movement. I need to figure out a way to amplify the need for referencing when movement is involved.*

In a single session we have both a first and an obstacle; a little jog, almost a sprint and then a cramp. We don't simply want the skill of eye-contact, rather we want to see emergence of social referencing*. It is social referencing, in it's early stages, that causes the child to rely on his parents facial expressions to determine the relative safety of an unfamiliar situation. Then I remember, in infant development, the baby is not ambulating. They are learning profound use of facial expression without the distraction of walking, going to school or playing little league. Their zone of connection* with their parent is less than arm length. But, Jason is 3 and he is walking, running in fact. We need to slow him down so he can pay attention to the important things his parents want to teach him. We need to keep him close.

June 20, 2003 - Carmen

I set up a very simple motor course for Jason. He was supposed to bounce on the ball with me to 'Humpty Dumpty' and after the fall, move to the tunnel and go through as mom sang 'Itsy Bitsy Spider.' When he came out, mom would hold him and finish the rhyme. Well, Jason loved 'Humpty Dumpty', showed us fantastic gazing and then happily went to the tunnel, with a little touch. Jason went in and that is where he stayed! No amount of encouragement from mom worked. I finally picked up the end of the tunnel and literally shook him out. Dana picked him up and finished the rhyme. I'm not sure why this didn't work, each of the elements seemed fine, but the whole wasn't working.

In my early training, Dr.Gutstein spoke of a principle which seemed to be written specifically for me, "Plan to make mistakes." As I remembered it, this principle came as a big relief.

I decided the tunnel was too long and Jason couldn't see the whole picture. I somehow crimped the tunnel, making it only 3 feet long. Jason responded to this change and it allowed Dana to reach her hands out to him, giving him the physical security he needed to pass through the tunnel to her. Gradually we extended the tunnel to its natural length of 6 feet and Dana went from greeting Jason at the opening, to standing many feet away as he ran to her.

When something doesn't work the first time, we go back and look at ways to improve the frame; the way we set up an activity and what needs to be in place to make an activity optimal for learning through relationships. I should also mention that I've come up with activities that no amount of framing* could help. They simply didn't work no matter what we did.

RDI is dynamic in its nature. You have to be willing to take risks; you have to be willing to change, sometimes on a dime, sometimes with slow and careful consideration.

November 21, 2003 - Carmen

We've re-administered the RDA™ and this is now our second re-evaluation. I certainly wanted the reassessment to reflect the changes that Dana, Barry and I have all observed. Jason has made real progress and we're ready to move slowly to a new set of objectives. I will set up a few simple activities for Jason to use facial expressions and gestures as the most important information he uses to determine his actions. We will continue to weave these with familiar activities that he has already mastered.

Jason is now 3 years 11 months old. It is wonderful to see observable progress reflected in the re-assessment. He consistently uses gaze to share joyful interactions with his parents. He is beginning to seek out their facial expressions before he does something he's unsure about, opening a cabinet, picking up a new toy, or walking too far away from Dana or Barry.

Re-evaluation is a very important component of doing RDI. It is how we make sure we are meeting objectives, not just having a good time. When I was meeting with the family before RDI we were talking about typical behavioral changes. In RDI, we're talking about typical developmental changes. It's been a year and we are seeing progress. Jason is becoming a competent social partner.

February 14, 2004 - Carmen

Dana and I were working with Jason on moving between two coaches independently. We had faded all assistance. We would simply sing 'to mommy' or 'to Carmen' and off he'd go to play with one of us. He had just finished bouncing on a ball with Dana and she put him down and started singing 'to Carmen you go.' Jason took two steps toward me, turned around and looked at his mom, said 'to mommy' and turned around and climbed in her lap. Dana looked at me and said, "I feel like I got my baby back."

Watching the two of them, I knew it was true. I knew that I was witnessing a very special moment, one that would now be repeated thousands of times.

April 2, 2004 - Barry and Dana

On our vacation, if Jason was a few feet away from us he would turn and look at us. If we said 'stop', or 'come to mommy or daddy', he listened immediately. This was VERY helpful. We didn't have to chase him or stay right on top of him. When we put our arms out even if he was far away in an enclosed space or room, he ran excitedly towards us. We're feeling pretty good right now.

These are the stories a consultant loves to hear. The work is beginning to pay off in more challenging settings. Events like vacations and holidays are often the markers parents use to measure progress. In day to day life, it's hard to appreciate changes. It's far easier to remember last year's vacation or last year's birthday party compared to the most recent. As a consultant I'm grateful we video tape as much as we do. It is a wonderful tool to see how far we've come.

April 30, 2004 - Dana

Jason loved the new activities. He had trouble with the 'shake' part but did great with 'take' and 'pass.' His participation was great. He really loved 'trade.' He was so excited. The best part was that he was so into the sharing of enjoyment that he stopped in the middle, ran into my arms and gave me a big kiss. The enjoyment sharing and the connection were more important than the activity. This was one of our best RDI moments ever.

Often parents want to know about the RDI® activities. "Give me more activities," is something I hear quite a bit. I need to help those parents see what Dana and Jason discovered. It is not about the activities; it is about what happens between two people as they engage in the activity.

I love baseball but when I go to a game with friends, it's not the game I remember. I suspect that the reason Dana felt this was one of her best RDI® moments is that for Jason, it was all about being with mommy; one more lesson here, treasure the small beautiful moments. Treasure the one you have and enjoy the anticipation of the next, it will come.

July 3, 2004 - Carmen

Grandpa brought Jason to his RDI session today. We were playing a simple sender-receiver game. I was sending cars down a tube to Jason. I'd hold one up; he'd look at me and say, "yes," even adding a little nod from time to time. I'd send it down, taking my time and holding his gaze. He was delighted and really seemed to be enjoying our interaction. After sending about 20 cars down the tube, I gave the box of cars to Jason and indicated that it was his turn to send them to me, which he did. Grandpa took me aside and let me know that Jason was sending the cars down in the exact same order I had sent them to him! Well that certainly wasn't what I wanted him to get out of the activity, that's for sure.

Besides being another reason to videotape, though I doubt I would have caught this without Grandpa's help, this session speaks to things looking better than they might actually be. I had hoped Jason was enjoying sharing the delighted emotion of the activity with me. It is so important to constantly check what is really being attended to. Jason was using gaze, nods, smiling and enjoying himself. I suspect he was most enthralled with his ability to repeat the order of the cars. Needless to say, we put this activity on hold, where it still is today.

July 30, 2004 - Carmen

I worked with Barry and Dana on creating a memory book for their upcoming vacation. I encouraged them to take pictures but to stay away from concrete labels like 'Jason standing in front of the brown house with a big tree'. As I'm saying this, Jason is repeating 'brown house with a big tree'. Lesson learned. I encouraged Dana and Barry to simply share emotion over the picture. Glance at it, use a great deal of facial expression and then share it with Jason.

What we were seeing in this session was a new obstacle. Jason was indeed becoming more verbal, but we needed to remain focused on providing an opportunity for him to attach his words to the social context. It's easy to want the words no matter how or why they come, but we needed to be careful to support Jason's language development within the context of relationships.

November 12, 2004 - Dana

Jason is referencing in so many ways. He references me when I call his name. He watches me to see what I'm doing and what I'll be asking him to do. For example, when it's time for school, he watches me to know what he should be doing. He goes to the car by himself even if I just say, 'okay, ready', or if I start putting things in the car. Jason is beginning to learn by watching. He is taking in lots of information to make a decision about what to do. He's becoming an observer of the dynamic nature of day to day life.

December 10, 2004 - Dana

We have not done anything new or different since last week. I intentionally ignore Jason when he requests certain things so he will reference me and persist instead of getting what he wants so easily. (I don't do this for every request because I feel bad.)

We're in the walking phase of the marathon. I recognize this as fatigue. We need to re-energize, remember to breathe and reflect. The truth is, running a marathon is exhausting and sometimes you focus on how far you have to go, not on how far you've come. Dana is trying to keep the bar raised, but moms get joy out of doing for their children. My children are grown and out of the house, but when they come to visit, I make their morning coffee, do their laundry and in general become the same mother I was when they were 2 years old. It's a hard habit to break.

I admire Dana and Barry. They have an amazing attitude. They are running this marathon beautifully and they are doing so with both boys. They began an intensive RDI® program for David 6 months ago. While both boys have RDI® programs in place, their programs are different and each boy's needs must be addressed in ways that are specifically designed for them.

This requires an incredible amount of energy, fortitude and commitment. I'm their RDI® Consultant*, but I'm also their cheerleader and biggest fan. I need to make sure that they are taking care of themselves and each other. To this end, they've added a healthy dose of couples' time. Dana and Barry go out to dinner once a week. While I'm sure they talk about the boys, I also know they give each other plenty of time to talk about themselves. They also give each other permission to do things alone and have some time to pursue personal interests.

January 12, 2005 - Dana and Barry

Jason was selected pre-schooler of the year! We were pretty proud at the awards ceremony, but the best part was how much he seemed to enjoy all the attention. He was clapping and giggling and running to us for cuddles.

Especially nice here is that Jason was recognized not just for his academic ability, because certainly he is one smart cookie, but for his social development. Jason's long-time classroom assistant remarked about the noticeable change. She commented that Jason used to come into the classroom, walk past everyone and settle in with a toy or book. Now it's his teachers and peers that he seeks out. She describes him as a joy in the classroom.

February 14, 2005 - Dana

Jason is now referencing me at the curb by school everyday. He helps me put laundry in the basket and he's starting to put things in the garbage when I indicate that it's yucky. So, I may hand him a dirty napkin and just make a disgusting face and point to the garbage can. I let him know what a big boy he's being, how happy he makes mommy when he helps. He seems pretty proud of himself.

In this entry Dana demonstrates the power of the master-apprentice relationship.* She is teaching Jason to watch her, to learn from her example and rewards that behavior by letting him know how happy it makes her. His good feeling comes from hers. The master-apprentice relationship is the parents' invitation to have the child join them in learning about the world. Day to day chores as well as why the sky is blue.

April 1, 2005 - Carmen

Dana and Barry continue to express concerns regarding Jason's use of a bottle and his very limited diet. They wonder if there is a way to incorporate RDI principles to tackle this.

I wonder about this too. Being trained as an RDI® Consultant has answered many questions, but it raises others. One new question is, "Does the lack of facial gazing during the critical first year impact feeding issues?" We know in Jason's case, he did not use facial gazing during his first year and not at a typical rate in his second year and that things were quite hectic at home during his first year. Barry recounted once in family therapy he couldn't remember the last time he had eaten a meal at home sitting down.

I can't help but wonder, remembering how all of us parents got our babies to take that first spoonful of mashed up sweet potatoes or carrots, if this doesn't come into play. Most babies I have known, take that first spoonful and, despite all our reassurance, spit it right out.

After all, what baby would go from nursing or bottle to pureed spinach if not for the reassuring face of their parent, the zooming airplane into the hanger, and those silly verbal "yum yums" and smiles? Without a parent's reassurance, guidance and trust to go where no baby really wants to go, are children with autism left to deal with this based on only their sensory systems? I don't know the answer, but I'm willing to try expanding some old activities to include drinking from a cup initially and eventually eating something new.

We have done this very simple game called 'take, shake, and pass.' In the activity, mom or dad takes a small piece of laundry out of a basket, sings, 'take, shake, and pass' and gives it to the child. The child does the same and the laundry winds up in another basket, or at home, in the dryer. Jason loved this activity and was very good at it. He sang the song, could initiate and complete it and was able to do it at home with laundry.

So, to address Jason's eating issues, we adapted that game. We sat in a small circle and played, 'take, sip, and pass' with a water cup. No germ phobia here. We were on a mission. Jason was now an active face gazer, so we had no trouble getting him to watch us sip from the cup. On our first attempt playing the game, Jason took the cup, but put his fingers to his lips then the cup to his fingers.

We accepted this. Within two weeks, he was putting the cup to his lips, but the water was falling out of his mouth. As we write this we're pretty sure he has taken his first sip from a cup. At home both parents are finding every opportunity to have Jason watch them eat, offering tastes and accepting any movement toward the mouth with celebration, "yum yums," and smiles.

Being the Parents We Wanted To Be
Where We Are Now - Dana

We were at the surgeon's office. Barry was playing with Jason, blowing on his toes and Jason kept initiating it and laughing, shifting his gaze to me, like he was saying, "Look at us mom!" He was laughing, which of course made Barry laugh, which kept the fuel in the interaction. And, there I was thinking, "We're in the surgeon's office, but we still have the capacity for shared enjoyment."

When Jason does share enjoyment, gazes and references us, we are so grateful because we thought that it would never happen. When people ask us, "What has worked?" We answer, "RDI is the only intervention that has paid us back as a family." We have put hours and hours into other therapies and not have received what we've gotten out of RDI. It has helped us get back to being the parents we wanted to be.

Having children with autism has changed every aspect of our family life. It is physically exhausting, emotionally devastating, socially isolating, financially draining and spiritually challenging. It has also changed the dynamics of our marital relationship, the parent-child-sibling relationships, and even our extended family relationships.

The results of our efforts with RDI, under our consultant's guidance and wisdom have given our family a renewed sense of positive energy and an abundance of happy moments and memories. RDI has not cured or taken away our children's autism but it has enabled us to experience more love and laughter where we had once expected only sadness and pain.

We both wonder what things would have been like for Jason if we hadn't done RDI. I don't think he would have been so content. We can be engaged through gaze, silly noises and songs. We've been able to maintain connection.

He's secure. In the hospital, through the worst of it right after surgery, when he looked at us, he responded to our words and our expressions of reassurance. He would look right in our eyes when he knew that something was going to happen, a blood test, or something with the IV and we'd say, "It's going to be okay - you're going to be okay." We could watch his whole body relax. To have him seek out comfort and be able to give it, that's what being a parent is all about.

Just last night, we started to let Jason scoot around on the floor. He would go about 10 feet away from us and would check back for security and reassurance. He certainly had reason to feel a bit insecure with this newfound postoperative freedom. He needed to know that we were watching him and that it was okay.

He wouldn't go any further away from me at first and kept coming back towards me and moving away while repeatedly referencing me. When he built up some courage, he stopped at that 10-12 foot distance and said, "Ready, set, go," to me. I figured out he meant for me to follow him. If I didn't follow him, he wouldn't move. But when I did, he moved a little further and checked back in with me before every scoot to make sure he was safe. If I remember correctly, this is similar to what babies do during the reapprochement stage, checking in with their mom to make sure they're safe.

Here's the silver lining, his broken leg gave him the opportunity to be uncertain and do what babies do when they take those first steps to venture away. He didn't do this when he was a baby.

We didn't get to have the kind of relationship we wanted with Jason when he was a baby. We had moments, but they were so brief. The first thing we both noticed after starting RDI was his gazing. He would look at us with this loving gaze and we would gaze at him. We could feel this energy of love between us. It filled our hearts with joy. To have that was amazing and we realized what we were missing.

When you have a child with autism, it is what you think you'll always miss. To parents that didn't have that experience with either of their babies, there is no way we can describe what it means to us. But now we have it and it doesn't feel too late; it feels as natural as can be. We don't believe that this is true but, let's just say if we never went any further, at least we got our baby back.

In Our Own Time
Consultant's View - Carmen

I did a triathlon in Galena, Illinois a few years ago. Those of you who live in mountainous country may not appreciate this, but I'm a Chicago girl and expressway overpasses are the only "hills" we have. Galena has hills - serious hills. The night before the race, my friend drove the cycling portion of the course with me. He said he would understand if I decided at the last minute not to cycle. Though I was determined to do it, as we drove I remember thinking, "I could die on this course."

Then it was race day; driving it didn't even begin to prepare me for actually cycling it. As everyone with his or her alloy titanium bikes passed me by at break neck speed, I seriously began to wonder if I hadn't made a huge error in judgment. Approaching the first big hill, I discovered a trick that was to help me for the next 16 miles; instead of looking at the whole hill ahead of me, I kept my eyes on that little bit of pavement no more than 3 feet in front of me. By knowing where I needed to go, but at the same time limiting my horizon, it seemed manageable. I finished the race in third place - third from the end that is. However, I finished like everyone else, in my own time, in my own way with my very own clunky bike.

I appreciate the notion that we all get where we're going in our own time. I could not have chosen a better family to start me on this journey. Their ability to accept guidance, keep their eye on the 3 feet of pavement in front of them and slow down and walk when they needed has been an inspiration. Given our experience so far, there is no reason to believe that we won't keep going. They have proven change is possible, desirable, and doable. They have helped me be the therapist I have always wanted to be.

As for Jason, we're dancing, literally and figuratively. During our last session before he broke his leg, Jason and I were dancing. All the hard work of shared enjoyment and social referencing has led us to it. And as any girl can tell you, a guy that can dance, well now that's something!

✎ **Carmen Gendel is a Licensed Clinical Social Worker. She is a partner in Sweeney, Gendel and Associates in Skokie, Illinois and has been working with families affected by autism for 23 years. She has been a RDI® Certified Consultant for three years. Carmen lives in Chicago and is the mother of two beautiful daughters, Lauren and Julia. You can contact Carmen at sloop23@aol.com.**

2

Finding Each Other Again

by April Choulat & Debbie

Names have been changed to protect the family's privacy.

She's a girl (!), she's a teenager (!!) and she's autistic (!!!) Put them together and it places our 14 year old daughter Michelle in a sub-category that's highly unusual even by autistic standards. If autism is completely baffling for most families with children on the spectrum, it's even more-so for us. Clearly we're in uncharted territory, but we always have been.

We live in a backward state, in a city that had absolutely no resources for us when Michelle was first diagnosed at age 2. Born in June of 1991, she was a very typical baby, adorable, sweet and engaging. I have vivid memories of that time and pictures which show a side of her I haven't seen since. One of my favorites was when Michelle was 11 months old and we took a trip to visit our relatives. She and I had so much fun together that I decided we'd make it an annual tradition. She charmed everyone, but especially her two little cousins. They doted on her and I have a great picture of all the girls smiling for the camera on a very happy day. Another favorite is a great video of Michelle and her big brother playing together in her crib. I remember how she would cry in the mornings until he came into her room. When he arrived her tears would dry up immediately and she'd get so excited in anticipation of more fun. I cherish those memories from her first year.

Michelle was very normal, except for one thing: she had more than her share of sinus and ear infections and was constantly on antibiotics. Then, at age 15 months, something very abnormal occurred. She had a particularly bad sinus infection. It stood out from the others because she screamed all day and night, completely inconsolable, obviously in pain. We treated her with antibiotics as usual, but to no avail and from that day on she was never the same. We know now that autism took hold that day and within 2 months, she had slipped away.

My husband and I began the rounds of appointments with different children's specialists, thinking it was a temporary problem that would be resolved. In quick order Michelle was examined by her pediatrician, and then came the avalanche of referrals: pediatric ENT, neurologist, audiologist, psychologist, and more. We became absolutely stunned by what we were hearing about our precious daughter. It seemed that no one really knew what to think, but it also didn't sound like a short term problem, like we first believed it to be.

At that time, autism just didn't happen so long after birth, so the experts were baffled and began calling it other things, and so did we. "Hearing Impaired...Secondary Autism...Autistic-Like...PDD-NOS...Learning disabled...definitely not Autism...definitely Autistic." As confusing as the labels were, the treatment plans were even worse, if you could call them plans at all. "Don't over-do the speech therapy...more antibiotics...she'll never talk...we're cautiously optimistic...drop her off with nice church ladies for a mother's morning out...put her in developmental pre-school...no pre-school if she's not potty trained...there's nothing wrong with that baby....hopefully she'll grow out of it...you have to get her talking by the age of 5...everyone is a little quirky...she looks fine to me...we're seeing more of this but we don't know why." Panic set in. Most of these labels and suggestions came from the top children's clinic in our city! Obviously we couldn't get answers or second opinions here, so we frantically began to get evaluations from major universities up and down the East Coast.

Our hunt for answers eventually stopped in North Carolina, first at Duke University where we met a child psychiatrist who had fresh ideas that were based on typical development, and at UNC-Chapel Hill, which taught us about the TEACCH method, another developmental approach which seemed logical. At the time we had no idea what we were in for, but we were determined to get our daughter back. We embarked on this path and gave it everything we had, but little did we know how twisted and tortured it would turn out to be.

My husband is a physician, so he knew more about autism than I did. His initial shock at the news was replaced by helplessness when he discovered that there was nothing that medical science could do for us, not a single thing. Up until then, he had always been the one who solved medical problems, because that was his job. He helped strangers all day long, but the one time when there were no answers was when it concerned his own daughter. All his training, knowledge and professional contacts couldn't help him. He was devastated, but committed to the effort anyway he could. His contributions were to work harder, so as to support the cost of non-stop therapies, and to distract our very demanding young son so he'd be unaware of the huge amounts of time I was spending with his sister.

I totally threw myself into the job of fixing "not-autism-but-something-like-it." This became first my full-time, then round-the-clock occupation. Quickly it moved into being my total preoccupation and before long I was spending every moment thinking about (and even dreaming about) autism. I simply couldn't turn it off and our friends and family began to tiptoe away. I became obsessed!

Along with the rest of the world, we were completely unprepared for autism and weren't even sure what it was! The definition in the DSM IV described someone else's child, but not ours, or so it seemed at that time.

We'd gathered from the evaluations that it was up to us, her parents, to pull her out of this "thing." But where were we supposed to begin? Matching up symptoms to treatments was the first step.

There was one common theme to all the experts we consulted and all the research we had done, and it was this: get her talking by the age of 5! We heard that loud and clear and it became our mantra, our whole reason for being. Besides, it made sense that if Michelle had talked before the autism took over, then she would talk again. She had become strangely silent; a mute. It was reasonable to assume that if you can't talk, you can't make friends. Everyone knows that, right? So speech therapy became the first job at hand and our primary focus.

Meanwhile, we noticed so many other symptoms popping up which were also alarming, like: Michelle averted her gaze, was mostly aloof and engaged in solitary activities, even when in the company of others; she became very hyper and jumped off counters, out of trees, and even off the garage roof. She would take off running so fast, she'd get away before we even realized she was gone (at age 3 she ran right down the middle of a busy road for half a mile before someone stopped and waited with her until we found them); she stayed up very late, then awakened in the middle of the night for hours on end; she rubbed tree bark, shredded leaves, and turned over and over in the wading pool; she began to use people in instrumental ways, like taking our hand and making us point to a cookie she wanted; she stared into space and laughed for hours at seemingly nothing; she seemed impervious to pain; developed many tics and quirks like eye squinting, toe-walking, tongue clicking, little vocal stims she repeated constantly, lined up her toys, was mesmerized with spinning objects, did full body jerks, punched her arm forcefully into the air; she lost interest in other children and was largely unaware of what went on around her. Worst of all, she lost interest in her family, and even her brother's best efforts to engage her were usually met with indifference, sometimes even annoyance.

The list of what we recognize now as autistic traits goes on and on. One by one we tried to figure out how to deal with the problems, but it felt like stamping out a lot of little wildfires. Each time we managed to extinguish one, another would immediately pop up somewhere else. We weren't making fast enough progress and Michelle's autism was on the verge of being out of control.

I led the charge, and first thing every morning, Michelle and I were out of the running blocks at full stride. Given the directive of at least 8 hours of 1:1 interaction a day, her daily schedule was loaded with activities designed to meet her many needs. Through diligent efforts and dedicated therapists, teachers, and others, we made some gains. She did intensive speech therapy, OT, playtime with typical peers, play therapy, interaction with college student helpers, a language based preschool, special diets and TEACCH. All propelled by the Duke doctor's chant of, "Stimulation! Stimulation! Stimulation!" Michelle started talking again by age 5. She also learned a lot of good skills, like imitating peers, sitting in circle time, attending to her therapists, learning to complete a task and expanding her attention span. She even initiated games like "Patty Cake" and "Ring around the Rosie" and seemed to enjoy it (albeit briefly) when children came over to play. Also, many of her sensory issues abated and she got potty trained.

Despite these types of advances, most of which we'd now recognize as "splinter skills," our darling daughter was getting worse instead of better. She still didn't interact and her talking was meaningless for the most part. Emotionally she was either flat, or she responded wildly to some secret, inner thought. In the 3 years since her diagnosis, Michelle had actually slipped further away from us. So at that all-important age of 5, I felt like a failure and when I called the doctor who had overseen her treatment program, he told me that we'd done our best and we needed to accept her for who she was.

By that point, the stress and strain of autism had taken its toll on every aspect of our lives, especially our marriage. But the disappointing assessment at age 5 changed that. My husband and I really needed each other. Slowly we began to repair our relationship, by getting a baby-sitter every Saturday night no matter what. We made a rule that there would be no talking about the kids! Toward the end of each week we would start to get really excited about our 'date', and looked forward to our adult time. It was the single best thing we did for ourselves as a couple, and over time we were a team. We found each other again.

Over time, in an effort to establish some normalcy, we began to go on little family outings, activities we missed out on that other families did. We went to our son's soccer games and sat on the sidelines with our daughter, armed with a bag full of enough goodies to last way past the hour we spent there. We became experts at keeping her happy and placated, which allowed us to relax and chat about typical kid issues with the typical parents who made up most of the spectators.

We repeated this scenario in lots of variations along the way, expanding our repertoire and accommodations, taking two cars and being prepared to leave with her if necessary. We always had a contingency plan and sometimes that plan included a helper, someone who would assist Michelle while the rest of us carried on as a separate family unit. This system was, on the one hand useful because it allowed me, especially, to enjoy the activities of our typical son who was the opposite of Michelle. He was extremely social, quick-witted and charismatic. At the time, he was pretty comfortable with having Michelle come to his activities and usually she liked being a part of the scene as well. Through him, we were able to experience what other parents take for granted; the ups and downs of typically developing boys. His feelings and welfare were of equal importance, so spending time with him was imperative.

On the flip side of these family outings was the constant practice of making Michelle content. Across all settings outside the home we were determined to try and keep her worst behaviors under wraps and we instructed everyone around her to do the same. Public displays of her outbursts were not only intense, unpredictable and draining, but blew the cover off family normalcy. Your life is limited if your child is out of control and I was determined to go boldly out into the world and live a little. I simply ignored the questioning looks and uncomfortable shifting of those who accepted our version of taking autism on the road.

Looking back, I see how we spent just as much time on preventing her bad behaviors as dealing with them, but there didn't seem to be any other way to carry on. To pull this off, we had to almost lead a double life, and as Michelle's behavior worsened, it became more difficult to depend on our goody bag. This became apparent one morning when my family came to visit for a few days. I would invite guests to come stay, which would give them the mistaken impression that things with Michelle were fine.

They weren't, and one morning we met my parents, my sister and her family for breakfast at a local restaurant that was popular in our neighborhood. Michelle was about 7 years old, and at the end of the meal she threw her first very public, very loud tantrum. I had to physically pull her out of the restaurant (which had come to a complete stop), and my sister pried Michelle's hands off the door frame so that I could get her out! This was to be the first of many such incidents.

Other similar scenes stand out, like the one at a McDonald's, on a road trip with 'the girls', myself, Michelle (age 9), April, her young sister-in-law, and my sister. We forgot Michelle's cup of water, and she flipped out at our booth, bringing the busy lunchtime crowd to a complete standstill. Again, the scene of dragging her out the door and getting her into the car is a slow motion movie that replays over and over from this period of her childhood. We took her snorkeling on that same trip, and I clearly remember her tantrumming in the water! Security has removed her (and us) from a theme park and the mall. We've stood in sadness as Michelle threw herself on sidewalks, store aisles, parking lots, and even airport jet ways. Through it all we just kept going, but honestly I don't know how.

Meanwhile an epidemic had begun. Autism was more prevalent and at the same time, the internet came of age. I joined message boards that became my lifeline to the autism world. Parents began to 'talk' and share information about our traumas and triumphs. Through age 10, in a desperate attempt to help our daughter, we researched and tried almost every autism therapy out there. We did it all! Vitamins, Secretin, ABA, FastForward, Verbal Behavior, Special Ed Programs, Home-schooling, Part-time with Mainstream Supports, ABLLS, Son-Rise, GF/CF diet, Floor Time, Teach Me Language, OT, SLT, Behavior Modification, Medicines, Social Stories, Social Skills Play dates, Shadows and more.

After attending workshops and researching many of the popular interventions at the time, we would throw ourselves into one treatment or another, discarding them as they failed. And, unfortunately, most of the treatments not only failed, but failed miserably, leaving us to dust off, find more strength and try again. It all blurred together, as we unwittingly beefed up her splinter skills and her ability to blend in better. All the experts were cheering us along, insisting that she was doing great. Apparently, things like riding the school bus every day, sitting in a class and being on the playground with her peers, qualified her as a success.

Although proud of her accomplishments, I wasn't crowing along with the others. On paper it looked good, but observing her was a different story. Look closely and you would see a child who was extremely tense, unable to control herself, easily angered and unaware of what was happening around her. She took a seat on the bus and immediately sank into her own world. At school, she looked around at everything else in the class except the teacher and on the playground she played solo and repetitively, mostly ignoring the imploring invitations from her well-meaning peers. Interventions on my part or the part of others would temporarily make things a little better, giving us hope that all our efforts were working after all. But deep down I knew this wasn't the case, and as time went by, the feeling of hopelessness began to invade.

The years of intensive intervention all culminated with an evaluation at Yale, at age 10, which bluntly revealed that Michelle was not only classically autistic, but probably mentally retarded as well! With all that humongous effort, she'd actually gone backwards! It seemed that almost every intervention had been a complete failure. Except for one, and that one thing was very telling. We had hired a college girl named April Choulat to help us and every day after school she took Michelle to play at her family's little farm. I would get reports (and finally a video) about how much fun they had and how happy Michelle was there. Also, April accompanied Michelle to a typical camp in the mountains for a week each summer, for 4 years in a row.

The reports back were in stark contrast to the horrifyingly self-injurious, tantruming girl we were living with and the out of control child that her school was dealing with. When I saw the video of Michelle at the farm, or visited the camp and heard from the staff and April about how relaxed and social she had been, it hit me like a brick. The problem wasn't with Michelle, but with us! She was perfectly capable of happiness and there it was, documented on tape for my eyes to see - told to me in gushing stories by teary-eyed camp counselors. But, with the pressure of all the therapies, the intensive work and years of over-scheduling, we had turned our happy girl into a completely miserable child! It was a huge revelation! We were the ones who were out of line! Our daughter could definitely interact, emotion share and learn just about anything. We just weren't going about it the right way.

Other than April's natural abilities and a few other beams of light, there wasn't anything out there to address the social and emotional aspects of autism. By then it seemed obvious to us that this was the next sub-category to tackle, yet none of the experts could offer any programs that would address these issues. When pressed, they'd admit that this was a very important area and it was worrisome; that was all, just an admission that they observed the same things we did! When it came time for April to move away to another city in order to finish up her degree, we didn't even have that anymore. School and therapy were all about instrumental learning, individually taught rote skills,* static systems that could easily be documented with a standardized form. Michelle's behavior issues became more problematic, gradually increasing with time.

By age 10 she was self-injurious, banging her wrists together, or banging them so hard against surfaces like the edge of a granite counter top, that they were always terribly bruised. Oddly, she didn't experience any pain, but those witnessing it sure did! She had frequent and intense outbursts, and would suddenly yell out, startling those around her. She began biting her hands and arms, eventually her fingers and it got so bad that she routinely drew blood.

The self-injurious behaviors intensified as she got older and as bad as they were, the tantrums increased, in frequency and duration. She would go berserk, breaking so many things in the house that we spent thousands of dollars on repairs. She would kick out windows and doors beat the walls with anything that would punch holes in them, ruin carpets by upsetting food or liquid containers, throw furniture, and kick in air conditioning vents. She would stand outside and scream and howl, raising the suspicion and concerns of neighbors and passers-by. She ran away and had to be retrieved by the police, rode her scooter in manic circles around the house, all the while screaming and banging. She had some language, "Help Me!! What's Wrong With Me? Why am I doing this? Oh no, not again!"

The closer Michelle got to puberty, the worse her behavior. There were so many factors contributing to the problems and nothing we did seemed to work. Finally, we hired a Certified Behavior Specialist to help us. We needed to address these issues and until we did, a social program seemed hopeless.

Of all the work we'd done up until that point, behavior intervention was by far the hardest. My husband and I, plus the few college girls and tutor who worked every week with Michelle, attended the initial intervention. It was a heart-wrenching weekend of tough work, during which we each had to kick up Michelle's behavior, then be coached on how to consistently deal with it. Before this happened, I'd been required to attend a month long course on the subject of behavior, so I was designated the in-house coach. Emotionally wretched as it was, the intervention eventually seemed to work. Michelle's behaviors decreased a lot, some of them even went away and over the course of the next year, she learned to handle herself much better. I was completely ready for something new, something positive for a change.

Meanwhile, we were still in touch with April, who was learning about something called RDI. As soon as she showed us some information on it, immediately we knew that we had found what were looking for! It was the best feeling in the world to have our hope restored. We got the book, *Solving the Relationship Puzzle* and highlighted nearly everything on every page, it all rang so true!

Over the next few months we interpreted and tried to implement the activities ourselves. We had enough success to know it was worth pursuing, but it was more complex than we had thought. April decided that this was what she'd been looking for too and wanted to become certified in RDI. Michelle became her supervision case and that's when we began to see real results! There were changes little and big, every day. Right away there was improvement in her language. We used to ask her a million questions every day, but switched to making statements, called Declaratives. Suddenly Michelle began piping up with her own, very original thoughts about a variety of things. She also began contributing to our conversations, which were novel and not an extension of her own. We noticed small changes in her behavior and eye contact, which were too coincidental to attribute to anything else. For the first time in years we felt encouraged!

Eventually, April graduated from college and simultaneously became one of the first RDI® Certified Consultants in the country. She was the only consultant in our state and she was dedicated to helping Michelle! This was an amazing turn of events and we felt the tide was finally turning. But there was one last hurdle in store, before we could turn it around for good.

Just after her 12th birthday and her first RDA™ (Relationship Development Assessment™), Michelle's bad behaviors began to show up again. She was just about to hit puberty, so we assumed that it was hormonally related. By then some doctors in our area had become much more experienced with autism and we began seeing them for advice. We were addressing these issues medically, ruling out conditions we were worried about, like seizures and Tourette's. Michelle was put on hormonal pills, and anti-anxiety meds which made a really big difference. These wonderful doctors were available to us in our time of need, and we felt like we were getting good medical support, something my husband especially, was relieved about.

Ironically, just when we were feeling like we had gotten back on our feet, the lowest moment of all came; Michelle had such a bad tantrum, she ended up cutting herself on a mirror that she'd smashed. That was it. We took her straight to the hospital and she was admitted into the psychiatric ward for adolescents. As hard as it may be to believe, there was a silver lining to her hospital stay. We realized that our new doctors were there when we needed them and our community responded to an autism crisis. Finally the worst was behind us. Finally, we were going to get our daughter back!

The RDA™ was an eye-opener. Like all parents with kids on the spectrum, we felt there were so many more strengths than there actually were. Also we were dazzled by the glow of splinter skills, so finding out that Michelle was functioning at such a low social level was a shock! After all, for years she had attended a regular school and had typical 'friends.' The assessment immediately revealed the superficial aspect of those friendships* and how stressed she was by trying to remain in such a lopsided arrangement. It showed that she had almost no referencing and was emotionally unresponsive. We were given our first assignment: be non-verbal and practice Declaratives. We relished the opportunity.

One day April accompanied Michelle and me to the mall, to prove how well these two concepts worked in all environments. Michelle enjoyed the mall and had a regular routine there, which usually resulted in me keeping up with her, while she visited her favorite stores. This time, April and I lagged behind, waaaaay behind and I was instructed to pretend I was interested in something else. Michelle was so far away it was worrisome, but then suddenly something remarkable happened. For the first time ever, she stopped, turned around and nervously began looking for us! It was the beginning of something ground-breaking!

Soon after, I attended two different RDI® workshops and learned first hand about the core deficits, the theories behind what we're trying to accomplish and the practical application of all this information. A huge revelation was learning about co-occurring conditions; the other issues besides autism that impeded progress. In Michelle's case, stress and anxiety were definitely co-occurring conditions, as were her language deficits.

April followed Michelle around school one day and made us realize how horribly instrumental and stressful the whole experience was, information which helped us stay focused on our goals for her. I took her out of school and home schooled her for six months. While at home we were able to spend a lot more time on our RDI® objectives, slowed things down and learned about so many different things, academic as well as practical. She has speech therapy at home once a week with a therapist who helps us by employing RDI® principals and goals. Little by little, April helped us become more self assured about using RDI as a lifestyle and taught us to recognize the small opportunities as well as big.

With April's skillful coaching, and goals garnered from the assessment, we started practicing RDI® concepts. We began by learning games in a controlled environment in our home that would target specific areas that we wanted to work on. Once we played the games with Michelle, and understood what we were looking to achieve, then we could transfer those same concepts across all environments, or what's referred to in RDI as 'lifestyle.' For example, we learned a game we called "Follow my Eyes." Either my husband or I would accompany Michelle out of the room while the other hid a toy under a pillow. When she came back in, she would have to watch the eyes of the person who hid the toy, in order to find it. Then it would be her turn to hide the toy, and move her eyes as we tried to guess where it was. We grasped the concept of non-verbal referencing (among other things), and were then able to recognize it in countless ways throughout the course of the day. We did this in daily activities such as doing the laundry, washing dishes and the car, setting the table, cleaning a mirror, packing lunch; the list is endless!

Once we really got it we were able to do more and more enjoyable activities together, like going to the gym and working out, taking long walks and bike rides, cutting up in movies, watching her brother's sporting events without bringing along a single distraction! Even more amazing, chores have become 'we-go' activities with virtually no resistance, like weeding the garden, cleaning the kitchen, planting flowers and putting away the groceries. What a difference from the days when she refused to do any of these, fun or otherwise. She wants to be with us now and that's the sole motivation!

Along with these changes are so many others: she expresses herself emotionally now, able to either verbalize how she's feeling or able to regulate her own emotions so they don't escalate. In the past year she's had only one small tantrum and not a single incident of self-injury. She's become concerned about others and gives me back rubs if I simply say that my shoulders hurt. She's in tune with the group and recently went to her first pro football game, where she eventually began to anticipate the action on the field along with the rest of the stadium and jumped for joy when our team made a touchdown, even sympathizing with an injured player on the field. She's curious about many subjects and asks a lot of questions. She went to a very crowded theme park and kept up with her friends, never once needing to be reminded to do that, and needing no over-compensation on the friends part. She's initiating so much, in speech as well as actions; she's playing little tricks on her family members and can't wait to share her delight when we get the joke.

She now attends a regular middle school, but this time without any aide and without becoming overly stressed. Her focus is on keeping up academically and meeting new friends. She tells me that she has to pay more attention in class, like her teacher tells her. A few weeks into the school year, she took it upon herself to find her guidance counselor and ask her some questions about her schedule. The counselor was floored and told me that Michelle expressed herself well, so that she fully understood why she had come to see her! None of these things were happening before we started RDI and we're certain that all these and more resulted from it.

We've practiced RDI with Michelle for two years and it's been the single most important therapy we've ever done. The changes in Michelle have been amazing, but most of all it's been the change in our relationships with Michelle and even with each other, that have been the most meaningful. For instance, Michelle used to stay in her room almost all the time, rarely coming out except for meals or TV. We tried to attribute it to being a teen, but since we began RDI, she hardly ever spends time in her room and is always seeking us out. She enjoys time with us and proves it's the relationship that matters by doing things she would've never done before, just so she can be with us.

For instance, she likes to cuddle so much that she's become her dad's #1 TV partner when he watches the (mostly boring) international soccer matches! She and her father have the kind of bonding that's enviable and they're so happy because of it. Michelle is much more patient with her brother and he notices her improvements as well. Michelle and I spend a lot of time together and that's brought us closer than I'd ever imagined. We really enjoy doing girl things together, hanging out in a girl way that is special with mothers and daughters. It's all so much more relaxed and calm and the pressure of fixing autism has abated.

Also, it appears that the manic work through the years that preceded RDI wasn't in vain after all. A lot of the individual skills she learned were assimilated when her brain began functioning in a whole different, more natural way, so she made advances right away that we didn't even expect. Our whole family has changed because of RDI.

RDI is in its infancy though and like anything else that's just starting out, there are some big learning curves for everybody! It began with a very broad concept that we studied and over time has evolved and been reduced to some essential parts, which is great, but it's caused some confusion for those of us who began early on. Even though RDI makes perfect sense, it's not always easy to grasp or to implement and there have been times when I needed to just take a break and free up my brain! Fortunately that's perfectly acceptable and even encouraged. The first two stages of RDI are the hardest to achieve, but this is where everyone begins. Some children respond faster and some parents get with the program more easily. For us, there were definitely some frustrations along the way.

With older parents and older children there are many obstacles, like burn-out, skepticism, and exhaustion, because we have done so many interventions over the years, mostly with disappointing results. We know our children so well, and they us, that we have trouble breaking old patterns. The demands on our time have increased, and we're stretched in many directions to accommodate siblings, spouses, home, work and school. We're anxious to do some of the things we put aside over the years, like reconnecting with friends, family, and interests. And of course, as I've already described, there are many co-occurring conditions that mask the gains and make the work of remediation even harder, until they are identified and dealt with.

Looking back on the last 12 years, I only wish that RDI had been available from the start. When I watch old videos of Michelle from when she was very young, I see many RDI opportunities, and wish we could've been on the road to remediation a lot sooner. But thankfully, its here now, and Michelle's progress in the 2 years since we've practiced RDI can be measured in quantum leaps, which proves that it's never too late to make real, meaningful changes. I feel an incredible gratitude to Drs. Gutstein and Sheely for developing this brilliant therapy, and for restoring our hope and our competent role as parents! RDI is a powerful tool with which to help our daughter accomplish all of life's goals. Throughout the years, we have been supported by the wisest, funniest, most creative and whimsical people that a girl could ask for. Those same people, in turn, have been profoundly impacted by Michelle! Helpers, therapists, teachers and peers have all reported that she has changed their lives. Michelle is a powerful force, and it's been amazing to witness her impact. Autism has had far reaching effects well beyond its DSM IV definition.

Finding Our Way
April's Story

I remember the day we met: Michelle played with a yellow school bus on the floor as I spoke to her mother. She repeatedly lined up her little plastic people and one by one, put them on the bus. Just when the boys and girls got on the bus, Michelle took them off, one by one. Over and over she lined them up and made the people get on and get off the bus. At first I was puzzled at Michelle's behavior. I wondered why she did not seem to notice I was in the room. I thought it was a little odd that she did not look up at me or her mother as she played. After a few minutes I learned that Michelle had autism, though I really didn't know what that meant at the time. Michelle's mother wanted someone who could take her to the playground, interact with her and occasionally drive her to therapy appointments.

At some point, in the midst of our conversation, Michelle sat next to me on the couch. She did not say anything or look at me directly. Initially she scooted her foot toward me and then reached out to touch my hair. Then she scooted her body next to me and grabbed my arm, placing it around her as if to give her a hug. Still she did not look at me. It was as if she was trying me on. I knew at that moment this was an unusual gesture for Michelle. I could tell by her mother's reaction that it was rare for Michelle to express interest in people at that point in her life. I was hired. It was the beginning of one of the most important and meaningful relationships in my life. Little did I know she would impact my life so much and drive me to help other families with children who are affected by autism.

Before meeting Michelle I had never met anyone with autism; I had no idea what it was. I was told that she first put two words together when she was 5 years old. I knew that she did not talk like other children and that she rarely looked at people's faces. Her play was repetitive and lacked imagination and creativity. She did not play with other children, or even appear interested in social interaction. My job would be to interact with her for a few hours a day so that she would be occupied in a meaningful way. I was supposed to keep her occupied and engaged after school until dinner time, at which point she would be able to eat and get ready for bed. I basically tried to wear her out every day.

Sometimes, as part of my job, I took Michelle to her speech and occupational therapy appointments. But, the majority of the time I played with her and when possible, attempted to facilitate play on the playground with typical peers. At that time, Michelle was extremely active and enjoyed hanging on monkey bars, repetitively moving back and forth, to the point that her hands were so calloused that they looked like little bear paws. The week I began working with her she had broken her arm and I remembered how baffled I was when I had to repeatedly prevent her from hanging on the monkey bars with her broken arm! She was persistent and did not listen very well. Although her initial reaction to our first meeting was somewhat encouraging, she quickly expressed her dissatisfaction when I began to intrude upon her space.

I repeatedly attempted to join in her pretend play with little success. If she made the children line up to get on the bus, I would try to expand the play by driving the bus to the park before she took them off again. Often this resulted in her turning her back to me, or moving the toys out of my reach. But, sometimes she smiled at a novel variation, though the smiles were very rarely directed at me. I also had to bring my own markers to attempt to engage her through her favorite activity, drawing. Michelle refused to let me use her markers – until she realized I could really draw! Drawing became a vehicle for me to coax Michelle into further interaction. She, who had so few reasons to communicate with others, was motivated to speak to me in order to convey the pictures she wanted me to draw. Michelle also drew lots of pictures by herself. They were repetitive themes, reflecting her lack of cognitive flexibility. Previously drawing had been a solitary activity, but it became a starting point, a sort of bridge which would be built upon and which held the promise that other types of shared interactions would follow.

Looking back, I know now that Michelle created static systems with her play - she repetitively performed the same play sequence over and over, controlling her environment and frequently became upset if her play was interrupted or elaborated upon. Taking Michelle out of the house when she was playing with her toys was an art; I collected her toys and marched her to the car, singing, "The ants go marching one by one." This was no small feat, since she went through phases of collecting every Polly Pocket or Barbie Doll known to man. I could not leave one doll behind; she was an all or nothing kind of girl! I lugged a crateful of tiny Polly Pocket dolls, shoes, clothes, various pets, and other pieces of the house into my car. Once she was in the car, it was off to the playground. I joined her in her favorite playground pastime, monkey bars. I became very good at monkey bars too and we monkey-barred together until we both had bear paws!

I remember the first time Michelle showed the tiniest inkling of interest in a peer. We were at the playground and she approached a little boy who was about her age (6 or 7 at the time). Well, she didn't exactly approach him, per se; I should say (to my horror) she approached his sand castle and proceeded to stomp all over it. The little boy was understandably upset and proceeded to put his hands on his hips and yell at her at the top of his lungs. At that moment Michelle began to cry. It was the first time I had ever seen her become emotionally affected by someone else's actions. This was not the same kind of upset as if someone had interrupted her play or asked her to do something she did not want to do. She was crying because this boy yelled at her.

I knew then that I was witnessing something that was qualitatively different than anything I had seen her do before. I picked her up in my arms, put her in the car and drove her home. She sobbed the whole way home until I handed her over to her mother. My heart broke for her that day, as I realized that she had made some kind of breakthrough, a connection that somehow affected her in some way; she was feeling something she had never felt before. I wasn't sure exactly what it was, but I knew as tiny as it might be, it was important. On some level she knew another human being was very upset with her (though I do not think she made the connection of exactly why). Soon after that day, Michelle began to take notice of other kids more often, though she still did not initiate with them or attempt to join their play. She began to watch them and imitate them, but she was still very difficult to engage and preferred the periphery.

Michelle's interest in others began to blossom over the next year. My sister-in-law, Tori, was two years older than Michelle and in desperate need of a playmate. Tori was creative, talkative, full of energy and very exciting to play with! We all jumped on the trampoline together, picked berries in the bushes, fed horses, rode bikes, hiked in the woods, made 'clubhouses' and occasionally went swimming in a less than hygienic pond on the property.

Michelle enjoyed being with Tori, even though it wasn't an equal friendship. Tori led and Michelle followed. Michelle participated in the best way she could and there was no pressure for her to behave in any particular manner. Tori became Michelle's template for the perfect gal pal – outgoing, smart, creative, a real chatterbox with long blond hair. For the next several years any girl who resembled Tori in appearance or personality was a Michelle magnet.

Michelle's language (that coveted behavior we sought so desperately back then!) exploded with original thought and spontaneity during these after-school play dates. We all hung out just to play and have fun and when it came time to come home, Michelle began to get upset because she wanted to stay and play with Tori at the "farm" (it was really just a few acres of land with horses on it, and a vegetable garden).

Her mother was thrilled! Almost every day I had wonderful stories to tell of Michelle's successes and small miracles I witnessed as she and Tori explored the woods together or played games on the trampoline. I really enjoyed being able to tell Debbie how much fun Michelle was having and the great interactions she had with Tori that day. It felt good to see Debbie's face light up because her daughter was so happy. As nice as that feeling was, what was so obviously lacking was the fact that Michelle did not come home and share with her parents what she did during the day; I was her voice because she did not have the awareness or motivation to share on her own.

What I also missed was being able to help Michelle have this kind of enjoyment with her own family – her brother Sam frequently attempted to play with her, usually with disastrous results. Michelle was very resistant to interaction with him; he could be unpredictable and rough in his play and she didn't know how to handle it. If he attempted to play or talk with her she frequently overreacted and resorted to yelling or tantruming, sometimes having outbursts over seemingly insignificant things. As a result Sam began to tease Michelle and annoy her to get a reaction, which continued the cycle of rejection and avoidance. Michelle responded similarly to her father's approaches, often turning away, or becoming stiff in response to his questions about her day. She very rarely looked comfortable and relaxed around the guys in the family. In these early years, her mother was the only one she really seemed to be comfortable with.

At 9 years old Michelle was not really a part of the family. I do not think at this point she had a very developed sense of self, much less a sense of having a role in the family. She was not expected to participate in family roles or have any responsibility. (She was just too unpredictable and unstable in terms of her behavior and emotional regulation*.) It was a good day if she was happy, and her contentment was not worth jeopardizing by placing demands on her. Often she was out of touch with what was happening in her environment and entertained herself with her own thoughts. She did not share what she was thinking, or seem to care if people were curious, distracted, annoyed, or downright angry that she giggled to herself. Sometimes she giggled to the point where it drove us crazy. At other times she could get extremely angry very quickly. She needed warning before any changes occurred and required a visual schedule of the day's activities.

It was difficult to predict her ability to manage family functions or neighborhood birthday parties for any significant period of time. Debbie once described Michelle's difficulty with birthday parties as seeming to result from her inability to match the mood of the party. With so many kids in one place, inevitably some are excited, others are tired or cranky and everyone shifts rapidly from one mood to another. It seemed to Debbie that Michelle could never figure out what the mood was. During times when most families are enjoying themselves, for Michelle and her family, the stress level just got worse.

Michelle's parents attempted to lead normal lives, including going on family vacations. But there was no vacation from autism. No matter how nice the destination, vacations still involved planning ahead, drawing picture schedules, preparing Michelle for the next change, packing special foods, not forgetting the bag full of markers and drawing pads, thinking of "Plan B" if Michelle would not or could not go somewhere with the rest of the family. Sometimes I was Plan B. She was my 'charge' so I helped out when needed, and provided brief periods of respite so her parents and brother could have some sense of normalcy.

I remember a trip to the mountains where the whole family was preparing to go on a white water rafting trip down the river. We were driving up the mountain and almost there, when suddenly Michelle became upset. She yelled and banged her fists the rest of the way up the mountain and continued for over an hour as I waited in the car with her, while everyone went on the raft without us. It was sad to see her so upset and miserable, so obviously having no control over her emotional state. It became more apparent a few years later that Michelle had an emotional regulation disorder along with her autism. It was difficult to tell the difference between the tantrums (because she didn't get her way) and the meltdowns (more physiological in nature). Her parents tried many things to reduce the tantrums as well as their polar opposite, the uncontrollable giggling. Nothing seemed to work.

Throughout Michelle's elementary school years, her parents did everything they possibly could to provide the best opportunities for her, with varying degrees of success. By all accounts Michelle was considered 'high-functioning' and had made huge strides in some areas, as a result of her parents' efforts.

While Michelle had made a tremendous amount of progress in the years since I had known her, she still was quite limited in communication skills and social interaction. Her family continued to seek interventions as needed for Michelle's functioning. When Michelle was around 10, she began to experience a great deal of stress, and in combination with puberty, behavior problems began to worsen. After a while, her behavior problems became not only unbearable, but dangerous, and a local psychologist helped the family to get Michelle's behavior under control. Soon after that, her parents read the book, *Solving the Relationship Puzzle*, and began to learn about RDI.

When Michelle was 12, I began professional training in the Relationship Development Intervention® Program. The theory of RDI made sense to her parents. However, implementation was not so easy without a consultant. After several months of trying RDI® activities from the activity manual with some results, Michelle received a formal assessment as my supervision case. Having known Michelle for so long, it was a painful and sobering realization that she was not as 'high-functioning' as professionals had led her parents (and me) to believe. As much progress as Michelle had made over the years from various interventions, it did not scratch the surface of her deficits in relationships and emotion-sharing. Although she had years of language-based therapy, she had not learned to use language for true communication. Her language before RDI was very repetitive and limited to mostly making requests or obtaining information. Michelle started RDI® functioning at what some parents now refer to as "Stage 0." She had not developed the reasons for sharing joy through face-to-face gazing, or learned to use her parents as a reference point to resolve her uncertainty– something a 9 month old infant has already mastered.

When her family first began RDI, Michelle had several obstacles in her path. While Michelle had a lot of skills, she was unable to use her parents' emotional expressions to resolve her uncertainty, or to maintain her end of a simple play interaction. Though she could speak, her language was used primarily to get her needs met, or to engage in static scripted interactions disguised as jokes. One popular joke was to tell family members they had an alphabet letter on their forehead; for example, "You have an F on your forehead, for FAT." The predictable response was a forced laugh from the target of the joke; any other reaction and Michelle did not seem to enjoy it as much.

Michelle was extremely passive and prompt dependent* in the beginning, and on top of that, was in the midst of a very stressful school situation which caused her a tremendous amount of anxiety. She was actually hospitalized just before her assessment due to a major meltdown and self-injurious behavior. She began to withdraw from adult-initiated interactions and seemed to want nothing to do with her mom and dad. But after a few months of RDI, I noticed some major changes beginning to take place.

In the early stages, changing our style of communicating was a big focus. Though she was verbally fluent Michelle had developed little true communication and could not hold even a simple conversation. Being the respondent, all those years, to question after question, left her with few tools for real social interactions. I remember the very first time I had a true conversation with Michelle. Also diagnosed with a language disorder, Michelle had always been quizzed: "How was your day?" "What do you want to eat?" "Do you want juice or water?" "Do you like your food?" I was just as guilty as anyone else of this tendency to overcompensate.

I remember taking Michelle to a restaurant and making a general statement about my food, not expecting a response. After several seconds, Michelle became very anxious. She shook her legs under the table, she picked her finger nails. Then suddenly she made a comment. Not only that, but a comment that was related to my comment. We had a really nice conversation that day. It was slow and for most people, would have been painful to wait so long for a response. But, Michelle had never been exposed to this before. It made her very nervous that I said something that did not require a "yes" or "no" answer. Within 6 months she was able to have meaningful fluid conversations, at a more natural pace.

Over the first few months Michelle began to seek her parents' company instead of retreating to her room. She and her brother began to play together more successfully, without culminating in inevitable breakdowns and fights. They developed a repertoire of playful games and began to enjoy each other's company. She started teasing him like sisters do.

Another thing Michelle also began to do in the first months of RDI was to have a genuine social smile. I remember the first time I walked into her house and Michelle greeted me with a smile. I couldn't believe it. It was one of those things that you don't realize is lacking until you see it for the first time. I saw many more of those social smiles, and many more little signs of progress, and was convinced it was a result in the changes the family was making in their communication and interactions with Michelle.

During this early stage Michelle looked generally happier and her previously flat affect was replaced by smiles and affectionate teasing of family members. She walked around with a joyful glow that I had never seen in her. Little signs of progress began popping up unexpectedly. Her mother reported to me the small daily changes she had noticed. Some big changes had occurred, too - Michelle began to develop true enjoyment of her father's company and started hanging out with him on a regular basis. They went to the gym, took the dog for walks and went to the grocery store on Sunday mornings. I remember the first time Debbie described how excited Dan was when he got home from the gym with Michelle – they had a great time playing various games with the gym equipment. For the first time he had been able to interact with his daughter and they were able to experience the payoff of a true relationship with each other. Michelle, who for so long was anxious and stiff in her father's presence, was enjoying spending time with him, and spontaneously exclaiming to him, "I looooove you!"

Debbie also reported to me an unexpected phenomenon; one day on her way to school, Michelle suddenly began waving to them from the school bus window. For years she had always gotten on the school bus and seemed to be oblivious to the separation from her parents. One day Michelle began to look for her parents from the bus window. She waved to them and it was another instance of not realizing Michelle hadn't ever done something before, until she suddenly did it! It seems like such an insignificant event, but for a child who never before realized the disconnection from her family that took place when she got on the bus every morning, this was a milestone.

Suddenly, Michelle's steady progress came to a screeching halt as hormonal changes and stress of middle school made it difficult for Michelle to be available to relate to her parents. She began to be emotionally flat again and sometimes spontaneously began to cry for no apparent reason. Working on RDI® objectives became difficult. Debbie asked me to observe Michelle at school to verify what the school was telling her –which was that Michelle was doing great.

I remember the day I observed Michelle in her middle school. I was devastated by what I saw; a ghost of the girl I knew, a phantom wandering the halls, completely shutdown and disconnected from everyone else. Sure, she could walk from point A to point B and stop at her locker along the way, but she was so stiff, tense and anxious all day long and didn't utter a word to a living soul. She tuned out in her reading class, twirled her hair and was easily distracted by kids talking in the back of the room. She ate lunch by herself. She sat alone in the locker room after dressing out for gym, furiously picking her nails as the other girls chatted and waited for the gym teacher. I had to step into the bathroom and cry, Michelle looked so lonely and afraid. I had never seen her look so incompetent in my life and it broke me right then and there.

Later on, a fight broke out in gym class and every kid in the class turned around to see what was going on –every kid except Michelle. (And here, her mother and I had been concerned she would be aware I was observing her, as if she would have noticed the other kids looking at me!) My assessment of the benefit of Michelle's school day was that it was not only useless, but damaging. She was spending her whole day as a passive observer; incompetent, stressed out, not socializing and on top of that, not learning anything.

The funny thing is Michelle claimed that she loved school. She did not associate school with her anxiety or increased stress level at all, although clearly she was in a state of shutdown the majority of her day. She loved the fact that she got to dress up in the latest fashions, have a locker with a combination lock and change classes.

When her mother picked her up from school she usually was in a great mood and was a chatterbox the whole way home. No doubt, because she didn't speak to anyone all day, Michelle was excited to finally see someone she could interact with. The few times I had caught her eye at school during that visit, it struck me how she transformed from an emotionless zombie to just bursting with excitement when she saw me, as if she was not used to even recognizing anyone she knew in that chaotic environment.

In addition to Michelle's anxiety, I was also concerned about Debbie's anxiety –dealing with school personnel, worrying about Michelle's ability to handle middle school, and thinking about IEP meetings. All of these things took time and energy from Debbie focusing on what Michelle really needed to learn, which was how to function as an independent adult. After spending all her energy providing supports to Michelle in the classroom and training teachers, it was really taking a toll on Debbie's ability to carry out RDI in the home. At this point the school was a drain on the whole family's much-needed resources: emotional, mental, and physical, as well as precious time needed to focus on developmentally appropriate goals.

After many months of putting out fires and attempting school accommodations, Debbie finally decided to home-school Michelle. The stress level was just too high and the resulting anxiety impeded progress. At one point Michelle, masked by the flat affect and survival mode she had to operate in just to make it through the day, actually regressed, from previously mastered stage one and two skills. For several months I was really worried about her. I missed the upbeat, interactive Michelle that had been blossoming in the previous months. I knew if we could just control the anxiety and stress we would get the old Michelle back.

Once the decision to home-school had been made, the change in Debbie was remarkable – she seemed much more relaxed and reported how relieved she was that she was not stressing out about Michelle's school situation. Michelle was also much more relaxed and at ease. Debbie reported the daily teachable moments available to her now - Michelle was helping her with household chores and they were able to go on daily walks and regular outings. Michelle was learning something significant; from how to cook and sew, to writing papers relating to local history, after visiting historical monuments in the area. She was not sitting in an autism classroom folding socks or zoning out to cope with an overwhelming mainstream middle school environment. After 4 months of home-schooling and incorporating RDI throughout her day, Michelle made more progress in relationship skills, adaptive living and academic skills than she had in a whole year in public school.

Of course, not every family can or should home-school, but in Michelle's case, it was necessary to remove the obstacles that hindered her progress for so long. When she is an adult, it won't matter if she went to public school or not. What will matter is if she is able to function in a rapidly changing world, if she can solve problems on her own, make her own friends and hold her own job. Will she be able to think for herself and know what to do when an unexpected problem arises? Will she be able to make plans for her future and alter them if they don't work out as expected? Or will she be paralyzed by the unknown and rely on rigid rules and scripted rote information? Will she be dependent on others to solve problems for her? Will she understand the difference between a joke and a hurtful remark, a friend or an enemy?

The challenges for Michelle's family have been mainly about finding a balance and simplifying life so that they can focus on developmentally appropriate objectives. This can be difficult with a long history of child-led interactions and with Michelle's own motivation to be like her peers (e.g. in her mind this means dressing the same, going to school, driving a car, etc.).

Michelle historically has always had ups and downs in her development. I recently went through all my emails over the last two years and Michelle's down periods have been associated with increased school stress (which equals increased family stress). Just as consistently, Debbie has reported how nice things have been during the times when they are able to slow down and simplify life for a while.

I have seen firsthand how increased family stress frequently leads to crisis mode, which results in the need to feel like one is doing something (in the autism world doing something frequently means making sure the child is in as many therapies as possible, or as many peer groups, as much exposure to typical kids, etc.) For Michelle's family, as well as so many others I have worked with, the challenge has been to take it slow and not force more complex interactions and environments before the child or teen is ready.

Part of my history with Michelle has been going to summer camp with her for one week out of the summer. Every year since she was 8 years old I have attended different camps with her and each year she has progressed in different ways. However, the difference in Michelle's functioning since her family has learned about RDI has been qualitatively different, certainly relating to her increased referencing and being more focused on social information in her environment.

For the first time this summer I did not have to narrate or translate to Michelle what a speaker was saying in a group setting. For the first time Michelle referenced me for reassurance or approval in large group settings, often informing me of her intentions before she left to go to the restroom or run an errand. For the first time Michelle referenced various instructors in small and large group settings, when she was confused about what was happening or had missed out on part of the instructions.

In the past Michelle had always imitated other kids indiscriminately without thinking; if they raised their hands, so would she, with no idea of what was being asked or even being aware that if she got called on she would have to provide an appropriate answer. This past year Michelle was much more tuned-in, aware and interested in what was going on in her environment. She no longer raised her hand if the speaker asked something that did not apply to her; she was able to participate in dialogue with the group in an appropriate manner. She was even able to relate other children's conversations to me, something she had never done before. For someone who has always had severe speech and auditory processing deficits, these were huge gains given that these issues had not been specifically addressed with therapy. Due to Michelle's increased ability to reference, she was able to pay attention to the important information in her environment and did not need nearly as much support as she has needed in the past.

This summer Michelle was able to function with a much greater amount of freedom and selected several new challenging activities that she wanted to learn. I noticed an overall increase in her motivation to try new activities and learn new skills, instead of hyper-focusing for hours on one particular activity. She even made the comment she did not want to go to gymnastics one day, because they were doing the same things they had done the day before. This coming from a girl who historically reveled in repetitive, static activities - here she was, telling me, she wanted to learn something new!

Another huge change between this year and last was Michelle's ability to stop in the middle of an activity and transition without needing to finish it or get to a particular point. She was able to immediately stop what she was doing and shift to a completely different task. Gone are the days of singing, "the ants go marching one by one," to get her out the door!

Michelle has started to develop a true sense of self, commenting frequently on her likes and dislikes. At circus camp she frequently commented to me that she used to not be very good at some things and now she has gotten good at them, by practicing. She was okay this year with making mistakes, and did not feel the need to compulsively practice a trick until she got it right. She will say she is tired of practicing and take a break, go to something else and come back to it. This is a huge difference from even two years ago, when Michelle compulsively practiced the same activity over and over again, sometimes working herself up into a frustrated frenzy, unable to recognize when she was getting tired and needed a break.

I was so proud of Michelle when she accepted her certificate of achievement on the last day of camp. She received recognition in several areas of circus arts due to the fact that she voluntarily participated in three shows. Last year she did not perform in any shows; she was not tuned-in enough to be aware that she needed to plan an act for the performances. This year, after she tossed the Diablo (Chinese yo-yo) into the air, she referenced the crowd with, "How was it?" The whole crowd shouted "Good!" and she gave them one last trick for good measure.

It was amazing to me to see this girl, who last year had to take breaks in group settings because she could not keep track of what was going on, now able to reference her turn in a show, perform her trick, then reference the crowd's enjoyment, as well as the announcer, to know when to sit back down. It might not seem like much to you and me, but for her this was a huge feat. In addition to the Chinese yo-yo, Michelle performed on the trapeze and participated in a gymnastics act, all of which required referencing skills that were clearly non-existent at 12½ years of age. As Michelle stood in line on stage to receive her certificate, I could see that she was anxious. She paced a little, swayed side to side and rubbed her palms together. Then she scanned the crowd, looked at me and was visibly relieved when I smiled at her. Again, this seems like such a small feat. When Michelle began RDI at 12 she did not seek facial information or even know when she was uncertain. In a new, ever-changing and sometimes overwhelming environment, here she was referencing me to relieve her anxiety.

None of this would have happened if it hadn't been for the countless hours of interactions Michelle has had with her parents. Interactions focused on enjoying each other's company and coordinating together to achieve a common goal, instead of focusing on eliciting specific responses from her or trying to teach her a specific social skill. Her parents are incredible people who have not been afraid to follow their instincts. I admire their courage and hope, and am glad they have not given up on Michelle's continued improvement just because she is older. I have high expectations for Michelle, and I know they do too. It has been an amazing journey for Michelle, her family and for me. I am hopeful of Michelle's future and know that with continued focus on the edge of her development, she will make great strides.

Just recently Michelle has begun talking about her future; where she will go to college when she is older, having a job and about getting married one day. She frequently makes comments about things she used to not be able to do, that she can do now. Michelle expresses caring and concern for family members that she did not show before. She also will often ask for family members' opinions and form general appraisals about her experiences, with comments like, "I think I'm having a bad day."

None of these things have been formally taught to her. Michelle's parents have not brought up college or what to do if someone feels bad. Just the other day her mother told me a story of how Michelle would not leave her alone as she attempted to speak with her doctor. She kept chatting with her mom and interrupting her conversation, so Debbie casually suggested Michelle hang out in the car with her brother. Michelle immediately said, "But I want to stay here with you." Then she appeared to contemplate this and suddenly said, "Maybe Sam is lonely in the car. I'll go sit with Sam." This is a good example of the type of thought process that Michelle just did not have before RDI.

We will continue to raise the bar for Michelle and strive for the highest quality of life we can help her obtain. Michelle has hopes and dreams that she expresses to us all the time; things like friends, college, a job, marriage, and a house. She desires the same things anyone else would want, and her parents and I want to help her achieve these goals. I do not have any reason to believe she cannot achieve these things just because she is older. She did not have a social smile or the ability to reference at 12 years of age, but I have seen those things develop. Why should I expect that she won't be able to accomplish her hopes and dreams, as long as we provide her with the opportunities to learn?

RDI is the only autism intervention that is based on quality of life. It isn't always smooth sailing, and it's certainly not the easiest way out –it takes dedication and determination for parents to choose to remediate their child's autism. But, the results are truly incomparable to anything that has come before it. Which means that, even though many of these parents have tried every therapy, seen every doctor, worked 24 hours a day, everyday; they are still willing to take all of the hopes and dreams that they have put in everyone else's hands, and try putting them in their own.

✎ **April Choulat has been devoted to helping individuals with autism since 1997, and was the first RDI® Certified Consultant in Florida. She provides services to clients that range in age from 2 years to adulthood. April resides in Florida with her husband, Trevor, who is completing his RDI® Certification process, and their cat named "Kitty!" April and Trevor will the very first husband and wife RDI® Consultant team. You can reach April Choulat at rdifl@hotmail.com and at Spectrum Therapies of North Florida, Inc., 340 Third Avenue South, Suite B, Jacksonville, FL 32250.**

3

Milking Cherries

by Rachelle Sheely, Ph.D. & Frank and Arabella Mills

For parents of children on the autism spectrum, there is often little surprise by the quantity of isolated bits of information their children collect and interject into their experiences and the conversations they have with others. Milking cherries might be considered one such piece of information if one were not privy to the journey it has been my pleasure to have had with a creative, disciplined family from Northern California. Their story takes place on a vineyard, a beautiful farm which one day may be shared by two brothers, Frankcarlo and Henry. This is their story.

Autism always seems to come to the surface with a nagging suspicion that something is not as expected. This is not always negative, however, and for Frank and Arabella Mills there was a gradual realization that their child did not necessarily think about the world the way other children did. There were the amazing questions at the age of 3 such as "How does God get to earth?" countered by no response at all to, "What's your name?" In the end, however, it was an experience with another child the same age in a doctor's office that shifted the balance from brilliance to problem; from gifted and talented to autism. "I was in the waiting room with Frankcarlo and there was a little girl there. She was talking up a storm, having a real conversation with her mother. I asked her age and was told that she was 3. I thought she must be at least 5 and remember thinking, "Frankcarlo doesn't have conversations like that." Then, other differences became more apparent. "We'd walk down the street and he wouldn't stay with me. He would just wander off. I became worried for his safety."

Like many parents, the mixed message is one of confusion, especially if the child is the first—and this is the statistic—a predominance of first-born sons. Encountering the dance of a typically developing newborn quickly exaggerates the difference from very early on. We often forget that our infants teach us to parent and so when the wrong signals are sent we often adjust to those signals, increasingly doing so since the child is not regulating* to get into synch with us.

There were many early signs of a confused, disorganized child. Things that didn't stay the same were upsetting, a closed rather than an open bathroom door; a preference of Play Doh over imaginative play. Arabella, [Frankcarlo's mother] remembers, "He was never a postman handing out letters. The Play Doh seemed more an interest in texture than exploration. Then there was the disorganization. While he could remember complete books, he would stand in front of the wash basin needing help to: turn on the water, wash your hands, turn off the water and get a towel."

There were also disastrous consequences, complete meltdowns when something went wrong. For example, before RDI, Frank and Arabella had to buy two of everything. If something broke, they had a second in order to avert comforting an inconsolable child. A popped balloon could be quickly replaced with another, but crayons were a different story. The tape had to be handy at all times so that a smashed crayon, which happens nearly every time a child picks one up, could be immediately repaired.

Arabella recognized the dissimilarities between Frankcarlo and his sibling, "Having now experienced a typically developing 3 year old, it is easy to pinpoint these differences. I can say 'Go tell daddy it's time for breakfast,' and he will not only tell him, he will come back and have a conversation about the conversation he had when he returns." Like most parents, if their children were born in an opposite order there would be an earlier recognition of the need for diagnosis and intervention. This, however, brings its own justifiable fears. Turning a child loose into a world that focuses on his weaknesses and overlooks his strengths is frightening to most of the parents I see. And, so like many of us, Arabella would observe those similar things that other children did like her son and think, "There is nothing's wrong, they all do the same things, he just does them more."

As a professional who has now seen hundreds of children on the spectrum, I can say that this is often true. It is repeatedly a matter of degree. Emotion sharing and referencing, even joint attention* may be observed, but so infrequently that they can be remembered. With a typically developing child, these things often go unobserved because they are part and parcel of the interactive every day experience, too numerous to count.

Like many parents, it was the pre-school experience that underscored the difference in behavior and led his parents to move Frankcarlo from a teacher-centered classroom into a co-op where Arabella could accompany her little boy. In this situation, the differences were more prominent and easily observed by the parents.

One thing I notice about successful parents is that they seem to hold onto their sense of humor. Arabella light-heartedly recalled, "I moved from bedtime reading of romance novels to books on autism. The latter put me to sleep more quickly." Also, "The attitude in these books bothered me, they all seemed to see the children the same. It was hopeless and had nothing to do with the strengths of my child. I didn't accept this and it was what led me to you."

As I reminisced with Arabella about her little boy, I remembered our first encounter. Frankcarlo was a really cute little boy with a lovely temperament and a sweet relationship with his parents. There was always a tendency to be passive, but neither of these parents had ever given up their ability or right to parent their child. They'd never become dependent on the therapeutic community to raise their child. This was significant because as an architect, Arabella often provides a plan of what needs to happen. She was the last person that was going to let other people tell her what she could and couldn't do or tell her to give up the control over her child's future.

Something that Arabella and Frank also related about Frankcarlo's initial visits, is that the things we did [as consultants], as a matter of course, were also influential. The appointments were on time, the room was clean and the staff were all friendly and positive. (This is Texas after all!) But more important was the sense of joy in the activities and in the relationship of the child and caregiver. We also have an inordinate amount of respect for children and never have discussions about them in their presence. But, probably most important, the experience was focused and fun. While this may seem like a given for parents of children who do not have autism, fun is rarely part of the initial visit.

I love hearing the parents say that it was fun because, while RDI is not always fun—there are those times when it just seems grueling—I remember that first visit as hilarious and easy. Frankcarlo was a quick study and once we had thought carefully about the modifications that would make the world a more user friendly place for him, he shone with a wonderful brilliance.

There were a number of things that were important for helping Frankcarlo become more independent in the world in which he operated. There was the co-morbidity of ADHD that could not be overlooked. Medication was and has been very helpful for him. There was also the need for a low stimulation environment to help him know what to focus on. Without this, it seemed that his little body would go in any direction on which his gaze settled. Finally, there was the problem with response to the language of others.

Three things were helpful. First it was important to slow down speech. This gave him time to think, and rather than forcing a rapid answer, we engaged him mentally and gave him time to come up with a thoughtful response. We also realized that, in addition to the speed of language we used, we needed to provide silence. It often seemed like an eternity, to give him time to think and respond, keeping that old bugaboo of anxiety that so many of our children experience at bay. Finally, the use of Declarative language, although difficult to learn and practice, made an enormous difference.

In the beginning, Frankcarlo's little brother had not been born, so his parents were able to follow through both individually and together. Because they lived so far from Houston, we worked out an arrangement for them to forward a video tape to me every other week, and I responded over the internet. Their videos provided invaluable information for me and for them. Both parents were full of creative ideas and energy and I absolutely thrilled to observe tape after tape from these amazing parents. Many parents that we work with today use these ideas with their children, not realizing their origin. One of my favorites was a simple game Frankcarlo invented called "Word Crash"; parent and child settle on a word and then break it down into two parts and move their hands toward each other until they've coordinated their efforts to bring the word together. Mother says snow and moves her hand toward her child; child says man and moves his hand toward his mother. This continues until their hands touch and they shout "snowman" in celebration.

We have always known that generalization was problematic with our children [the patients we care for] because of the strong associational memories that get stuck within the static systems they create, to reduce the chaos of the environments within which they operate. It is not unusual for a parent to say, "We're going to grandma's house," and for the child to demand that he wear the same thing he wore the last time, and that they take the exact, same route. We knew the things that parents taught needed to have the ability to have greater influence over children's lives. Thus, the tension between lab and lifestyle is an area that clinicians have attempted to resolve in a variety of ways.

In RDI, lab time typically refers to a planned session. Frank stated, "We needed the lab activities to retrain and focus our patterns for interactions. In other words, I am glad we had the activities to create a foundation." We have different ways to think about it, but usually we follow a simple pattern of identifying a basic objective as a starting off point. For example, RDI currently has 26 stages, each with its own title such as emotion sharing, social referencing, caring for others, and so on. Within each of these, however, objectives are broken down into functions and skills—the functions being the reasons why typically developing children learn skills. Interestingly, in autism, the approach has often been to teach the skills and not the functions, a dead end since the children already are able to learn skills easily; it's the functions that are missing from the basic developmental repertoire. These stages are broken down into sub-functions, easily understood and evaluated.

With RDI® lab time, one would chose a sub-function and concentrate on this for at least two weeks. This doesn't necessarily mean that it will be mastered within this period of time, rather it's a source for keeping family organized in their work with their child. Then there are other things that go into a lab time activity: scaffolding*, pacing, elaborations, environmental modification and; always in the background, regulation, the master-apprentice relationship, Declarative language, episodic memory, to name a few.

Frankcarlo's family started out at the very beginning. According to his parents, his ability to respond to these early stages was so natural and easy that it didn't feel like work. They were enjoying him in a different way and he was bringing more to the table. As I watched these tapes, I often found myself at my computer, earphones on, laughing out loud to the uneasy stares of staff and strangers who might be in the vicinity. One memorable tape was when parents were playing "Monster in the Mountain," during which the child, within the safety of one parent calls to the other parent who is pretending to be a monster from behind the beanbag mountain. On one occasion as Frankcarlo and his mother called for the monster to come out, shrieking in anticipation, the father began to produce an earthquake, rumbling the bean-bags to build anticipation, finally jumping out wearing Mardi Gras beads and mask.

Little examples of lab-style activities, such as these simple interactions, underscored many of the games this family developed that were not only fun, but worked toward the generalization of functions through the development of episodic memory. It is often surprising for parents to realize that their children have a memory deficit. Frequently, they fail to realize the deficit because of a child's ability to memorize complete books, lists of where soda is manufactured throughout the world or capitals of obscure countries.

Episodic memory, however, is an autobiographical memory, often of a shared emotional experience, that we are able to use as a building block for future experiences we encounter. Frankcarlo's parents were especially capable in helping him develop this critical type of memory. For example, with "Monster in the Mountain," it was previewed* with a simple statement such as, "We're going to have fun"; encoded with a hug while shouting, "go away monster," and "we're a good team," followed up with a review. The review might be a video of the experience, a snapshot or even a trigger word such as "monster" followed by peals of laughter. It is these early games of childhood, and the encoding of our episodic memories, that teach us that the real monsters in our life are kept at bay through the important relationships we develop with the people we love.

But, it was not only the lab-style activities that provided the impetus for the growth we saw with Frankcarlo, it was the experiences that his parents took advantage of in their every day life. There is often confusion about the difference between lab and life-style activities. A lab experience is carefully planned out within the framing context, while lifestyle is an opportunity that presents itself within the context of every day life. So, washing the car, if it is planned within the framing context, would be considered lab-time activity. But, if a parent and child were washing the car and the parent saw an opportunity to spontaneously spotlight the sub-function/objective, this would be considered lifestyle.

Our emphasis on lab and lifestyle opportunities has shifted over the years. While we still feel that a significant number of planned hours are important, we've come to realize that they needn't always occur within a sterile low stimulation environment. While some children may need an environmental modification like this in the beginning, all do not and none need it indefinitely. An example of this shift in emphasis was the experience the Mills family had with the birth of their darling little Henry.

Henry's arrival was preceded by much needed bed rest and limited activity for Arabella. During this time Frankcarlo was busy thinking of a name for his little brother. It was unclear why he settled on Henry W. Mills but the W for Wong didn't seem to fit this Anglo-Italian family. The change to Walker was more acceptable to everybody and presidential as well. Not only did the naming of the baby herald an exciting milestone for Frankcarlo, it also demonstrated the importance of life-style RDI. Because the family had been involved in RDI for a limited amount of time, I was, of course, concerned about regression as they were forced to spend almost no time in the lab setting. What they did do was maintain the discipline of sending a tape every two weeks so that I could consult with them about their son.

Much to my amazement, Frankcarlo did not regress, but continued to make progress for the months preceding and following the birth of his brother. The primary reason for this was that the family was doing more RDI than before. It had become a way of life and Frank and Arabella were able to concentrate on specific objectives, using opportunities as they presented themselves in every day life. There were moments on the combine, in the car going to school, lying next to Frankcarlo reading a book, that were clearly as productive as those spent in the low stimulation, lab environment.

Another important lesson learned. Once a family understands RDI and feels competent implementing it, RDI becomes a way of life. It becomes not a 40-hour a week program, but an every-minute- of-the-day program. It is during the small, elegant moments of the here and now, the every day experiences that are so easily taken for granted with typically developing children where the miracles occur.

Many families of ASD children have difficulty thinking of activities to do with their children that are age-appropriate and not within a child's restricted range of interests. While not all children have restricted interests, many do and catering to these, often odd, streams of information is not really helpful for the child. Our honesty with our children will take them further than our pretense that we would like to hear about something that, not only we are not really interested in, but most other people are not interested in as well. If we fail to be honest, we do not help our children develop a true appreciation of what they must do to maintain a conversation or friendship. Talking to them about Egyptian hieroglyphics, their collection of yellow pages or small town airports; sends a false message of how human beings relate to each other. One question we always ask parents is, "What do you like to do?" Not only for the above reasons, but also because all of us will be able to stay disciplined if we're enjoying our child within the context of something that we enjoy. We have children rebuilding bicycles with their fathers, cooking with both parents, going deep sea fishing and sawing down trees to get ready for a new house.

The Mills family had many such memorable moments as they enjoyed the company of their little boy. Many of these have been viewed at our two-day workshops and also on our DVD. There are a number that stand out, following the birth of Frankcarlo's little brother Henry.

The Tree House

Frankcarlo had wanted a tree-house for some time. With an architect for a mother and a father who was quite good with machinery, the project could have easily been completed by Frank and Arabella during a weekend of hard work. However, the family saw this as an opportunity, and so the tree house which could have been constructed over a weekend took many months to complete.

The project began with Frankcarlo and his mother planning the tree house. This discussion went on for several days as she brought books that illustrated different methods of construction and types of roofs. This opportunity presented itself at an extremely important juncture in his development, because the problems he was facing were related to a specific core deficit of autism that we have come to understand as a poorly developed sense of self. Frankcarlo had been quite happy to have somebody tell him what to do, think for him and keep him organized. While most of us would not see compliance as a problem, for his parents and myself it was evidence of a more serious problem.

Often referred to as executive functioning*, the ability to plan is an intricate by-product of our children's differing neurological pathways. Thus, while typically developing children store proud memories of experiences where they have met challenges and overcome obstacles, our children are more likely to retain memories in a more isolated fashion—small pieces of information that do not provide tools or building blocks for future self-learning. For this reason, the time spent planning this tree house was crucial to help Frankcarlo begin to have preferences and to develop the hindsight and foresight that most of us take for granted and use effortlessly in our every day lives.

Even though his parents had worked hard and long on episodic memory, Frankcarlo continued to over rely on his procedural memory, the ability to memorize books or videos over episodic memory, the sharing of emotional experience. For our children on the spectrum this is an enormous problem that must be targeted careful and consistently. In Frankcarlo's case, he might have a wonderful time with his family and remember, not the emotional component, but rather that the mask was purple or another secondary, unimportant piece of information.

The tree-house carefully targeted this deficit. Each step of the way was documented with video footage and Frankcarlo's parents were careful to stress the important information. "We're a great team," as they went to the lumber yard to order a piece of wood, carrying it together back to the truck. "We did hard work," as they rented and drilled a hole to set concrete posts in the dirt. Once the planning was done, the rest of this project was clearly a "guy" thing. While not that well-coordinated, Frankcarlo worked alongside his father and learned about heavy equipment such as the large power post-hole drill, as well as equally difficult machinery for him: hammers, nails and small hand drills.

A beautiful example of work on episodic memory occurred spontaneously one day as Frankcarlo and his father were drilling fairly large holes in wood so they could bind the posts together with nuts and bolts. Frankcarlo had been doing fairly well with an electric drill when his father brought out a very old hand drill and showed him how to use it. "The electric drill is faster but this one belonged to your grandfather. Sometimes I like to use it better because it reminds me of him."

Egg-Dying

At Easter, Frankcarlo's family like many others have a traditional Easter egg hunt. Typically, the two children ran around looking for the beautifully dyed eggs their parents had hidden the night before. On one occasion, however, I noticed a difference in Frankcarlo's deference to his little brother. Although still a serious contender for the most eggs, he frequently monitored where the little guy was heading and steered him in the direction of a "find." There were some very nice signs of joint attention during this Easter egg hunt, distal pointing, following gaze. Most fun, however, was the sincere celebration when Henry found an egg and put it into his very own little basket.

Following this dramatic morning, the children decided to dye eggs again, have another hunt and re-experience the fun. This required an enormous amount of organization that was quite difficult for Frankcarlo, and it was only as his parents broke down the process for him that he was able to present the dying process to his brother in a way that helped each boy feel competent. I mention this, not only because it was difficult for him, but because it heralded a milestone, not yet formed - a harbinger of what was to come. Just as children need to build memories on which they can build new competencies, parents need these benchmarks as well. The struggle to remember and organize all of the steps in the process was a difficult one for him. Yet I believe it signaled that he had accomplished many of our earlier stages and was ready for a substantial developmental leap.

Reading to Henry

Frankcarlo had never had trouble reading but did have some difficulty with various forms of comprehension. Especially difficult was information related to text that didn't necessarily have a right or wrong answer. The notion of testing a hypothesis, experiencing the creative edge that comes from uncertainty was completely outside his repertoire. If the world in which he operated became too dynamic, he had few resources and often simply deferred to anyone in his proximity and asked, "What do you think?"

They say that if you want to learn, teach. As a former teacher, I know that this is true. Many things, such as spelling, came easily to me once I was in the position of teaching another person about these things. In college, prior to a test, I often found somebody who hadn't studied and tutored them. Following the lesson on Easter eggs, Frankcarlo began to spend more "big brother" time with his Henry. This included reading. And, it was about this time that there was a shift in the way he spoke with Henry, very similar to the way most of us change our syntax and tone of voice when talking to an infant or very young child.

Frankcarlo seemed aware of the effect of his behavior and tone of voice on Henry and was also sensitive to his brother's feelings. While the reading was fairly absent of questions related to content it was appropriately significant for use of language that was Declarative and involved the sharing of emotion. For example, commenting, "That was funny" and "it was a nice puppy. " And, when Frankcarlo added novelty, he did so in a way that was just right for a little brother. It was encouraging to see that in this situation and in others as well he adapted his language and his ideas to maintain coordination with his brother.

Cherry Stand

Approximately a year from the building of the tree house, Frankcarlo asked his parents if he could have a cherry stand alongside the road that runs beside their home. Whereas the tree house was something he wanted, it was his parents that made it happen. There was significant prodding to maintain focus and a good deal of organization that was not reciprocal. The cherry stand, however, was quite different. It began with Frankcarlo saying, "Let's do a cherry stand. Let's make some money." Most significant was that this was his idea and he had some very definite opinions about how he wanted it to look and turn out. For a child who had problems communicating and organizational difficulties, this approached amazing.

Once the idea had become a possibility Arabella agreed and said, "Well, what are the steps?" From this point, Frankcarlo took it over. He owned it and it became his project. Once started he was diligent and organized: "Okay, now we have to get started." According to Arabella, it was December when they got started and there were no leaves on the trees. Frankcarlo was already asking, "Are the cherries ready yet?"

There were many steps to this business venture. First, similar to the construction of the tree house, there needed to be a design. Frankcarlo had in mind a small building, but agreed to his mother's idea to take a drive and see what the neighbors were using to sell their cherries. It was necessary to review the competition. There were many very silly moments as they looked at the neighbors' signs and structures. They talked about what they did and didn't like saying, "You like that," and "that makes me sick," or, "I really hate that." Frankcarlo set out to develop a slogan that would entice and compete. My favorite, "Pit Stop - Cherries" did make the finals, but the other side of the sign, "Tasty Cherries - Life is Pitless Without Cherries" brought in the business. Finally, the collection of money—it was an honor system but they "didn't trust people too much." A can with a lid, nailed to the sign came out to the penny.

The desire to make money brought to the foreground many of the things parents and researchers worry about. There are a number of very bright, unemployed adults on the autism spectrum. It's not their intelligence that creates the difficulty, but rather the core deficits of autism in the areas of episodic memory, dynamic thinking, co-regulation* and experiencing sharing communication. In each of these, I was pleased to see mastery of the core deficits of autism and a strong emergence of capabilities in these areas.

As I mentioned before, it is often difficult for parents of a child on the spectrum to consider that their child might have a deficit in memory. It often appears that it is actually too well developed. Children quote videos; they can name every child in the fifth grade class and easily remember obscure information about dates of musicals. But, the memory that provides the basis for using the past to plan and work for the future, is a different kind, requiring that the brain utilize the pathways between the pre-frontal cortex and limbic system. When a child is able to do this: he can recall how proud he felt when he helped his father build a tree house, he can remember that at each juncture, decisions had to be made, and that in the future he will be able to use a hand drill that belonged to his grandfather as he builds something wonderful with his own son. The cherry stand that signaled how far Frankcarlo had come.

He was able to use the experience of the tree house for decision making about the cherry stand. He now had the ability to develop organizational strategies that resulted in having a dream he realized, one that came true through hard work and sufficient planning. Frank commented, "Many of our activities, such as the cherry stand, have given me a better picture of what and how Frankcarlo perceives things."

As Frankcarlo and his mother talked about the kind of stand they would construct, and the name of their cherry stand, there were many answers that might have been correct. The task called for divergent thinking; thinking up multiple solutions and deciding on one together. For children on the spectrum, this ability for cognitive set shifting and flexibility is very difficult. When they are presented with unexpected information they are unable to shift gears and generate novel thoughts and take action on those thoughts. Not only was Frankcarlo able to do this, he was able to accept a good enough solution. This freed him from the anxiety of having to make a perfect choice.

As with the tree house, the cherry stand was documented in video tapes sent by the Mills for feedback. The RDI® Program protocol lends itself well to distance learning and encourages that consultants and families videotape and provide feedback either by phone or over the internet. The Mills family has forwarded tapes now for well over 4 years. By now, Frankcarlo is used to being videotaped, knows me and every now and then sends a message directly to me. Once asking, "Do you have any girls at your office?"

When it was time to pick the cherries from the tree and sell them at the cherry stand next to the driveway, Frankcarlo demonstrated on video exactly how cherries should be picked if they were to last longer. First of all, pick the cherries, but not all of them at the base of the stems and they will last longer. If you pull them off of the tree without the stems they won't last as long and will be harder to sell. Looking at the camera and laughing he said, "That's called milking cherries. That's what Henry does." I watched as his little brother "milked the cherries" or ate them immediately after Henry put them in the bucket, savoring them, one by one while his big brother looked on laughing and enjoying the antics of the smaller one. No sales from this pail!

Frankcarlo's coming!

The Mills family has always been generous in their willingness to share their journey with other parents of children on the spectrum. We have widely used video footage of their work with their son and so in some respects he has become a well-recognized little boy, his cherubic face, becoming more grown up as we have spanned the years with him. On one occasion, the Mills were in our waiting room with two other families, novices who had come to Houston for an evaluation. As I walked into my office with the "new" family, I heard them whisper, "That's Frankcarlo and that's his mom and dad." The introduction seemed like meeting a celebrity, although if my memory serves me, there was no official autograph signing. But there is always the buzz around our office when Frankcarlo is coming. While it's not exactly like Christmas, the electricity seems to pulsate as the staff looks forward to seeing him and his parents again.

On one occasion, as mentioned above, before he came he contacted me to ask if I knew any girls. We had wanted to observe him with peers so he furnished a nice segue into the idea. Waiting for his dyad partner to arrive, Frankcarlo was clearly interest and excited. She walked in with her own agenda, "Do you like my highlights?" having just had her hair done. In honor of the occasion, she had been to the beauty shop and arrived not only with highlights but a big bow in her hair that matched her new capri pants. As Arabella recalls, "He bent his head the way he does when he is shy and then on his own said, 'Allow me to introduce myself, I am Frankcarlo.' Years later when they met unexpectedly, she didn't remember him. Further conversations about her now end with, 'She didn't remember me - I can't believe she didn't remember me.'" While none of us want our children to experience the heart-break of lost love, it is through the range of emotional experiences, not just those that are positive, that we develop the breadth of ourselves as humans and the capacity for compassion and empathy.

In RDI, we believe that a social skills curriculum has value for learning good manners and social rules. But we also recognize that it has limited benefit for children who are attempting to make friends and interact with their peers. Ten minutes observing children on a playground demonstrates the keen ability children have for playing together and effortlessly responding to the dynamic systems* they create together. For our children who have had to learn the rules, this simply does not apply. Children rarely check in verbally before changing the way they are playing an activity together and are more apt to send nonverbal cues to indicate that they are moving from one part of the playground to another. This speaks to a specific deficit that people with autism encounter. They simply aren't able to take advantage of potential opportunities with others because they lack the flexibility to not only engage productively with peers, but to be able to assess the social and emotional disconnects and take responsibility for repairing them or re-engaging their peers.

In observing the children together, we were able to assess a number of abilities Frankcarlo had developed over the previous year. We knew that he was able to manage a variety of skills that are typically strengths for children on the spectrum. In school and in his spare time, he was able to easily take in knowledge and store it. This isn't unusual. He was also able to retrieve information that had been learned and had shown an increased but varying ability to even manipulate the information internally and think divergently. Linear acquisition of information was, of course, his forte and so many educational demands were easy for him.

We, however, were interested in a different capability. We wanted to see if he could now "think about" himself in relationship to others. While it is common knowledge that children on the spectrum have difficulty making friends, it is less well known that more basic is an inability to have a relationship with self. Over the year, Frankcarlo's parents had worked very specifically on this.

We began this work by helping Frankcarlo work specifically on perspective taking. We defined the overall goal as being one where the highlight on an interaction is comparing and contrasting unique evaluations and/or interpretation of external referents. For many children, the problem is one of accepting and inviting others to share their ideas as they co-create a project together or discuss something of mutual interest. Frankcarlo had easily mastered this, but had also become prompt dependent in the process. It was not uncommon during conversations for him to ask for his parent's ideas, "What do you think?" and, "What would you like to do?" A quick review of "Perspective Taking" (an RDI® function) showed vigilance in being curious about the ideas of others; soliciting the interpretation of others when uncertain and valuing the differing ideas others interjected into play or work.

More difficult was the sharing of his own perspective or even understanding or being aware of what his perspective and preferences were. The suggestion for doing something a different way typically resulted in Frankcarlo immediately agreeing with the suggestion and throwing his own idea out the window. His parents came up with a number of creative ideas for working on this. One idea that proved fun for the whole family was "four-square." As they sat on the floor a pillow was thrown from person to person and each had to tell what he liked best about an experience. Other simple activities such as this seemed to help develop a sense of self.

Imagine a world where you lived completely in the present. You had acquired no memories related to pride in achievement when you were faced with a challenge or play was remembered primarily for its content rather than the emotional sharing of experiences with others. The memories that you had were of a static nature. This would mean that you had little ability and few resources for mentally using the past to approach current problems or the foresight to anticipate future problems with the understanding that you would be able to figure things out. Self regulation might also be a problem, because it would be difficult to understand that even in new situations there are patterns that you have learned in the past and that these numerous patterns will sustain you in an unfamiliar setting. There would also be the question of how self conscious you are on an on-going basis. Finally, how would your sense of competence support the identity that is unique to you? These are some of the core deficits of autism and were the things we had been addressing.

The evaluation began in the waiting room as the two children waited for their therapist to pick them up. They oriented toward each other with some curiosity and introduced themselves. The session was set up so that the environment would support the children's ability to play together without the constant prompting of the therapist. It was also arranged so that there would be maximum opportunity for things to go wrong. Typically, we think of our dyads as venues for practice with play as a side benefit. This was quite important because if the situation contained no elements where things could go wrong, there would be no evaluation of Frankcarlo's ability to observe these disconnections and do something about them. There would also be no opportunity for him to learn that in situations like this he could figure out what to do and continue to interact with his partner.

Most interesting, Frankcarlo not only had a good time with his playmate, but also showed a surprising amount of self-efficacy*. In each of the areas addressed with his parents, he was able to demonstrate competence with a peer. It was good to see that when faced with challenges, he was able to continue to participate with his friend. He seemed capable as well of integrating his past knowledge and experiences with his parents into this situation and in the process create new ideas and strategies for playing together.

This was not a complete surprise because, since the birth of his little brother, Frankcarlo had been tutored by his parents on the importance of being a big brother. Interestingly, many of the things that Frankcarlo missed as a baby and toddler were now done over, but with his little brother. He taught Henry many things, but learned from him as well. So, while Frankcarlo had to be taught by his parents to share emotion, he had an additional go-round with his infant brother. Except, that this time he was able to do a good deal more of the co-ordination for regulation and his baby brother countered with an equal ability.

Stories such as these become part of the history of each child, but the experiences serve another purpose as well. Frankcarlo was beginning to pen his own internal autobiographic memory. He was now able to use a mindful analysis regarding this experience to use later. In recalling experiences such as these with a little brother he was building the foundation to anticipate, to plan and to project into his future an understanding of what it means to be in an emotional relationship with another person and to be able to take responsibility for it. Frank has noticed that "during the last 2 years, Frankcarlo has begun to reference and copy our neighbors. He looks to see what they are doing and then expands this information into more complex actions." Thus, the foundation for a personal identity and self concept are formed.

There were other experiences that heralded a burgeoning self-efficacy with Frankcarlo. A new puppy (to replace a much loved deceased family pet) belonging to Frankcarlo created an additional "growing up" experience for him. Rather than training the puppy themselves, they assigned Frankcarlo to a class where he would be able to further explore the master-apprentice relationship with himself as the master. We know that practice makes perfect and this class called for a disciplined regimen of practice. Each day he walked the dog four times, each day he practiced four times teaching his dog to stay and sit. By now Frankcarlo had achieved a good deal of confidence in his ability to take on projects such as this one and so there were very few, if any, reminders from his mother regarding the need to practice with the dog or take him for walks. A video documentary of graduation showed a well-behaved dog and a competent master.

Being a child, Frankcarlo didn't always know exactly what to do. He did know, however, exactly where to look. Social referencing which had been in place for a long time served him well. By definition, we reference when we're wary or uncertain of how to change our behavior in response to what we see. This was evident as he referenced his coach, the other owners, and took actions with his puppy. A final video segment is something that will stay with me for a long time. Graduation was over and this young boy with a puppy almost as big as he, smiled with enormous pride into the camera; another autobiographical memory, stored for the future.

The first part of this story is important because in relation to broken balloons and smashed crayons it seemed a miracle that the loss of a family dog was taken in stride by Frankcarlo. He joined the search party and without falling apart, accepted with finality that the dog he had known since birth was no longer with them.

There are a number of authors who have influenced our work with children in the spectrum. They are responsible for our understanding of the core deficits of autism and coupled with their excellent work on typical development, we now know that deficits in mindfulness are the most critical, important areas to be addressed. Mindfulness* does not refer to a child's intellectual capacity; rather it describes the important abilities that are necessary for adult relationships and employment.

As Frankcarlo's parents provided opportunities for him to participate in increasingly demanding relationships with them, he was also showing an ability to think more divergently about other areas as well. This didn't come easily and often required that his parents help him feel, see and understand patterns so that they could deviate from them and help him find assurance that he would know what to do when things didn't remain exactly the same or weren't exactly the same as he predicted. For all of us, once we get outside our zones of comfort we can feel that the world is too turbulent for us to bear. So long as it doesn't become too chaotic, however, we emerge with a new sense of ourselves, our capabilities in understanding the new patterns that we now become more instrumental in forming.

It takes mindfulness to do this. It requires that we have not only the ability to respond to our environment, but to reflect on our ability as we do so. Two important, but painful milestones heralded the solid formation of this mindfulness with Frankcarlo. The first was when, during a family conversation, he confided that he had trouble with long-term memory. The second was when he became upset and said, "I don't know my own preferences." A magnificent, beautiful challenge had now presented itself to this bright boy. He was on his way to becoming a mindful person. And, it is only through the development of the various aspects of mindfulness that he and the other children with whom we work will ever achieve a sense of self and emerge from situations with new perspectives.

Imagine the thrill his father feels now when Frankcarlo sincerely inquires about his day. He is genuinely curious about things like picking corn and the number of trucks that were filled. "These aren't scripts. His self awareness, where he fits into the family - he is curious about all of the things I did as a child, for example, the boat I drove as a kid, and wants to copy them," said Frank.

Frankcarlo's parents have never given over their ability or desire for parenting to therapists or the professional world, which has sapped so many others of their energy and confidence. They have, however, allowed me the privilege of walking alongside them and sharing the ups and downs familiar to all parents, but often more extreme with a child who is on the spectrum.

Frankcarlo's mother described their journey this way: "When I was in high school I took art from two different teachers. One was an artist from birth and as a result could not teach what came naturally to her. The other teacher had to learn art herself and was able to teach us step-by-step what we needed to do to create our own art. RDI is like the second teacher. It gives us the structure we need to teach our child something that comes naturally to us, but not to him. Understanding that has allowed us to parent Frankcarlo on our own."

When I see Frankcarlo, now, I can see what his mom is talking about. There are so many different components to him, so many capabilities and motivations. He is not only a physical representation of them, but an emotional manifestation. He carries not only his parents hopes and dreams, but more importantly his own. There is no telling where he will go and what he will do when he grows up, but his parents have given him the foundation to spread his wings and fly.

✎ **Rachelle Sheely, Ph.D. is the clinical director of the Connections Center and co-author of two books with Steven Gutstein, Ph.D. When she is not on the road, she is at home in Houston, Texas with her two daughters, bright red jeep, poetry, knitting and of course, Mistletoe.**

4

Believe is Something

by Amy Arnoff & Jan Amodeo

Life Goes On

While climbing on a pile of beanbags, Jan invited Nicholas to play with the swimming noodle. Nicholas declared, "I'll be the shepherd to watch my sheep. We're gonna do angels all around." Jan asked how many angels there were. Nicholas stated "all around, all around." Jan wanted to pretend to be angels, Nicholas said, "Only angels fly and you're just a person." Jan wanted to pretend they had wings, Nicholas replied that "they only have hands." Jan pretended the noodle was her wings. Nicholas quickly reminded her that it was "just a noodle." Nicholas said, "The shepherds went back to their sheep, praise God all the way. Let's go learn all about God. Believe is something, write this down, write believe mommy. Write it down and read it." Even when mom pretends to lose her voice (one of the activities in the Relationship Development Assessment™ where a parent no longer uses their voice or words to communicate), he asked over and over for her to spell believe. She wrote it in the air and on the carpet, over and over and over. This was December 2003, our first RDA™ with Nicholas.

On February 10, 1993, Joe and Jan gave birth to a beautiful, healthy baby girl. Although Ashley brought them abundant joy, life was certainly different after she entered their lives. Before Ashley, Joe and Jan liked to dine out at ethnic restaurants, attend the symphony, go on outdoor vacations, bike, hike, read, garden and take advantage of what life brought their way. Joe and Jan both traveled in their careers. After Ashley was born, Joe continued to do this while Jan stayed at home and learned to provide care for her daughter.

When Ashley was only three days old, Joe broke the news to Jan that they needed to move from Cleveland back to Chicago. Joe and Jan both loved Cleveland and knew this would be a very hard move. Joe started work in Chicago approximately one week later. Jan visited Joe every other weekend. Eventually, Jan was forced to leave her wonderful Cleveland with its beautiful paved biking path, "the Emerald Necklace" which stretched from one end of Lake Erie to the other. They moved into a newly developed suburb on the far west side of Chicago. Jan adapted to fewer opportunities for nature and biking. Their neighbors were friendly. Life went on.

One ectopic pregnancy and six miscarriages later, they were still trying to have a second child. When the opportunity presented itself, they decided to participate in a research study for recurrent miscarriage. They wanted to do what they could to have another child and knew the study was their last hope. They stepped out in faith one more time.

Approximately 14 months later, they gave birth to a baby boy. Nicholas was born on September 2, 1998. When Nicholas first came home from the hospital, Jan marveled that she had delivered a live baby. She remained frightened for the first few days that something would happen and he would not live.

Away We Went

Jan would pick Nicholas up from the bassinet, and was surprised at his lack of muscular response. His trunk remained floppy. As an occupational therapist, she was a bit concerned. However, she had brought home her baby boy and was thrilled! Their family was now complete.

Life was, of course, different with a new baby at home. Ashley was 5½ and already somewhat self-sufficient. She helped hold and rock her new brother. Jan was tired after giving birth and her husband had also recently had surgery, so life was a bit overwhelming at times.

They soon discovered that Nicholas had reflux particularly while he slept. The pediatrician recommended having Nicholas sleep more upright in a car seat. He slept this way for the first 7 months of his life. Nicholas was also fussy in the evening. Sometimes they would take him for a ride in the van to calm him. Other times, Jan would carry him up and down the street while cuddling him. They even put him in a car seat on top of a running dryer and stood there trying to calm him.

Ashley seemed proud of her new brother. She wasn't keen about his crying during the night, but became accustomed to it. Joe was at work during the day and Jan became acclimated to staying at home full time to provide child care.

Jan was a bit concerned when Nicholas crawled late, not until 10 months. When he crawled, he tucked one leg in at a right angle. Her neighbor had a child who was a month older and he was already walking. Nicholas pulled himself up at 10 months and he started to walk around 16 months. However, it was nearly 18 months before Nicholas was walking all by himself. He also fell a lot and had bruises on his face and limbs.

Jan also noticed that he was a bit behind with some developmental milestones, besides the late crawling and walking. Nicholas was late talking and only had about 5-6 words that he used appropriately at his 18 month check up. This check up was notable after the fact. Ten days after that doctor's appointment, which included immunizations for polio, DPT, and Hib, Nicholas no longer spoke at all. He did not respond to his name when called and was notably more irritable.

During this time, Jan remembers taking Nicholas outside on a bright sunny day. There was not a cloud in the sky. Airplanes were flying overhead en-route to O'Hare Airport. Jan was very concerned when Nicholas did not look up or even seem to hear the jet engines. She tried to lay him horizontally in her arms and hoped that he would notice the airplane. She pointed at the airplane and said, "See the airplane?" but got no response from him. That seemed very strange to her. After all, it seemed that normally, children would look up into the sky to see where the sound was coming from.

A friend, who had attended occupational therapy school with Jan, came to visit a couple of weeks later. Her baby girl was 2 months older than Nicholas. Sharon [the baby] was way ahead of Nicholas developmentally. Without any prompting, her friend said, "I would get him evaluated if I were you."

Joe and Jan discussed this for approximately 1 month. Jan remembers Joe saying, "I don't want Nicholas to have a label if there is nothing wrong with him." However, they did decide to have their pediatrician take a look at Nicholas. Jan remembers this appointment well. "One of my concerns was possible muscular dystrophy. Nicholas seemed to fall so often. It seemed like his poor little head was bruised at least a few times a week if not more. It was great to hear that this was not the problem. The doctor said that Nicholas did not have muscular atrophy, so that was not the issue, but did say he could have a hearing problem. He ordered a hearing evaluation and away we went."

The audiogram was not particularly fun. Nicholas squirmed and whined, unable to sit still on his mom's lap. A week later, Nicholas had a more in-depth assessment of his hearing. This was difficult because the technologist put electrodes on Nicholas' head and Nicholas would not stay still for the test. Jan stood by the gurney stroking his head and arms. She leaned over to hug him and held his hand.

Life was starting to get very hectic with all of the medical tests and developmental screenings. Jan would never forget the moment when the pediatrician called one sunny afternoon, while Nicholas played in a kiddy pool with their neighbor and good friend, Jack. Her friend Maureen watched the boys while Jan took the call. The doctor said that Nicholas might have neurodevelopmental degeneration, autism, or a brain tumor.

They scheduled an MRI the next day to rule out a tumor. It was very hard to watch their 20 month old child receive an I.V. and be sedated on a big gurney in preparation for the MRI. They received good news almost immediately. Nicholas did not have a brain tumor. In an attempt to learn what was happening to their son, they went to the University of Chicago hospitals the next day for further evaluations.

The neurologist ordered further blood tests to rule out genetic abnormalities. They came back a week later for the tests. Nicholas also had an EEG, which was very hard to obtain, and some type of visual evoked response test. At that time, Jan was concerned about possible seizures since Nicholas was very restless while he slept, often kicking, jerking and finally waking. Luckily it was July 3rd and the offices were relatively empty. "We were ready to cry by the end of the testing. Fortunately these tests came back negative. The neurologist concluded that Nicholas had PDD-NOS."

They were relieved and dismayed at the same time. Almost immediately, they had a developmental play specialist come to their house to do an evaluation. Nicholas scored in the 3 – 6 month category for most skills. They soon entered into a therapy filled existence.

Reflections

It is ironic that Jan was once a nurse and is currently an occupational therapist. She was always the person doling out the care. Some of her best strengths as a nurse were compassion and advocacy. However, she never completely understood what it was like to walk in her patient's shoes.

When Jan learned she had a child with autism, she finally understood how confusing it was to figure out which therapies to pursue and how to obtain insurance coverage. One of her best resources was an autism internet support group. However, as to be expected, opinions varied. What worked for one child, didn't work for another. With limited knowledge, the family embarked on a trip with no end in sight.

The Journey

To begin with, Nicholas had physical, occupational, and speech therapy every week at the rehabilitation clinic where Jan worked. She was not sure how the speech pathologist even endured working with Nicholas three times a week. He mainly screamed and cried. Blowing bubbles was about the only thing that would interest him. Nicholas was also in a developmental play group, one time per week, with three other boys.

Jan started attending a support group for moms with special needs children. One woman recommended a gluten/casein free diet to help with all of the tantrums and sensory impairments. She plunged into this and started studying every food label before she bought a product. They ordered expensive food via the internet. She also tried new recipes, which sometimes were palatable, and others times were not. This lasted for one year. Jan and her husband had varied opinions on the diet. It became more difficult to continue, and they returned to a regular diet. Nicholas was starting pre-school and he wanted snacks like the other children. Her husband was not convinced that the diet showed that much improvement and thought the money was better spent on other therapies.

Jan also researched some biomedical approaches to autism. Nicholas had testing to determine heavy metal levels in his system. They started to give him daily compounded nutrients to try to help in his recovery process. Jan continues to feel that Nicholas made good progress as a result of the nutrients. Her husband remains more skeptical.

Nicholas also went to a developmental pediatrician. Jan had actually worked with this physician when she was a nurse in pediatric rehabilitation. This was the first doctor who took extensive time to sit and talk with them about Nicholas and his daily strengths and challenges. He diagnosed Nicholas with high functioning autism. The doctor suggested an inclusive pre-school setting for Nicholas. She did not think Nicholas would need ABA, but Jan and Joe decided to pursue it anyway.

They found a woman who did ABA programming with a school system. She came into their home approximately 10 hours per week to work with Nicholas. This was very trying for the trainer and for Nicholas because he cried constantly. Eventually he became accustomed to the drills and cooperated.

Nicholas started in an inclusive pre-school two days after his 3rd birthday. Jan was worried that the teacher would not want him to be a part of her class, because he cried and at times tried to bite or hit Jan. He was the only child who cried on the first day of school when she dropped him off. Jan walked away slowly as the teacher gently guided him into the building. Then she walked back to the van and tried not to cry herself. By the end of the first week, he did not cry when she left him at school. That was a relief.

Nicholas was extremely fortunate to have a wonderful team working with him at school. He had a 1:1 para-professional and the staff tried to make school fun for him. She remembers, "The school year ended and Nicholas attended a park district camp in the summer and also received 30 minutes of speech therapy through the school district for six weeks. Of course, the established therapies continued on through the rehab hospital. We were no longer doing ABA."

Jan hired a college student to work with Nicholas at their house who was studying speech pathology. Interestingly enough she was working with another child on the spectrum who was embarking on a program called RDI®. Jan bought the purple book (*RDI for Young Children*), which explains RDI® activities and showed it to Nicholas' teacher from the previous year. Jan thought it looked interesting. Looking back, she now considered the purchase to be an act of divine intervention.

The student and Jan tried to implement their own RDI® Program that summer. It actually was kind of fun. She invited Jan to meet me at a home where I was working. Jan went and listened to an informal presentation that I was giving and watched me work on some emotion sharing/referencing activities with the other child. Jan was very impressed.

After sharing her enthusiasm with Joe, they hired me as their consultant. Their son's pre-school teacher came over to get training with me in some of the beginning techniques of RDI. They were encouraged and wanted to dive into the program.

Everything for a Reason
Amy

I became interested in autism back in high school. I loved to read and picked up a book about an autistic child. After I read the book I decided to volunteer at the Easter Seals Foundation and was an aide in their birth to three programs. This is where I was introduced to my first autistic child. The experience really resonated with me and I began to get more and more involved in the autistic community.

Every autistic child I encountered was so different. They seemed like lost souls to me. No one knew quite what to do with them. I would try to engage a child in an activity and it was challenging and frustrating for me. I could only get the child to pay attention to me for a second and then I would have to start over from square one the next day. The kids did pick up routines pretty easily and that part I felt I could help improve.

Eventually I went to school part time studying psychology and Special Ed and was trained to do ABA. I found the work to be rewarding and yet I didn't feel like I was seeing these kids get what they needed. One day I was browsing the internet and I discovered Dr. Gutstein's book. I read it for myself and then gave it to one of my clients to read. This book made so much sense. I could not figure out why it took this long for someone to put this type of program together. It was so obvious that this was the missing piece. One month later, we flew to Connections Center for an evaluation. I immediately started working with Jan and Nicholas on RDI® and we saw great results together. Two months later, I was training to be an RDI® Consultant.

I have spoken with a lot of families and many of them were not given much hope for the future. They were basically told to accept their child the way they were. Doctors, teachers, parents…all misunderstood children on the ASD spectrum. And, as a result, their children remained lost in their own world where they felt safe as long as things didn't change. When I discovered RDI, I introduced it to my current families. I noticed that the kids I was working with started to look at people, not through them. It was like giving the parents their child back, little by little.

As life went on, I would venture down new career paths, but every time I was guided back to working with autistic children. For instance, I have three grown boys of my own and was a stay at home mom, but continued to do volunteer work in the autism community. Even when I was indirectly involved with autism, I was still gaining a lot of information for what I now believe is a specific reason. Asking, listening and believing are what it takes. God is watching and guiding, waiting for us to take the steps needed to continue on our path.

Soon after hiring me, Jan threw herself into the process. She immediately went shopping for beanbag chairs and her husband seemed pretty tolerant of her plunking down additional money for yet another type of therapy.

I gave them a number of suggestions to follow through with at home and returned once a week to guide them in this new therapy. However, the distraction level was too much for their son at home. So, they decided to drive the 45 minutes a week to come to my office. Jan's initial impression, upon arrival, was that the room was very small and stark. I had a cabinet and shelf for supplies. It just didn't feel warm and fuzzy to Jan. However, Jan could soon appreciate the lack of distractions and understand why my work space was so barren. Nicholas was very difficult to work with at that time. He mainly cried, kicked, hit and bit Jan. At other times, he just burrowed under beanbags for a long time.

Working Hard

Jan grew up with two German parents on a farm in Michigan. There were four children in her family. They worked very hard to help with chores around the farm and Jan still functions that way. Jan was taught that if you work hard, you can accomplish anything. Nicholas' poor behavior and lack of immediate success in RDI was frustrating for her.

One thing Jan really worked on was Nicholas' attitude during the car trips to my office. Jan wanted Nicholas to be calm and happy when they arrived. She said prayers in her head and out loud asking for God to bless them with a good session. Jan said, "Eventually Nicholas joined in and we prayed for God to bless me too. God is good and he was listening." Not every session was great, but she usually learned something that she could take home and work on with Nicholas.

One day I was going over mental engagement with mom. Nicholas could not get the Uno attack game to start. He referenced mom, she pushed the button hoping that the, problem was solved. Nicholas then could not get the cards to spit out. So, again he referenced mom, but this time mom just smiled and Nicholas had to come up with his own solution. He said, "What if I took some cards out?" He referenced mom and again she smiled, he took some cards out and tried it and again it did not work. He referenced mom until he was able to solve the problem. He trusted that she would not let him fail.

We began working on episodic memory. Episodic memory is the ability to encode the event and the emotion associated with the moment and put it into your own unique perspective. I took a picture of Jan and Nicholas running and knocking down a beanbag tower together. The photo caught them in mid-air with the sunlight behind them. Nicholas smiled, looked at the photo and said, "We look like angels." That was in 2004 and Nicholas could finally pretend they were angels with make-believe wings.

Getting to that wonderful emotional referencing took a long time. Emotional referencing happens when you use the reactions of a trusted person as a reference point. You "borrow" someone's perspective. After a lot of work, Nicholas was finally able to check with mom when he was unsure of what to do.

Training for the Marathon

When they initially started RDI, Jan was a bit frustrated because she had hoped for quicker results. Her husband was good about cheering her up, but she felt that they should be further along in the recovery process after all of the therapy. Jan eventually heard the phrase, "Autism is not about training for a sprint. Rather, it is like training for a marathon."

Life at the their home revolved around Nicholas. It was difficult for Jan to have any quality time with Ashley. Nicholas clung to her and whined without her. Jan had very little time for any type of "non-therapy" conversation with her husband. It was not very conducive to a happy household. Jan often battled with exhaustion. Nicholas was not a good sleeper for the first few years and Jan often got about three good hours of sleep per night. Jan spent many nights on a mattress on the floor in Nicholas' room to help everyone sleep better. Bedtime was a continual nightmare as far as the family was concerned. Jan tried to let Joe sleep during the week so he would be more rested for work. On Friday and Saturdays, Joe would sleep on a mat in Nicholas' room so she could be rested for her weekend OT job.

Slowly, the family stopped saying, "Look at me," to Nicholas when they were trying to converse. They also stopped physically turning his head in their direction. His eye contact started to be more natural and was not prompted. He eventually learned that it was critical to look at someone in order to understand how to adjust his own response to their action.

Jan posted laminated sheets of Declarative statements around the house. She had a hard time changing her language, from asking questions of Nicholas, to making statements that elicited more language from him. Jan's husband and daughter often heard, "Quit asking Nicholas so many questions," from her. Personally, Jan thought that the switch to Declarative communication* was the key to success. Declarative communication is verbally or non-verbally sharing an experience or feeling with someone else. There is no specific response required, no right or wrong answer. The only goal was experience-sharing. It encouraged Nicholas to think and respond with more than one word.

They set aside about a half hour per day to work on specific objectives in a distraction free environment, working one-on-one with Nicholas. The only time they were able to do lab time together was late in the evening which was probably not good for any of them. However, that's when Joe was home from work and Ashley was done with her homework. Jan wanted the entire family to learn these new and promising techniques. At times, Nicholas would balk and say, "I don't want to play RDI games." However, there were successes along with the setbacks.

One day we were working on referencing at a mall escalator. In the past, Nicholas would demand to go up and down as many times as he could before mom or dad put a halt to it. Nicholas and Jan met me at a local shopping mall on an autumn morning when the mall was not busy. We spent time teaching Nicholas to reference Jan in order to go up and down on the escalators. Within a short time, he had mastered this activity. Afterwards, we went into a Christmas store and looked around. Nicholas and Jan decided to buy some handmade ornaments that could be personalized. The clerk needed some information about names. Nicholas started to speak with the clerk and had some real conversation going on. The woman was impressed with his politeness and they both seemed to enjoy the short interchange.

Nicholas was also beginning to recognize gender differences. For years, he called boys, girls and vice versa. Over time, he started to call his sister Ashley a girl and not a boy. That was big hit with her.

Hey, Look!

As a health care professional, Jan used to stress to patients that they must follow through with exercises at home or they wouldn't continue in their recovery. After Jan finally got Nicholas to bed and settled into bed next to her husband for the 10 p.m. news, she still had things to accomplish. Usually Jan read her own Bible first and then went on to read Dr. Gutstein's "activity bible," *RDI for Young Children*. It would often take her a few evenings of reading to really understand what I wanted them to work on. Sometimes Joe would just look at her and wonder why she was reading the RDI® book again. Jan repeated over and over that she had to be prepared for the next day, so Nicholas could keep moving ahead.

Jan said she remembered me saying that when Nicholas got better at emotion sharing, he would ask to play the games. She thought, "yeah, sure…I will believe it when I see it." I mentioned that another child was making progress with two sessions per week. So Jan decided that was the way to go. It was tight, but they fit it in. She drove 45 minutes to therapy, had an hour session, and then drove one hour in the opposite direction for Nicholas to attend afternoon pre-school. With a heavy foot, they usually got there just in the nick of time. Once again, she felt exhausted and it was only 12 noon. Jan felt that Nicholas really began to achieve more success when they started coming twice a week.

One day we were doing an activity and Nicholas stopped and said, "Hey, look!" He was pointing and looking at both our faces as he proudly pointed to the squirrel sitting on the fence right outside my office window. This was the first time he ever noticed a squirrel, let alone wanted to share it with someone! Joint attention was coming into his world. Nicholas finally wanted to share his world with us. He would show us things and look at the reactions on our faces. It was great!

Another fun memory was when we went for a walk outside to work on coordinating our actions. Nicholas would walk and I would indicate by clearing my throat when he should start and stop walking. We then would occasionally "shoot" him with silly string. Initially, he did not know where the "green" stuff came from. Eventually, he figured it out. We had some good laughs.

Nicholas was starting to break out of some fixed routines in therapy; for example, always having to read a book with me before leaving my office. It was very difficult for Jan and me to discuss Nicholas' progress and obstacles at the end of a treatment session. We could not even talk to each other during our sessions. He would pull on Jan, hide under her shirt, sometimes bite, or whine when we tried to have a conversation. This was a common occurrence. One day Jan and I looked at each other and noticed that Nicholas was tolerating us talking to each other. These things happened little by little.

One of the activities Jan really missed was scrap-booking. Jan used to show Nicholas pictures in her scrapbook. Now, she longed for the day to do more of it. When she paged through photos with Nicholas, there was some recognition of the people by him, but the photographs certainly did not provoke any emotions. This was sad to her, as she remembered their daughter from one year old looking at pictures and really grasping what was going on in the photos. Usually smiles and verbal recitations of the event exuded from Ashley. Why didn't Nicholas experience joy and smiles when looking at these pictures? Why didn't they trigger emotions in his brain?

Jan and Amy decided that they needed a sophisticated "memory encoder," a Polaroid Camera! She took lots of pictures, but didn't know how to properly use them for Nicholas to encode* the memory. Encoding an activity meant that Nicholas had to be able to talk about and describe the activity. He needed to tell us what happened, how he felt and tell us his perception of the activity.

Jan learned how to take the photo at a moment of productive uncertainty. A state of uncertainty exists every time we encounter something new. It is during this time that learning takes place. During an activity, Jan would create a moment when Nicholas was uncertain about what was going to happen next. It was a part of the activity that was different than what we did before. Nicholas labeled it and then identified the emotional tone of the photo. They did this immediately after taking the picture. At a later time, they revisited the experience through the photo in order to remember the emotions.

Starting to Come Together

Transitions were always difficult. The smallest change in routine could precipitate a major meltdown. Nicholas would tantrum if Jan decided to take a different route to therapy. He screamed if his dad backed the van into the driveway instead of driving in forwards. Stores were horrid. He often balked so much when they drove into the parking lot that Jan would decide not to go in.

Jan started to work on RDI in the grocery store. She was beyond worrying about what other people thought. After all, Jan had lived through the Costco incident, one particularly momentous tantrum, when everyone in line including the cashiers, stared at this screaming, biting, unruly child.

Eventually, all of the practicing, hard work and playing began to come together. Nicholas had wanted to eat some popcorn. So presto, within 4½ minutes of microwave popping time, they had gourmet popcorn. However this time, he ate it with a bit of a twist (while lying on his tummy on their floor). Then Nicholas had popcorn on a plate and ate it with a fork. He was smiling and laughing as he tried to master this. Just then, one of their extenders came in to start working with him. They all got a chuckle out of this. She never in her wildest dreams imagined that Nicholas could become this flexible.

Life is Hard, But God is Good

Life was on an upswing. Even Nicholas' teacher was becoming more interested in RDI. Amy went to observe his classroom, "I gave the team suggestions about Declarative communication and ways to get Nicholas' attention without direct prompts. Jan was thrilled that others were seeing the value of RDI implementation."

At home, the family started to be increasingly silly. They put gloves on their feet, read books from back to front, put plates upside down on the table to eat off of and enjoyed wacky stories about an elephant and a clown taking a bath everyday in their tub. It became a daily routine to check to make sure they had cleaned up the water on the floor before they left. This was really starting to be FUN! They smiled and laughed a lot more than they had in a long time.

Nicholas would ride the bus home from school and arrive at 3:40 p.m. Jan had purchased a bunch of animal masks, silly hats and noses and wore a different one every day. After all, she first had to get Nicholas' attention before he could reference her. After a while, the kids started careening their heads in anticipation as the bus pulled to a stop. The bus driver and all of the children laughed and screeched day after day when it was time for Nicholas to get off the bus. They live on a busy street, so neighbors and motorists probably wondered who the weird person with the masks and hats was. That was fine by her. She was helping Nicholas to notice her without fail every day when he arrived home from school.

One of the phrases that go through Jan's mind from time to time is, "Life is hard, but God is good." Her faith has kept her going through this entire long ordeal. Jan is involved in a Bible study and gives credit to these women for their prayers. They attend mass weekly. She used to wonder why they went to church as Nicholas had such poor behavior. Now Nicholas prays and sings with the rest of the congregation.

There is a verse in the Bible that Jan clings to, " 'For I know the plans I have for you,' declares the Lord, 'plans to prosper you and not to harm you, plans to give you hope and a future.'" (Jeremiah 29:11) It is very important to Jan to pass on her faith to Nicholas. She prays that Nicholas will be able to serve God during his lifetime on earth.

They look to the future with hope for their family and hope that Nicholas will grow up with friends to enjoy life alongside of. They hope that he will live independently as an adult in the "non-autistic world." Their dreams include gainful and meaningful employment for him. If Nicholas desires to marry someday, they hope that opportunity will present itself as well.

Opportunities for Change

Opportunities for positive change are how RDI continues to transform Nicholas' life. Sometimes changes give them wonderful results and sometimes they have to think of new ways to implement changes. Ever so slowly, he's starting to tolerate more change. Now, they are able to drive over or under highway bridges without Nicholas crying. It has become a bit easier to go to the grocery store; a huge step, compared to what they had to deal with before.

Nicholas is now much calmer. They tell him what the main activities of the day will be when he gets up. And, they can often make changes without much resistance from him. He generally goes shopping without any problems now. Nicholas is excited to try any new restaurant or go to new destinations for a vacation. He does not shy away from meeting new people. His volitional eye contact is much improved. Meals are more pleasurable than they used to be. The family changes their seating routines repeatedly in order to stimulate more acceptance of change. Jan puts the plates and cups on the table upside down. Someone asks for ketchup and Jan might hand them maple syrup.

As a result of these persistent antics, Nicholas continues to try new foods. He ate tomatoes the other day without any whining. Vegetables still cause him some distress but, he is gradually accepting them. In general, Nicholas appears to be less sensory challenged.

School also enabled Jan to give Nicholas more independence. During the first year of school, Nicholas car-pooled with a neighbor girl. When the girl moved to another neighborhood school, Jan was in a bind since Ashley got out of her school at the same time, 5½ miles away. Thus she opted to put Nicholas on the bus. Jan said she felt like a bad mom initially, but Nicholas really enjoyed this new mode of transportation.

Jan continues to attend many conferences on topics related to autism. She was happy to pass on an RDI® flyer to Nicholas' school staff for the 2-Day Workshop in their area and was pleased to attend with his teacher. She really learned a lot during those two days. Jan and Joe went to a 4-Day RDI® Parent Seminar a few months later. This really helped clarify methods of working on RDI with their son. It was especially helpful for her husband who cannot be as involved as Jan, because of his job.

Last year, Nicholas started to attend the local neighborhood school as he moved on to kindergarten. He started to take the "big" bus to school. The transition appeared to go fairly smoothly. They all adjusted to a new staff. Jan met with the team monthly to go over RDI® techniques. They tried to work on episodic memory at school. Jan learned that in order for school to be successful, Nicholas needed to incorporate the memories immediately.

Nicholas is more willing to try to play cooperatively with a few neighborhood friends. He still requires quite a bit of prompting at times, especially when he is fatigued; he also lacks imaginative play and is quite rule bound. He would prefer a board game to any type of creative play. However, he does surprise Jan at times and shows some imaginative play. Nicholas has "made" dinner for Jan in his play kitchen and really enjoyed serving it to her.

Something that has been difficult for Nicholas is imitating other's facial expressions. He has oral motor apraxia, which means it is challenging for him to coordinate his mouth movements. When we embarked on learning "Degree of Emotions" (noticing gradual changes in people's facial expressions), he struggled to recognize them; Nicholas could only make a "happy" or a "sad" face. Jan said it was even difficult for him to understand why people used other expressions. After all, he worked in front of a mirror time and time again, only to fail at copying mom's facial expression.

It took many attempts up until the age of 4 for Nicholas to learn to stick out his tongue. Other parents tell their children "don't stick out your tongue." Jan kept trying to get Nicholas to do just the opposite. It is important to have proper tongue movement for oral language and even chewing food. As a result of all of their hard work, Nicholas has become much more fluent in conversation. He can even manipulate words sometimes to his advantage. However, Jan stresses that he needs to tell the truth and not make up stories. Honesty is a very important family value.

Family, Friends and Seasons

Joe and Jan feel that family time is essential. Jan also greatly values friendships for them as a couple and for herself. She has lost friends along the road due to heavy commitments to therapy and friends who just don't understand the burdens of autism. Jan told me that a good friend sometimes reminds her that we all have certain seasons in our life. This is her season to be very committed to her children's needs.

Needless to say, they are also very busy with their daughter. Ashley is active on a local swim team, playing softball, swimming and piano. Jan admits that it is very difficult to manage all of their activity at times. Trying to avoid burnout and maintain sanity are her immediate goals on some days. It is also tough to fit in all of their home therapy. But, life in general is taking on a more peaceful tone.

This year they attended a swim meet for Ashley 5 hours away in Quincy, IL for the 3rd year in a row. Due to lack of rooms, they shared a two room suite with another family. The other family has a boy 2 years older than Nicholas. This child is somewhat quiet and the boys had some similar interests such as board games, playing in the pool, and video games. By the end of the weekend, Nicholas was calling Matt his new friend. One day at the pool, Nicholas came up to ask Matt's mother and Jan what they would like to eat from "the menu." He was holding up an invisible menu. So Jan and her friend told him what they wanted. He then walked off, moved his hands around in the air (gathering the food). All of a sudden the "restaurant" had run out of some of the dinner items that they wanted. He also brought them the wrong food sometimes. They ate and he came back to check if they wanted dessert. What a delightful, non-caloric meal.

A week and a half after returning home, they invited Matt over to play. He was there for 3 hours, which is a very long time for Nicholas. For the most part, the boys played together with only occasional prompting; taking turns during a game, and backing off on silly talk or singing at times. But, they came up with their own ideas of what to play. When it got late, Jan took Matt home before continuing on to RDI® therapy. Matt got in the door and asked his mom, "Can I have Nicholas over to play sometime?" As they were closing their door, Jan also heard Matt say, "Mom we had so much fun." Now in Jan's opinion, life doesn't get much better than that.

Ashley is less embarrassed to have friends over. She used to be disturbed by Nicholas' behavior, unusual language, and messy eating skills. Ashley still occasionally mentions to a new friend or visitor that "my brother has autism."

Jan believes that marriages can be made better or broken by a special needs child. They have been through many stressful times together and will continue to do so. It was sometimes difficult to make a point of doing lab time instead of enjoying family or couple time. Jan said she tries not to, but does often put Nicholas' needs ahead of others in the family. That certainly includes her needs as well. Jan still struggles with feeling guilty if she has some down time and is not working on therapy. Fortunately, Nicholas likes to ride his bike just about as much as Jan does. They have a lot of fun together as he tries to race her.

In July, 2005 Nicholas started to work in 2 different dyad groups. He plays with a 9 year old girl and also an 8 year old boy. Jan's eyes continue to be opened to the new possibilities that RDI presents. She enjoys seeing the differences as well as the similarities between Nicholas and these children. They certainly build on each other strengths. It is exciting to watch Nicholas adjust to more change and unpredictability in life.

At the start of the dyad, the kids had never met, so I took Nicholas and Jackie (the 9 year old girl) to a park. Nicholas led the way with Jackie following behind. When Jackie lost Nicholas, she stood at the top of the play set and looked and called for Nicholas until she found him. Jackie tried to imitate Nicholas by jumping off the swing. She hurt her knee and was upset. Nicholas tried to cheer her up by making silly faces at her. Eventually this worked!

One day while swimming with Jackie, I asked Jackie to guide Nicholas to go under water. In the past this was a difficult thing for Nicholas. He followed her and was able to go under water for a short period of time. I asked him how it was and he told me, "interesting." Then they went under water together and made silly faces at each other.

I also introduced Nicholas to another boy about his age. We went on a nature walk. Seth had been there before, so he led the way. Seth went to his favorite spot and walked right into a creek. He coaxed Nicholas in as well. Reluctantly, Nicholas went in the water. After they walked into a second creek, Nicholas asked me why he had to do what Seth wanted to do. I told him that sometimes you do what your friends like and sometimes they do what you like. Nicholas asked me if this was a rule or a law, because he only understands rules and laws! I told him that it was neither a rule or a law. And again he repeated that was all he knew. It made me realize how far we had come and yet how far we still need to go!

After a couple times of meeting his new friends, I could see a definite desire to play with them. I had Nicholas and Seth in my office playing. They started to throw beanbag chairs at each other. They wrestled, pounced on each other, knocked each other down and happily ran around the room chasing each other; they finally 'danced' to the song of co-regulation. The boys were spontaneous and unpredictable in their play. And they had to balance what they were doing to create a smooth social experience. They were careful not to throw the beanbags too hard; they "read" each others non-verbal cues. They made sure they did not get too rough with each other. They had to remain coordinated with each other. This was non-scripted and not controlled by either child. They had to continually make mutual adjustments to each other. It was awesome!

Ups and Downs

Sometimes Jan feels that nobody really understands the sacrifices that she has made in order to help Nicholas. Jan feels Joe doesn't always appreciate how the small things make a big impact with RDI. Sometimes her silliness is annoying to others. Jan often reminds her family that these techniques just need to become part of everyday life. The sun rises and sets daily despite their ups and downs.

Nicholas continues to have some "quirky" conversation and behavior. He is fixated on time and numbers. He will tell you throughout the day exactly what time it is and what he is doing or will be doing. He will then tell his dad and Ashley later on in the day, exactly what they did and at what time during that day. Recently they were at a Kane County Cougars game. He spotted the clock and frequently started to recite the time to others. Jan asked Nicholas to point to the clock so she could show others where it was. She then explained that everyone now knew where the clock was, so he didn't need to tell them the time any longer. It worked! In the past, this would have brought on whining, wiggling and eventually crying.

Jan's hope comes from seeing Nicholas' progress and remembering how far Nicholas has come in this journey. God and her family continue to be Jan's prime source of comfort and encouragement. Jan and Joe have even started an internet group through Yahoo called Prayer Spectrum. This was to support other families with members on the spectrum through prayer. Jan used to be a fringe member of some local support groups, but was always too busy to get really involved. In the last five years, Jan has been able to develop many wonderful relationships.

Nicholas will have a big change in school this year. This will be the first year that he does not have a 1:1 aide. He will share the aide with 2 other children. For the past 4 years, he was enrolled in half day programs in public school. Now his program is comprised of full days. Schedules will have to allow for after school dyads and Jan is looking forward to some "mommy alone time." Jan also looks forward to meeting new staff and hopefully having some great social memories emerge during this year. Joe and Jan hope that Nicholas develops some true friendships in 1st grade.

In Jan's own interview with Nicholas, she asked how he felt about RDI. Nicholas replied, "It's good. I just like it. Jackie and Seth are there. We play fun games." When asked to tell what a friend is, he said, "A friend is a best friend. Friends make you happy. Friends are happy. We get to play." Jan asked if it is more fun to play with kids his age or with adults. He replied, "Its better with kids. They are my best friends."

Ashley was 5½ when Nicholas was born. She had been at the very center of their universe. She enjoyed her brother as a baby and toddler. When he slipped into autism, it was difficult for her to deal with his tantrums and he ruined a lot of social outings. However, he didn't really get into her toys and things as he had no interest in them. He did not explore like typical kids. Jan remembers when he first started to take an interest in his sister. Ashley really enjoyed her brother's attention.

Ashley commented on Nicholas at this time in his life. "He is more sensitive now and a lot easier to talk to. He does drive me crazy at times, but a few hours later he cooperates." Nicholas' behavior and language have improved a lot over the past 5 years. They have a more typical love/hate sibling relationship. She picks on him. He annoys her. They argue.

Amy

These children find it very difficult to function in our world. We have the ability to teach them to enjoy life. Parents deserve to have their children back. Little by little I see these kids emerging from behind scared and confused faces and smiling as they are able to understand people and our complex world. Life just isn't scary any more! I see real laughs and emotion sharing with parents and their children. God gave us a big battle to overcome. It helps us to grow and develop as human beings. It helps us appreciate life, and value the small things. This job is very rewarding, yet very challenging.

I was not satisfied with the way these kids were developing with traditional methods. I felt there had to be some alternative method. RDI was that method. I am amazed every day at the progression of the children I work with. The families put in a lot of hard work, but the payoff is un-measurable.

Jan once told me, "All parents with children on the spectrum know how life-consuming autism is. We have all heard, but not heeded enough, the advice to take care of yourself. That seems like such an oxymoron. How can we keep working so hard to help our children recover and have any time or anything left for our husbands, other children, or personal friends much less ourselves?" To Jan, it is like trying to move along a balance beam. "Gymnastics never was my sport. Give me a bike or a pair of running shoes. I used to like to swim. Maybe I will become a Master's swimmer in my dreams. Or, I will ride the first Tour de France for women. Move over Lance Armstrong!

Smile and dream of the possibilities and certainly I will photograph it all to put into my scrapbooks when I have time."

Jan is in training to ride a quad century bike trip at the end of August.* Last year she canceled out in order to attend the 4-Day RDI® Parent Seminar. Jan is looking forward to some personal time for prayer and contemplation before tackling another school year.

**After this chapter was written, in August of 2005, Jan participated in the Quad Century Bike Trip! She completed 340 miles in 4 days. She loved being outdoors and on her own. She was able to meet new people while challenging herself physically.*

Dad's Perspective

After Nicholas was diagnosed with autism, Jan was the one who put the most effort into determining the cause and finding the best treatments. I would read information that she pointed me toward which greatly educated me on the autism. Sometimes I would have a different take on what I read than she had. We both knew Nicholas needed something, but the hard part was deciding where to invest our time and resources. RDI is one of the things which we both feel the effort has been worthwhile and beneficial. The search for treatments can seem almost endless. The trick is to know which ones to keep and which ones to throw out.

Nicholas has given us a lot of joy and stress. The early days of continuous crying were very stressful. I would take Ashley to the Y for swimming lessons, and sometimes Nicholas and I would sit in the car and there was nothing I could do to stop him from crying. Other times we would go walking and exploring. At this stage he was into repetitive activities. One time we went to a 4th of July party and Nicholas and I must have crossed the same crosswalk 50 times. Another time we were at a playground, and he would circle and go down the same slide over and over again. We also knew his behavior could be much worse. We heard of autistic kids who would destroy their homes. So overall I felt we were blessed in some ways because he was not regressing any more.

At this time, Jan was especially interested in diet and supplemental therapies, although I felt Nicholas did not seem to have the symptoms that a casein and gluten free diet would benefit. We did however have him on this type of diet for about 12 months and Nicholas still takes supplements. We also started a modified ABA program. I believe this gave Nicholas the foothold to communicating with the outside world. ABA helped him with early verbal skills and some one-on-one interaction with other adults. I was probably like many parents of children on the spectrum that thought that once a child could talk, the road to recovery was at hand. How wrong that idea is!

I knew that social interaction was imperative to a productive and happy life for Nicholas, but most therapies only touched this on periphery. I don't believe that the vitamins and supplements make a significant difference for most autistic children. I have not seen the rigorous studies that support those conclusions. Some people imply that the supplements will cure autism. I wish it were that easy.

What got my attention about RDI was it did not offer a quick fix cure. RDI addresses the emotional factors that keep these children from achieving their potential. The eye opener was when Jan and I went to the 4-Day RDI® Parent Seminar in Chicago last summer. Dr. Gutstein's goal is to have these children grow into socially happy adults - not robots who are programmed to say the right thing. This is our goal as well. The step by step methods RDI uses makes sense to me.

On a final note, before when I would come home from work, I was always happy to be home, but now I look forward to coming home and playing with Nicholas because he is fun to be with!

✎ Amy Arnoff is a RDI® Certified Consultant operating Essential Elements, a private RDI® Consulting Business, located in Plainfield, Illinois. She resides in Joilet, IL with her three children, Graesen, Seth and Tyler. She has been involved with the autism community since 1980. Beginning in 2003, RDI has become her main focus with individuals on the autism spectrum. You can contact Amy at aarnoff@comcast.net.

5

Enjoying the Silence

by E. Cheryl Fletcher, MA

Cheryl's Story

My initial interest in the field of speech and hearing came from my studies in linguistics. I found the study of languages, their development and structure to be fascinating. How did human beings ever learn to talk? Talking is one of the most difficult things any of us learn how to do. Nearly everything we say is a unique creation differing in some way from the previous utterance.

Unfortunately, I soon discovered that it was difficult to find meaningful employment in the field that I was fascinated with. When I tried to find work in this area I soon discovered that, apart from teaching, there were few practical applications. During my search, one of my professors at the University of Sheffield suggested that I consider speech and hearing. In those days this was a field in its infancy in the United Kingdom; America was the place to go. Thus, I decided to go to the University of California, Santa Barbara. I was fortunate enough to be accepted as a graduate student, although I did have to make up the missing undergraduate course work. It took a little longer, but I received a MA degree in speech and hearing science. I could have continued with the doctoral program but I felt it was time to have some real life experience.

At that time, autism was a rare condition about which very little was known. Santa Barbara was in the forefront of treatment of the disorder, with a newly hired professor in the speech and hearing department, Dr. Robert Koegel. As I took his classes and learned from him I became more and more interested in serving this population. Under his guidance many of us had the opportunity to work with children on the autism spectrum at the Camarillo State Hospital where Dr. Ivaar Lovaas was doing his groundbreaking work. This was an exciting time to be a student. Many of the well known names in ABA were at the state hospital. We had the opportunity to participate in research and therapy with a wide range of clients with the diagnosis of autism. We all seemed to be on a path of discovery.

For many of these children, the main focus was getting them to talk. Using behavioral methods, these children did learn some words, some even talked a great deal. However, as time went on we began to see that these children spoke, but did not communicate. The expressions they used were rote, or scripted, and often non communicative; they did not share experiences as other children did. Unlike many of the other children I saw in the clinic, they did not approach to share some new toy or just to talk to me or to tell me of something that had happened. Their communication was limited to phrases I had heard before or to asking me for some desirable item. At the same time we were using these strict behavioral methods, Dr. Carol Prutting was introducing us to the field of pragmatic language which looked at language in its social setting.

I came to realize that one could easily be fooled by a child's often uncanny ability to memorize and reproduce rote memorized speech. A client of mine was reported to politely refuse to do his class work by saying, "I don't think so, not today, thank you." The aide commented that he always refused so politely! He had actually learned this phrase from me. When I did not want him to do a particular activity, this was my response.

My clients with autism have taught me that while speech, language and communication are related terms, they are not synonymous. I would often feel frustrated when I read reports that stated that a client had excellent language skills when I knew that what had been heard were rote phrases from the television or videos, phrases which had no communicative intent. These terms have overlapping, but not identical meanings. Speech output does not necessarily imply communication, and even less so, language. This is one of the most difficult areas for family members and many professionals to understand. Most become focused on the use of words and forget the importance of meaningful communication. Perhaps this is because in our society we place such emphasis on verbal communication skills not realizing how much of communication is non-verbal. Parents become focused on the fact that their child is not talking whereas their friends' children are.

Helping children with autism to become better communicators presented a unique challenge, because generally these children do not truly understand the idea of communication. They tended to rely on highly unconventional means to express a narrow range of communicative functions or purposes. They make few attempts to repair communication (i.e. restate and reformulate the misunderstood message). I think of my own child as a toddler, who came home from the baby sitter and kept saying over and over again "ooie." I had no understanding of what he meant. He realized this and then pointed at the cookies, signed cookie as he said "ooie." He had recognized my inability to understand him and had modified his signal to me. This type of communication repair is beyond the capacity of all but a few children with ASD.

When I looked at the incredible diversification of the communicative repertoires of typically developing children around 20 months of age, when they discover the powers of symbols, and then saw the restricted range presented by many individuals with autism, I realized how great the communication gap was. Children start to understand that the word they use refers not only to the item present e.g they see a dog and say dog, but also to other objects that may not be present. They start to understand that the words they say have the same meaning for the communication partner. One year olds have learned to express a wide variety of communicative intentions, albeit non-verbally, including protesting, requesting, calling, commenting and showing off. Children with autism, even when talking in sentences, may remain at the context driven level of communication. Their communication may only be understandable to those who know them. A young man in my practice used to say, "No videos today, no videos today," meaning he did not wish to work. Clearly, this would only be understandable to those who knew him.

While most children run out to the playground, turn and look at you and perhaps comment about the swings; a child with autism may just stand close to the swings and say, "More swing." He will not turn to look at you; he may not even know whether anyone is close enough to hear him.

Many of their communications were highly context dependent as with the young man who at every mealtime would say, "He put the green peas down the chute." Little room is left for the negotiation and clarification that helps prevent behavior escalations. Many of the behaviors seen in autistic children were as challenging, but were often an attempt to communicate. One young man threw himself on the floor because he did not wish to transition to a table task, while the aide asked multiple times if he wanted to get up and sit at the table. Each question was accompanied by louder screams and kicking. Obviously he was answering her question but in manner she could not understand. Many so-called unacceptable behaviors are protests against changes in routines or an attempt to escape from a situation.

I found that a person with autism spectrum disorder has an extremely difficult time reading the cues of others. They do not notice when their partner blushes or looks away as a signal that they find the conversation distasteful. They may not respond to a change in conversational topic preferring to continue with their own conversation with no regard for the conversational partners subtle cues. One 3 year old I knew lectured me extensively on the prehensile toe of a dinosaur. This was not the kind of topic that would interest most other 3 year olds and he completely missed my attempts to change the subject. On another occasion a teenager with Asperger's Syndrome* responded to a visitor's crying child with the rhetorical question of, "Why doesn't someone throttle that child?" He completely ignored his mother's embarrassed look as he went on to repeat the statement several times.

In the face of many of these obstacles, children with ASD are sent to speech pathologists to teach them to speak and to social skills groups to teach them how to interact in social situations. But, as always what tends to emerge is rote repetition of learned phrases. For example, one of my young clients, many years ago, came into my office and said, "Hello Mrs. Flitstick (sic) what a nice dress you are wearing." I happened to be wearing pants at the time! The inability to be aware of what is appropriate and what might be offensive to the listener were continuing obstacles. One young man while in an elevator in Paris complimented a strange woman in the elevator on her a nice moustache. Fortunately, she did not appear to have understood him.

In 2002, one of my parents returned from having seen Linda Andron. Dr. Andron is well known in the Southern California area for her programs for children with autism. The parent returned from visiting Linda very excited about a new treatment method having to do with relationships and emotions. I investigated further and decided this was something I should try for myself. Linda is always at the forefront of new ideas. She explained to me that a psychologist in Houston had developed a program that seemed to address the many areas of deficit we had long talked about.

I attended my first professional workshop in Houston. As I watched the videos, I became excited. I saw these children start to blossom. They were interacting with their parents, perhaps not always verbally, but certainly non verbally. They became aware of other people. Above all, both parents and children seemed to be enjoying themselves and one another. They took pride in their mutual accomplishments.

I attempted my first RDA™ (Relationship Development Assessment™) with Dylan and his mother. Dylan was a very active little boy who danced and jumped around the room as his mother worked very hard to keep him engaged. She followed him from place to place, throwing balls to him, and talking all the time. Dylan's attention to her was fleeting at best. When we moved onto the lost voice segment, the changes in Dylan were extraordinary. He moved closer to his mother and tried to engage her. He finally sat on her lap and kissed her. I think for both the mother and myself that was our real moment of revelation. When Dylan kissed her, she hugged him back. I was moved by the close connection between mother and son. To this day when I show parents or professionals these contrasting video segments, I usually manage to extract an "ah" from the audience. The dramatic change in interaction always makes an impact.

Even today as I go back and review that segment of the initial video I am stunned by the difference in the quality of the interaction. The removal of the verbal input from this child had immediately changed the interaction. He now was initiating contact with his mother. He was much calmer. The dancing and jumping around the room had ceased. He seemed to be really aware of her for the first time. He was actively seeking her out.

When I redid the RDA™, approximately 10 months later at the conclusion of my certification period, the changes in Dylan were dramatic. In the free play segment he actively engaged his mother in a lively game with the floodle noodle. His mother picked up the floodle noodle and hissed as if it were a snake. Dylan then copied her and took the snake to chase her.

In the end they were both holding the floodle noodle, one at each end, and running across the room with it. Dylan constantly looked back at his mother to make sure she was with him. He no longer jumped around the room while she ran after him trying to engage him. She was also much more content to wait for him to reference her, and not constantly verbally cue him.

An unexpected benefit of the RDI® treatment for Dylan was a tremendous leap in his verbal skills. Dylan had always been a verbal child, but most of his output had been limited to short phrases requesting objects or activities. There had been very little commenting or emotion sharing. During my RDI® certification period I had provided no direct speech therapy in the traditional sense because I believed that the activities we were doing were actually working on pragmatic or social language in its beginning non verbal stages. By the end of this period he was using longer and more complex utterances. These utterances were novel and did not appear to have been learned rotely.

One day he walked in and told me he was going to the movies to see *Chicken Little*. He was also starting to understand and use humor and lie. The other day he didn't want to go to school, so he informed his mother that he did not have school that day. He will also tease his brother about Barbie commercials. He will look at his brother and say, "You want that," and then laugh. He knows that Barbie is a girl toy. He liked to sing the peanut butter and jelly song. I started to add silly changes to the song such as peanut butter and plums. Dylan prefers the variations to the game and makes up his own novel additions. He now responds to subtle hints. Once he was eating french fries and I said, "I do love french fries," he smiled and gave me one.

When children come into his regular education kindergarten Dylan will turn and greet them. I had the opportunity to observe Dylan in his previous special day classroom where he might not have the great verbal skills of some of the children with Asperger's, but he definitely has the better social skills. I watched as he made play and communication bids to several of the other children who did not respond to him. In contrast, on the playground or in the park, he cannot not be picked out from among his typical peers. In the mall play area he will initiate games of chase with other children. He is able to be both the child being chased and the child doing the chasing. He will take the initiative to keep the game going.

The great changes I see in Dylan led me to wonder whether I would see the same kind of effect in ASD clients with greater speech impediments. I, therefore, approached Caleb's parents and discussed the RDI® Program with them.

Caleb continues to be developing verbally and we have seen great changes in his social abilities. I think Gina and Caleb's story as told later in this chapter speaks for itself. But, I must include an anecdote from a California regional center service coordinator about Caleb. I believe this illustrates to the power of RDI. He visited Caleb's home for an annual review of services. Previously when the service coordinator had been there, Caleb would walk away and show little interest in him. During this visit, Caleb came and sat beside the service coordinator. He remained part of the group, smiling and looking at the other members for the whole meeting. He might not have been able to say much but his actions spoke for him. I am here, I am part of this meeting, and I am part of this group. I want to be here with you. I don't want to be off by myself.

The RDI® Program has profoundly changed the way I provide speech therapy services to all my clients with autism, not just those in the RDI® Program. I see many very young children who do not yet have a firm diagnosis of autism, but in whom autism is suspected. Sometimes clients are referred to me because their own speech therapist is seeking some guidance. I enjoy the stimulation of being involved in the Relationship Development Intervention® Program. It is not a static system but is dynamic; it is constantly changing, requiring us to change along with it.

I would like to share two families' stories. One is of Dylan, the young child who was my certification client. The other is of Caleb, who remains minimally verbal but whose story also attests to the power of this intervention and the lasting benefits it has for the family unit as a whole.

Dylan's Story

Dylan's parents, Susan and Freeman, first began to notice changes in Dylan when he was around 18 months of age. Prior to that time, Dylan had been developing like any other child with no causes for concern. He stopped responding to his name. Then he stopped looking at his parents and other people in his environment. Next to go was his speech. He had been saying ten words, but now he said nothing. He no longer pointed to things he wanted or just to share with them. He became very sensitive to noise. He refused to eat all but a few foods. His main source of protein was pizza. He would refuse anything else. He did not imitate speech sounds or gestures. He no longer copied his older brother.

Dylan had great difficulty sitting still. He was very active. He was always moving, running from one thing to another, opening doors, jumping off counter tops. His mother could not leave him unattended for fear something would happen. He had no idea of danger. His mother had great difficulty with this, because she was very much alone having recently moved to the area. She would go to the park and be unable to socialize with the other mothers and make friends because she constantly had to run after Dylan. On several occasions she was forced to leave Dylan's 4 year old brother unattended while she ran to catch Dylan. This dangerous situation led her to stay home and she was unable to seek out other families.

At 2 years of age Dylan was referred to the California Early Start Program for early intervention. Prior to applying for Early Start services they had had Dylan's hearing tested thinking perhaps he did not respond because he could not hear them. He received speech and occupational therapy services through those programs. Therapists found Dylan to be an exhausting client as he was so active. Dylan's parents heard the usual explanations: he's a boy, they take longer to develop, and he's a second child so doesn't need to talk as much. He'll catch up. The family felt frustrated by the pediatrician's inability to find out what was really wrong with Dylan. In hindsight, Susan believes the doctors they saw were just ignorant of the symptoms of autism. Usually somebody had a story of a family member or friend who was the same and was now doing well. No one else in their family or circle of friends had a child with any kind of problems let alone autism.

Dylan was being seen by one my colleagues at 30 months. She referred Dylan to our Hanen, *It Takes Two to Talk* class - a parent training class for children with speech and language delay, thinking that Susan might like to see if this would be a better fit for her family's needs. Dylan's mother attended the first few meetings by herself, and then came to me to announce that she thought Dylan was different from the other children in the class. She felt he definitely had his own agenda and his play skills did not seem to be as good as the other children's. However, she did not believe that he was autistic because he seemed so closely attached to her. One of Dylan's strengths is his memory and his recall of how he felt about past events. There was a little part of Dylan that still wanted to interact with her even if it was on his terms.

I suggested that she come to the Hanen *More Than Words* class for parents of children with autism and see if that class would better fit her needs. After the first class she came to me stating this is where she felt Dylan belonged. After attending a few more classes, she came and asked if we thought Dylan was autistic. As part of the classes, we also video taped the parent interacting with the child, so I had an opportunity to observe the interactions within the family. As speech pathologists, we were not allowed to diagnose autism. We directed Dylan's mother to the psychologists at our local regional center. When she received the diagnosis it did not come as a surprise to her. Susan was not upset; she now set out to educate herself about autism and, as she says, became a mom with a mission.

Susan went on an internet search. She investigated diets and supplements. They did not try a special diet, but did try supplements and detoxification in addition to his speech therapy, occupational therapy and school. Hours were spent on the internet. Dylan made slow improvements in joint attention, ability to point to desired items, requesting and expressive language. He was placed in a special day preschool class. Susan was reassured by the fact that there seemed to be many other children who looked worse than Dylan. He was enrolled in an in-home intensive intervention program based on social communication and play skills.

Dylan continued to make some progress. His language continued to increase. His play skills slowly improved. Then I invited Dylan, who was now my speech therapy client, to be my RDI® certification case. Susan was always ready to give a new treatment a chance. Following the RDA™, Susan was now committed to the program.

Every week, we would videotape lab time (exercises done in my clinic) to send in for review. In those days we did not talk as much about lifestyle changes. As the weeks progressed, we saw changes in Dylan. He became less active and more focused. He started referencing his mother and others. When he investigated my toy cupboard he would look at his mother and me rather than just dive in and pull everything out. The next step was the introduction of lifestyle changes. Susan seemed to be a natural fit with the RDI® lifestyle*. She was very flexible and willing to make adaptations. She tried to slow down and share the moment. When she and Dylan went walking down the horse trails near their home on the way to the park they used to rush down the trail. Now they started to slow down, smell the flowers (literally) and throw rocks in the pond together. They enjoyed the process of walking together; the end goal of getting to the park was no longer the important thing. Then she attended a 4-Day RDI® Parent Training Seminar and many of the ideas she had heard before began to coalesce. Through videotape review and clinic based activities the family's patterns started to change.

Susan reported that among the changes she has observed in Dylan is his awareness of his family. He now notices when they come and go. He became sensitive to their changing moods and responsive to the moods of other people. In the past when his older brother would cry because he hurt himself, Dylan would be oblivious. Now he will say, "Jordan is sad. Don't cry Jordan," and will attempt to comfort him. He spontaneously gives hugs and kisses. He tells his mother he loves her without prompting and without having been taught. He will sometimes respond to subtle verbal hints. I can now look at him and say, "I wish I had some bubbles," and he will hand me the bubble container to play with.

Dylan now plays with his older brother and other children. The games may be active like chase or hot wheels, but he is a full participant. He participates in team games such as soccer. He can even play a board game all the way to the end. (I am not sure that I thought that the active little boy I first met would ever be able to sit still long enough to play a game to the end.) He will initiate a game or play scenario or respond to another's play overtures. No longer are power rangers his only source of interest. He will stay in a group playing for long periods of time.

A difficulty encountered in his special class school placement was that none of the other ASD children in his class would respond to his play overtures. He is now in a regular Kindergarten doing well with the children. After playing at the park other children invite him back to play again. His parents are thrilled that other children find him to be a desirable playmate.

Dylan's sensitivities to noise have decreased and he no longer holds his ears and protests when there is a loud noise (with the exception of the fire alarm bell). He is now ready to try more foods! His diet has expanded from pizza to include some fruits, vegetables and different meats.

One of the most exciting developments is the change in Dylan's language skills. His non verbal interaction skills have changed immensely. He will now look to pick up facial cues. He is now able to carry on a conversation over several turns. When he becomes fixated on one topic, he can be diverted to another topic. Susan's own interaction style has also changed. Her use of Declaratives is significantly higher than her use of Imperatives.*

Dylan talks about the past and recalls the emotions that are triggered from those memories. While making cookies on Valentine's Day he was reminded of the difference between happy and sad. He and his mother were making heart-shaped cookies and one of them broke. Dylan said he was sad because he had a broken heart; he then went on to say he was happy because he had eaten the cookie and it tasted good! He will recall how he felt on a particular occasion. He is able to talk about the future and reflect on how an activity might make him feel. Every Christmas the family goes to Disneyland to see the Christmas decorations. It is now early November and Dylan is already talking about the trip, recalling how much fun they had last time. In fact, he even managed to go on to the computer and find the web site to help plan the trip!

Susan, Dylan's mother, wrote: "To other parents, I would say that RDI has helped my son (and family) tremendously. My son has started to seek out interactions with others and these interactions are so much more normal. More often than not, he is actively engaged in the interactions and does his part to keep them going. The weak points that we are still working on are variety and flexibility in these interactions, but I think that this will come over time. I believe that with continued work Dylan will become a competent and productive member of society. To the untrained eye, he is indistinguishable from his peers. It is only I (and Cheryl) who really see the deficits, as they are growing smaller with each passing day and year."

Caleb's Story
by Gina Vallis, Ph.D.

One day while my little boy and I were sitting on the couch, he turned and solemnly stared up at me. His remarkable gold eyes were neutral, and then suddenly focused. In real time, the contact probably lasted no more than four seconds before he broke it. For me, it was much longer. I felt a crawling sensation in my stomach I didn't recognize the simple act of looking into my son's eyes. Like one of those panicky dreams where you misplace something vital, I couldn't for a moment, remember the last time I had really felt him to be present in the room.

I remember Caleb before autism with such clarity: pointing and naming a bird from his stroller, abandoning himself to an enthusiastic stranger with waves and smiles, holding his doll up for kisses, plucking pictured fruit off of a magazine cover in the grocery line and feeding them to his father with delicious giggles, looking for my applause each time as he strummed his toy guitar. After that, came a blank period. I don't really remember the precise moment when he went missing. There was no accident, no wailing of sirens. When he turned 20 months old, I remember beginning to feel chronically and vaguely uneasy. I remember commenting to his father that Caleb didn't rush over to give kisses when we came home. I remember noticing he no longer used the word button, his favorite for naming anything that remotely fit that description, including the one on his belly. As time went on, I remember putting a blanket over his head for peek-a-boo and his rejection in a cold moodiness that I turned into a feverish tickling game that neither of us enjoyed and had more desperation than play in it. I remember I allowed a doctor to soothe my fears too easily. I don't remember much else. My child slipped away so quietly I didn't notice that he was gone until it was too late to say goodbye.

Various professionals have told me that I simply probably hadn't recognized early signs of autism. I didn't have to argue my point much, however. My child was conceived against very heavy odds over four years of trying and a painful surgery. Although his birth was textbook normal, we will never have another child. In other words, Caleb was a greatly anticipated child, and practically every one of his waking moments (and quite a few sleeping ones) was videotaped from birth. His videos showed a child so fully adept at social play, so active in communication, and so obviously cognitively intact that when I produced them, one professional asked to copy them for her childhood development class, in order to give an example of typical play behavior in a young child.

Yet no matter how clear my memory of that time was, or what accurate evidence I could produce, that child disappeared. At 22 months, four months after the first onset of his symptoms, Caleb was formally diagnosed. By then, he rarely made eye contact, and then it was brief. He was non verbal. He loved to watch videos, by which I mean the same videos over and over, with brief moments of attention followed by dashing around our dining table and flapping or watching, completely fascinated by the kitchen tile. He walked lines. His toys, including his beloved doll, gathered dust. He no longer stroked my face when I pretended to cry, or even if I was not pretending. He did not cuddle, but crawled over us, all sharp elbows. He could only start at one end of a banana; the pointy end would not do. He was afraid of water. He did not sleep. He walked all the time with his head down, on his tiptoes, looking at the floor. He laughed for no reason, cried for no reason, shrieked and moaned, and nothing I could do stopped it or shared it or helped it or gave him ease. He was utterly cut off, and was, in words nobody offered me at the time, a severely impaired autistic child.

Just as autism manifests differently in every child, every parent has his or her own horror when it comes to autism. Every parent can accept autism except for one thing. For one parent I spoke to it was the loss of grandchildren. For another, it was how other people were going to treat him. For me, it was my child's isolation. What scared me the most was that my child would be deprived of the ability to love, to relate, to play, to share feelings, to touch pleasurably, to anticipate a joke, to know others, and to feel connected. That was what I wanted for him so desperately. There is no more treacherous line to walk as a parent than the one between acceptance and reaching for something more. This is why autism never really allows you to move on after grieving. It is, in its own way, a lifelong wound re-opened by mystery as it is confronted by hope.

Like many parents, my grief was interrupted by a series of nagging questions: how do I approach a public agency? What are the dominant interventions, and how do they stack up? What does treatment look like? What are my child's chances? I was completely out of my depth. So I did what every parent does; I entered the realm of autism treatment. It is a strange realm, and difficult for parents. It could be easier; it should be easier. It is not.

I was asked what I would say to a parent whose child is newly diagnosed. I think I know my own answer, and it's a brass tacks one. If you want a program for your child, approach your provider, whoever they are, with an informed, open attitude. Keep in constant contact with them, be determined (like a pit bull) but courteous, and make it clear you are willing and able to work with them in coming to a joint decision about the best therapy for your child. Do not believe those people who tell you that: a) a certain program is not possible, or b) that the powers that be wake up in the morning trying to figure out how to deny it to you. These people are not in it for the money, and most of them want to go home feeling like they've helped the children that compose the overwhelming caseload they manage. Acknowledge that they are overworked and under-funded without letting go of what you know is in the best interests of your most precious charge.

If things get sticky, remind them of the first rule of autism treatment: the single most important factor in the highest compensation of an autistic child in the level of cognitive, social, and communicative skills, surpassing in importance the degree or kind of therapy the child undergoes, is the ongoing and active participation of a parent. This is why the Relationship Development Intervention® Program with its stress on the family and lifestyle changes spoke so loudly and clearly to me.

It is easy to become confused and even frightened by the verbiage of autism treatment. The major therapies are really ideas. These therapies move forward from an operating theory of autism. My dive into research constituted a year of submersion; I can speak the jargon better than most general professionals (and I'm afraid I often understand them better), and I have seen multiple children's progress over years under radically different and distinct treatment modalities. I have never regretted the path that I took; I remain in debt to those good people who helped me to travel it. My conclusion is that it is the idea behind the therapy that must make sense to you. I wanted a program that was eclectic and that addressed the goals that I wanted for my child.

In all honesty, I am forced to say here that this is only my child. I cannot speak for any other situation, except to suggest this: respect the world your child lives in. It has order and meaning, and just because it is the result of impairment does not mean it has less emotional significance. I say this because no testimonial to any model of intervention, including this one, escapes the political net of autism intervention. There are bitter contestants in the reach for resources, and I want to acknowledge here that my decision was not made entirely from an objective or academic viewpoint. Autism was not a career choice for me; I did not have the luxury of choosing the stakes of my decisions, nor of maintaining a clean, unemotional separation from real consequences of that choice within the fabric of my life. This absolute insistence on certain hospitality for the space that autism occupies within my son has colored every decision I have made concerning therapies for him. In other words, it goes against everything I know as a teacher, as a parent, and as a human being, to savage another to my own world view. Rather, what I wanted to give him was every opportunity to come home.

In choosing therapies for my son, my reasoning went something like this. First, I knew that autism causes deficits in the social, communication, and cognitive domains. My son was hit hard in all three, harder than a lot of kids. Yet for me, one of the most eerie symptoms of autism is inadequately described by any of these three things alone. It is that they often neither desire nor see the point in playing. Their play is, in the words of the treatment realm, repetitive and marked by stereotypical behavior. Play is important. It is especially important for those three primary areas where autistic children are often found to be in deficit.

Everybody knows that autistic children are not fun people to play with. They're downright rude, and couldn't make it clearer that you're boring. For my child, while he would physically manipulate objects (toys or otherwise) it was beyond him to imitate, imagine, or interact with me or anyone else. He would spin the wheels of a truck but would never push it or pretend that it was a real one. He would sift sand through his fingers but leave if another child joined him. When he was swinging, he was swinging alone. For me, play was the fulcrum from which my son's new skills were going to rest, the point of emergence from isolation. But I didn't just want him to play; I wanted him to play with me. I wanted a relationship with my child.

From my perspective, it made sense that the best medicine for my son was to enjoy doing what other people were doing and actively seek out other people to do them with. Although my son's program has consisted of a variety of interventions woven into an eclectic program that tries to draw the best from each; our primary tool has been one in which we develop a relationship through the steadily more complex rules of interaction with a partner. In other words, this interaction requires the child to pay attention to the other person in order to keep the play going, in that process stimulating between two people that spontaneous and mutually pleasurable activity that is for its own sake. The RDI® Program seemed ideal. These were the tools that I brought to bear, tools that seemed so somehow flimsy at first against such a formidable disorder, and that somehow gained such power as we used them. In the end, my child, whose prognosis was dreary, surprised everyone: he surprised me, he surprised his treatment team, his teacher, his family everybody. Maybe he even surprised himself.

It feels like a Herculean task to lay out the steps whereby we got him to interact, to make eye contact, to attempt language again, to communicate and to sustain an interaction. The changes we made as a family. The care we have taken to not to bombard with questions, but to use comments. For a highly verbal family, such as ours, it has been difficult to learn to lessen our flow of conversation, to enjoy the silence and not be scared of it. How does one example cover years of therapy?

I have to remember again, remember him after autism. I am holding his feet while he is swinging; I will not let him go until he references me. I call his name and he comes from the other room, looking at me, which shocks me. I have a book, and we snuggle up to read, and although he still likes turning the pages the best, he is following the words. He is standing on the edge of the bed in anticipation of my push and his eyes are wide and locked on mine; he will not fall until I have yelled, "Three!" He says "mama" meaningfully to me for the first time since before he was diagnosed. I ask for a kiss; he gives me his cheek, and I say, "No! A real one!" And, he kisses me and wraps his arms around my neck, a hard and confident hug. I put him under the covers and ask if he is in the bath; he laughs.

Then a whirlwind: he does not talk, but he has learned to read. How many words? We don't know yet. He cannot get his tongue to the roof of his mouth, but he mastered an "f" sound last week. He is sitting almost nose to nose across from his speech therapist; he is watching her mouth with longing, trying so hard his face goes funny. She laughs, surprising him in his concentration, and he laughs back with her. He tries; it is not right. He tries again, much better. I applaud; he turns to me and smiles, just smiles, proud of himself. Not the child that would have been, maybe, not typical but definitely my son, present and accounted for.

✎ E. Cheryl Fletcher, MA CCC, is a speech pathologist and has been a RDI® Certified Consultant since 2003. She provides speech and language therapy for children with autism as well as RDI® programming. Her private practice, E. Cheryl Fletcher and Associates, is based in Camarillo, California. She also provides distance consultation for RDI. She may be reached at ecfspeech@aol.com or by phone, 805.484.1671.

6

Mommy Sit Here MOO

by Linda Andron-Ostrow, LSCW & Jennifer

This is Jeremy's story. How Jeremy was wished for and came to be. How he used to say, "Mommy sit here moo," to mean, "Mommy sit here with me."

A few days before my wedding, I had a very lucky dream. I dreamed that I was on a boat sailing to some location. It was a beautiful day and the water was so calm. When I got off the boat, I landed on a green hill. Then I saw this wild female boar standing on top of the hill, snorting. Down below, I saw two wild boar's piglets. Instinctively, I grabbed the two piglets, held one under each arm and ran towards my boat. I hopped on and then turned my head to see the mother boar chasing after me. When I woke up, I felt lucky. Koreans believe pig dreams are the best dreams one can have. They believe it brings good fortune and luck. My mother, a Korean, was so happy when I told her about my dream. She predicted that I was going to have two sons. Sure enough, our first child who was born 2 years later was a boy. We named him Jonathan.

Just before I conceived my second son Jeremy, I had another dream. I dreamed that my husband, Joshua, was picking peaches from our peach tree in the backyard and he handed me the biggest and the juiciest peaches.

According to Korean superstition, this type of dream is called a "Conception Dream." My dream, in particular, meant that I was going to have a son. After I woke up, I was ecstatic. Being a tomboy growing up, I always wanted to have two boys.

Jeremy was born in February of 1994. He is 19 months younger than his older brother, Jonathan. We planned the pregnancies so close together because we wanted the kids to be close in age so they could play with each other. Having a second son was truly dream come true for me. I was so excited at the thought of all the fun we are going to have as a family camping, riding bicycles, climbing trees, roller-blading, playing with marbles and rocks, and, of course, catching tadpoles, frogs, grasshoppers and maybe even snakes. I couldn't wait for the boys to get big enough so we could do these fun things together.

When Jeremy was 2½ years of age, he still wasn't talking. He had some very unusual behaviors like temper tantrums around 50 times a day and obsessions with certain objects. He was impossible to engage, and seemed deaf at times. Jeremy was first diagnosed with autism at our local regional center. The way Jeremy was diagnosed was pure coincidence. We didn't think much of Jeremy's delayed speech, because his father didn't talk until age 4. So, the whole family just thought Jeremy was like his dad and didn't seek any professional help.

Then in the summer of 1996, I met a mom at Mommy and Me Swimming Lessons at our local high school pool. I noticed what a talker her daughter was, and I made a comment that Jeremy still didn't talk at age 2½. When I asked her for advice on what I should do, she immediately said, "You need to come see me." It turned out she was a Teacher Specialist at a nearby school district. After talking to me a little bit, she found out I lived in a different school district area and referred me to my school district and our local Regional Center for assessment. At the beginning of September I contacted the Regional Center. The entire time, I thought everything was going to be okay with Jeremy. When we arrived for our appointment, he was seen by a psychologist. At the end of the meeting, she gave him the diagnosis of autism.

I had no idea what autism was at that time. Nevertheless, I was shocked to hear something was wrong with my baby. I came home and shared the news with family. None of us believed the diagnosis. We didn't want to believe it. This couldn't be happening to us. I thought of all kinds of excuses for his speech delay and unusual behaviors. I thought the reason Jeremy was not talking was because we were speaking too many languages to him: Chinese, Korean, English and Spanish (we had a Spanish nanny). My mother-in-law thought that our Spanish nanny didn't spend enough time playing with him and that he had too much time alone, and was under stimulated. So, I let our nanny go, quit everything I was doing (including running a small business and a part time job as a pharmacist) to spend more time with Jeremy. I thought if I just spent more time with him he would be normal again.

After Jeremy turned 3, he was referred to our local school district. They did their battery of tests and assessments and concurred with the diagnosis of autism. My reaction was a mixture of devastation and disbelief. At the same time, I feared for Jeremy's future. I never planned this. This was not supposed to happen. We didn't let anybody, outside of family, know that Jeremy was diagnosed with autism. I still hoped that he would somehow come out of it, if I spent more time with him and we enrolled him in a TEACCH program provided by our school district. For about a year after the diagnosis, we were in denial.

I purposefully did not look up or study autism; subconsciously, I felt that if I did so, I would be admitting defeat. We didn't tell friends and neighbors about Jeremy's diagnosis. I kept finding excuses for Jeremy's odd behavior. When people asked me what school Jeremy went to, I just said that he was going to a special school because of his language delays. I never mentioned the word, autism.

We took advantage of all the programs available to us from our regional center and our school district. My thinking process at the time was, if it's there and it's free; why not take advantage of it? Through our regional center, we were able to send him to a local autism center. We didn't do anything extra at home. I didn't even enroll him in any program after summer school was over. I tried to engage him, but it was difficult to get his attention.

So, all summer, when I got tired of trying, I allowed him to just sit on the sofa watching TV. Then, one day I noticed he had started to pick the skin on his fingers, then the skin on his toes. His fingers and toes were raw and bleeding. We didn't know how to make him stop. We couldn't keep bandages on his fingers and toes, because he would take them off as soon as we put them on. So, we had to put them on when he was sleeping.

It was then that we realized that something was seriously wrong with Jeremy. How on earth, could a normal child hurt himself so badly? We began to take the diagnosis seriously and started to look for help desperately.

Once I started to accept the diagnosis, I was overwhelmed by sadness and a tremendous sense of loss. This was a tremendous burden to bear. Which was only compounded by the fact that, I had to deal with people who were largely ignorant, and often unkind to people with disabilities and their families. I never realized people could be so mean. Many times, Jeremy was yelled at by strangers who thought he was "just acting up." Other times, I was yelled at by people (some of them even knew he had autism) or criticized by family members and friends because they felt I was not disciplining Jeremy enough. The ones that hurt the most came from family members and close friends who said things like, "Why can't you be happy with what you have?" or, "At least you have your husband and another normal son."

Needless to say, I was physically and emotionally drained during the early years of struggle with Jeremy's diagnosis. I think everyone just wanted me to snap out of it. Unfortunately, that's not how it goes, especially if you have to face the loss every day. Eventually I realized that some people would never understand what it felt like to have a child with autism unless they actually have a child with autism. So, I learned to keep distance from those people and situations that hurt me.

A 3½ years of age, Jeremy still had no language (he was severely apraxic). He had no eye contact, no imitation skills and no social skills. He was not even able to call me "Mommy." He didn't know the alphabet, colors or numbers. He would constantly have tantrums during the day (due to his frustration from his inability to communicate and understand language). He had difficulty eating most foods and would sometimes eat things like sand and dental floss. He also had no self-help skills. He had severe auditory processing delays and had self-stimulating behaviors. He insisted on routines and had hypersensitivity to noise. He sought unusual tactile inputs including touching various textures of flooring (different types of carpet, linoleum) in public places or inappropriately laying down on them. His OT therapist wrote on her report, "Jeremy tends to be repetitive in his toy exploration. Jeremy needs constant and intense tactile inputs, which impairs his ability to stay on task for longer periods of time." He had gross and fine motor delays. He couldn't hold markers or crayons. He couldn't kick a ball. He had a hard time stopping himself when he was running and often ran into things, such as walls. He couldn't coordinate his gait and would often trip over his own leg and fall. He liked certain visual stimulations such as looking at objects or pictures very closely. He loved to watch repetitive movements, and liked manipulating objects or moving his hands very close to his face. He preferred solitary play and he was obsessed with lining things up. He liked to spin the wheels on his toy cars. The list goes on and on.

As parents, we knew we needed to find a way to help him. But where do you start? We didn't know who to ask, what to ask and where to find information. Back then, the internet was not an option. I felt alone, helpless and lost. It pained us so much to just watch Jeremy day by day, zoned out, unable to speak, hurting himself physically and completely disconnected.

We urgently searched for treatment options. Since his diagnosis 9 years ago, we have tried a variety of treatments. We were so desperate that we tried some therapies against my better judgement and professional training (I have a Pharm. D. degree from one of the top Pharmacy Schools in the country). At the time, our feeling was that if it didn't hurt Jeremy, we would try it. That is pretty much the mentality of a lot of parents who try various treatments for their children with autism.

I remember when Jeremy was young and still wasn't speaking; all we wanted from therapy was for him to call us Mommy and Daddy. Not knowing what your child wants, needs, what he thinks and feels is sheer torture.

For the first 2½ years, Jeremy was doing 20-30 hours a week of home therapy per the supervisor's recommendation. This was in addition to his school time, his daily speech therapy and his occupational therapy. We had to hire and train college students to work with Jeremy. At one point we had five therapists (more like tutors) working for us, putting Jeremy through a regiment 7 days a week of two therapy sessions daily, each session lasting 2-3 hours.

I wish I had more knowledge of autism then. I just assumed then that the professionals and experts knew what they are doing. In retrospect, I should have listened to my own concerns that I pushed aside. I first contacted the agency to put my name on the waiting list, so that we could be assigned a supervisor. This was part of their standard procedure. I asked the qualifications of the supervisors and was told that most of them had a BA or MA degree. I asked whether the agency director, who has a PhD, needed to see my son. The agency told me there was no need since they could come up with a treatment by looking at a questionnaire that I had filled out for my son.

Once a month, we had a team meeting where the supervisor, Jeremy and, all our therapists got together for a "Critique Session" where progress and problems were discussed and we also discussed what new drills to do with Jeremy. Instead of focusing on Jeremy, these critique sessions would often focus on me, the parent, and what I wasn't doing. Some people might ask why we continued with this program even after everything we had been through. The reason is that we knew Jeremy still needed help and we didn't know what else to do. We wanted him to have a better life.

One of my most poignant memories is when they tried to teach him emotions. At first they just had him match pictures and identify the emotions. Then they said it was time to elicit these emotions. This was done with five therapists, each told by the supervisor to elicit a different emotion. Jeremy was given a book to read and the first therapist yanked it out of his hand. He was very surprised and did not know what to say. She then prompted him to say, "I am sad because you took my book." The next therapist just yelled at him for no reason to elicit anger. While he was still crying, the third therapist went to him and started tickling him to elicit "happy." At this point, I told them to stop and asked them, "How many of you experience three emotions in five minutes?" At this point I promised myself that I would stay involved in all of Jeremy's therapies and would not allow a therapist to do anything new without my permission.

When Jeremy became more verbal, he was able to tell me how he was treated and how he felt. He said, "I was scared all the time." I realized that throughout Jeremy's early years, the therapists were generally inexperienced and even though I tried to screen everything they did, bad things still happened.

During these times, Jeremy developed eye infections 4-5 times a year, because he rubbed his eyes and cried so much. The problem was that even though we didn't like what we saw, we didn't stop the program because at the time there was no other option available and Jeremy still needed help. Looking back, I can say that those 2½ years, were the most painful part of my life. I became very depressed, nearly suicidal.

Understand that my son was able to learn a lot of academic and non-academic skills and we were able to change his behaviors with these methods. But, that wasn't enough. For our family, the biggest tragedy was the creation of a therapeutic environment where Jeremy always felt defeated.

With all the therapy and all the tutors going in and out of my house several times a day, we lost the peace and privacy in our house. Our home became a battleground. Jeremy was in therapy practically every waking moment. He hardly had time to play. I had to put Jonathan, Jeremy's older brother, in a lot of after-school programs, so he would be occupied and I didn't have to worry about him. I also asked my husband to focus on Jonathan after he came home from work every night so that he would get some attention from one of us.

When Jonathan was in second grade, we felt that it was time to tell him about Jeremy's condition. We got some brochures and information about autism that was geared towards young children. We sat down with Jonathan and explained to Jonathan why Jeremy had to have so many hours of therapies and why so many therapists were coming to our house. We told him at the end that even though Jeremy has autism, we know that God never makes mistakes. Jonathan immediately broke down and said, "But, I think He did this time!" He was crying bitterly and we could only hold him and cry with him. Jonathan was grieving too, grieving for the loss of a brother that he thought he had.

I first heard about RDI when I received information about a conference. At that time, I was still very involved in our current therapies and did not attend. Later, a friend asked if I had heard of RDI. My friend had heard about RDI at one of her Inclusion Support Group meetings. Some of the mothers had gone to a recent conference and talked about the concept of looking into each other's eyes, referencing, instead of just the 'Look at Me' drills. This seemed so much more meaningful to me. I was excited because all along I felt like I knew more about what would work for Jeremy.

I decided to look into it, got on-line and read about RDI. I realized that over the years of being Jeremy's advocate, I had learned a lot on my own. In the back of my mind I knew RDI was something that I had to learn. I bought the book *Relationship Developmental Intervention with Young Children*, but, didn't read it right away. Our lives were too chaotic at the time. Then I saw the information about the 4-Day RDI® Parent Seminar.

Linda Speaks

I met Joshua and Jennifer at the parent training in Orange County, California in the Summer of 2004. I was immediately struck by Jennifer's enthusiasm and both of their intense desires to learn. During the parent training, Jennifer and Joshua learned about the principles of RDI from Dr. Gutstein in the morning and practiced with Connections Center staff in the afternoon. Following the parent training, Jennifer and Joshua brought Jeremy to my clinic (about an hour's drive) for the RDA™ (Relationship Development Assessment™) and we began what has been a year of learning and growth for both the family and me.

This was my first case of distance supervision. I live far away from Jennifer and Joshua and have been able to see the family for three home visits, but most of the work has been done through video and through a reporting form that would allow them to ask questions. At that time, Jeremy was 10 years old. They were not doing any particular therapies and were frustrated with lack of interaction with Jeremy and yearned to have a meaningful conversation with him. We communicated mainly through e-mail, and phone. This was different than previous therapies because Jennifer and Joshua were Jeremy's main coaches.

Throughout, I have been impressed with Jennifer's organization and her commitment. She has taken to the role of coach like a duck to water. It has been a little more challenging for Joshua since he works long hours and is away from home most of the day. When he is home, he feels that since

Jennifer is doing such a good job teaching Jeremy and studying about autism he doesn't feel motivated to study it himself. "I can't keep up with Jennifer," is something Joshua often says, but, he has managed to incorporate RDI into activities that he does with Jeremy, including exercise and playing the piano.

Jennifer has lived, eaten, breathed and slept RDI. She carries her books with her wherever she goes so that if she has any downtime she can plan. She keeps careful notes in the Progress Tracking form and has systematically worked through the stages in RDI. She has been able to incorporate RDI into all aspects of family life, including cooking, exercising, and walking to school. She has now made a commitment to home-schooling, allowing her to incorporate RDI into even more of their life.

Jennifer Speaks

I took Jeremy out of school because I was not very happy with the impact it was having on him and our family. Also, I wanted to do more RDI with Jeremy and I felt that home-schooling will give me more time and energy to do that with him. It was at the 4-Day Parent Seminar where I first got the idea that home-schooling could be an option for Jeremy.

Jeremy was fully-included from Kindergarten until the end of 4th grade and was probably in one of the best elementary schools possible for inclusion. The principal and the teachers were really supportive and sincerely wanted the best for Jeremy. Frankly, without the support of our principal, I don't think I would have been able to keep Jeremy in full inclusion for as long as I did. One thing that really touched me and made a world of difference was that the principal awarded special recognition to a classmate who befriended Jeremy in special way. The principal also gave me opportunities to do disability awareness and sensitivity training sessions in school; as a result Jeremy was very well accepted by his peers.

We struggled to work with the district, to motivate, to inspire, and gently persuade them to make the best decisions for Jeremy. Sometimes we succeeded. Sometimes we didn't. We understood that the district is bound by a budget and it takes more than people skills to get services. Services are driven by IEP goals and objectives. At one point we were told that, "They were the trained professionals and we were just parents." I told them that they might be experts in speech, OT, and psychology, but I am an expert in Jeremy.

Miraculously, at that time we found a home-school consultant who was a handicapped learning specialist by profession. She home schooled her three children, including a daughter who was severely autistic. Within a month of starting the home-schooling program, Jeremy told me in his own words, "Before when I was going to regular school, my engine was running always high [ie. he was stressed out]. Now, with home-school, my engine is running just right." Now, Jeremy and I are both experiencing a tremendous reduction in our stress level. All the time and energy that I used to fight with the district is now channeled to working directly with Jeremy. I am seeing tremendous progress in academics and increased self-esteem and enthusiasm for learning. That's because I'm working consistently at his level, and moving at his pace. In homeschool, we can't compare him to anyone else, and that's a good thing. We set him up for success.

With RDI, I feel totally at peace knowing that I'm addressing his social needs. Jeremy learned instrumental social skills in the inclusion setting, but was not able to learn very much in the way of relationship skills. I still do not regret keeping Jeremy in public school. He learned what he could learn in that setting and we got to know our community well. Without that inclusion experience and seeing first hand how much work and stress that had caused us, I probably would not have considered home-schooling Jeremy. I feel that RDI compliments a homeschool program.

Linda Speaks

Jennifer likes RDI because is so natural, and includes the whole family. Jennifer's success comes largely from her always keeping her objective in mind and looking for opportunities throughout the day to incorporate RDI. I believe that RDI has been a very good fit for this family.

Jennifer always strives to have a RDI® lifestyle. She does this by first learning the objective of an activity in the book, trying it out a few times and thinking of ways to incorporate the objective naturally into daily life. For example, for Word Crash (an RDI® activity created by FrankCarlo and his parents. See chapter three): During dinner when somebody used a compound word, Jeremy and Jennifer would jump up and go to the opposite end of the room and start doing Word Crash. Before RDI® days, Jeremy would have thrown a fit if we tried to change or stop his routine but now he actually looks forward to this.

Through the years, Jennifer became more and more aware of the need for her to advocate for her child and to take control of the therapies he was having. RDI gave her the confidence to believe that she could in fact be the coach. It also allowed her to see that my role was to provide her with guidance, while she was the one who knew her child best.

During this year, Jeremy has made a great deal of progress. We have overcome many of his obstacles, including always having to be silly and becoming easily deregulated during interactions. In structured RDI® activities, Jeremy has developed emotion sharing, social referencing, and co-ordination with his partner. He can now deal with the addition of variation and even reversals and transformations without becoming upset and melting down. We are now working towards these actually being the highlights of his experience. We are also seeing more and more of these abilities in the broader range of his life with his family and community. Jeremy has become much more flexible and is no longer freaked out by changes in routine.

In fact, they have become so inventive Jennifer has modified activities in the book and, has developed many of her own.

Tango Dance

These are the steps to do the activity:

1. Jeremy and I pretend there's an invisible rope that we are holding, and that we have to keep a certain distance between us when we dance.
2. We hum the Tango music while we are doing this activity and we do not talk.
3. When I move forward, he has to move backward keeping that distance.
4. When I move backward, he has to move forward.
5. When I stop, he has to stop. When I slow down, he has to slow down, and so on.

Variations on Tango Dance

1. We change directions and speed.
2. Do coordinated start and stop, and role reversal.
3. We do it in the kitchen, in the hallway, upstairs or downstairs.
4. I trick him...I pretend to go forward but go backward instead.
5. Doing the Tango Dance in the upstairs hallway is especially fun since you feel like you are about to fall out of the stairs.

We are looking at each other the whole time we are doing this dancing, humming, and having fun. To encode the memory, I had Jeremy draw a picture about us doing the Tango Dance.

Walking to the Park Song

One of my favorite times to do RDI was when I would walk Jeremy to school in the morning when he was going to public school. Now since I'm home-schooling him, we walk to the park instead in the morning. We usually walk our dog, Snuggle, partly to give her exercise, partly because she adds variations to our routine (you never know when she will make her poop!)

Initially, I just worked on having fun together by singing and swinging arms together. Some times, we sing a familiar song with words changed. I also made up a lot of original tunes to sing on our morning walk. I started singing songs because this was one way to stop Jeremy's echolalia, per Dr. Sheely's suggestion. Then little by little I added different things and highlighted different things. Now, our walking to school lifestyle looks something like this:

1. When we leave our house, we usually start singing "Today is Monday" song.
2. I changed the words to reflect our schedule that week.
3. For example, "Today is Monday, Today is Monday, Monday Cub Scout, all you 5th grade children come and have fun. Today is Tuesday. Today is Tuesday. Tuesday trash day, Wednesday drawing," and so on.

In the beginning, Jeremy would throw a fit if I sang the song out of order. He always wanted to sing from Monday. Eventually, I was able to start the song with the day of the week that day happened to be and stop the song at "Today is Thursday." He actually is enjoying singing like this more now because he now gets a kick out of uncertainty and variations. In fact, the sillier and more confusing the song gets, the more fun we have.

There are also tons of opportunities for Declarative language during the morning walk. Jeremy started to use a lot of them on his own. "Watch out for the poop! Look somebody littered. It looks like it's going to rain."

Detour Through the Park

If we have time, we like to take a detour through the park. I do this by asking Jeremy, "Do we have time to walk around the park?" He usually looks at his watch to see if we have time. If he says yes, we start singing, "We will go around the (name of the park) Park, _____ Park, the ______ Park. We will go around the _______ Park early in the morning," to the tune of Going Around the Mulberry Bush. If we don't have time to walk around the park, we change the words to "We won't go around the _______ Park, ______ Park, the ______ Park. We won't go around the _______ Park later in the morning."

How Many _____ Do You See Today?

I made up another original song called "How many _____ do you see today." The song goes something like this:

1. "How many red cars, how many red cars, how many red cars, how many red cars, do you see today?"
2. When I sing the word today, we turn our heads to look at each other.
3. Then, we just started counting as we sing, "I see one red car, I see one red car, I see one red car, and I see one red car, today."

Variations on How Many __________ Do You See Today?

As we sing, sometimes in the middle of the song, the numbers of red cars go up as we see them drive by which is productive uncertainty. Jeremy gets a kick out of this. We can change the words of the song to count different color cars, different type of vehicles (trucks, SUV's, minivans, vans, motorcycles) specific kinds of plants, trash cans, newspapers, birds, dogs, doggy poops etc.

Jeremy Holding the Leash Song

I let Jeremy hold the leash as we get closer to school. I taught Jeremy how to hold the leash with a song I made up. The words go something like this:

1. "Make a fist, make a fist. That's how we hold the leash." *Repeat 1X.*
2. "Don't let go. Don't let go. Or else we will lose her. Don't let go. Don't let go. Or else she'll be flat like a pancake."

Variations on Holding the Leash Song

Later, I pause at the end of the song and let Jeremy fill in with a different noun. I.e. she'll be flat like a ______. Jeremy came up with tortilla, pizza, paper, road kill, Chinese pancake all on his own.

Eventually, we added this variation for a play on words activity. We change the first letter of the word "fist" to a different letter in the song (this was Linda Andron's idea). "Make a dist, make a dist", instead of fist. Or, "That's how we hold the deash," instead of leash. There is the rest of the alphabet for variation on this activity.

To help encode the memories of our morning walk, we started the 'Walking to School Song Book' where we write down all the lyrics of the songs we made up. Jeremy usually hates to write but for he has no problem doing this writing activity.

A Road to Follow

At my most recent home visit back in July 2005, Jennifer and I sat and talked. I asked her to share a little bit about her first year of doing RDI. Jeremy had turned 11 in February and they had been doing RDI for almost one year.

"I love that the parents are the main coaches, the main people working with the child. There isn't a specific time that you have to do this therapy. It doesn't seem like a therapy. It seems more like an interaction. I realized that I would be able to make up for the time that I had lost and that I would be the coach. This made me feel so much better. With other programs, it is almost like saying 'here is my son.' It is like giving up my son. With RDI, I can reclaim my son and the time I lost."

One of the first things that Jennifer did was to nurture Jeremy's abilities. Jeremy is an extremely talented artist. I asked Jennifer what she had done to foster this. "Early on I realized that I would need to develop anything he was good at, because he was getting so much negative [feedback]. When he was 4 and barely learning how to hold a pencil, I saw his drawing and there was a pig that looked so much like a pig and a dog that looked so much like a dog. And then I just bought him all kinds of art materials and made them available to him all the time. He just kept drawing and then I had all these materials compiled and I finally convinced an art teacher to take him on and at about 5 she started teaching him one on one."

At the time, Jeremy really had serious fine motor problems. He had lots of OT and if you were to see the amazing figures he sculpts, you would hardly believe it. Unfortunately, right now the art is very solitary. Our challenge will be to find ways for this to become part of the initiation of joint attention that Jeremy is now beginning to show in other areas.

Jennifer Speaks

We would like to see Jeremy overcome his disability (not cure, but overcome), and learn to enjoy life and have meaningful relationships with a few good friends. Jeremy wants to be a Daddy some day. He already has names picked out for all four of his kids (2 boys and 2 girls). He even thinks about what to do with his kids; taking them to Yosemite, Hoover Dam and Palm Springs. He wants to drive a car some day, to have his own home and a wonderful wife who loves him. Jeremy also wants to be an artist when he grows up. Our dream is to see him fulfill these wishes and reach his full potential.

We yearn to have a deeper relationship with him, one in which we can share our thoughts, our values, our aspirations for him, or just about simple things such as enjoying the beauty of the sunset over a cup of coffee. We would love for him to spend time with us, not out of need, but out of his own desire to be with us.

Before RDI, we thought that these dreams would be unrealistic in this lifetime, and we talked about being able to do all those things in heaven. However, since starting RDI, we started thinking that such dreams are possible in this lifetime, and we are full of hope.

✎ Linda Andron-Ostrow, LCSW is the director of FACT, an agency serving the needs of families of children with autism and Asperger Syndrome. She has been an RDI® Consultant for two years. She is the author of *Our Journey Through High Functioning Autism and Asperger's: A Roadmap.* She lives with her husband and dog in Los Angles, California. She can be reached at Linda@factfamily.org.

7

The Return of Maddy

by Katherine Lee, B.A. & Lorie

One Simple Presentation

I had the honor of meeting Maddy and her mom over 6 months ago. I first met Lorie at a talk I was giving on the Relationship Development Intervention® Program. Many wonderful families came to the event. As you will read, Lorie came to the meeting as a skeptical parent but, before my presentation was over, she knew she wanted to start RDI with Maddy.

At the time of the presentation, Lorie was beginning to wonder if she could ever have a mother/daughter relationship. In that brief introduction to RDI, she saw that she was the key to realizing that hope. Lorie has many wonderful characteristics, but one that stands out, is that she will do anything to help her daughter. There was no selling or convincing her of this truth. Intuitively, she knew she was the key.

Our hope, as a parent and a consultant, is that Maddy's story will encourage other mothers and fathers. And, let them know that it is not too late to start new dreams and revive old ones.

I'm known to many off my friends as Kat, for two reasons. The first is that I was called "Kat Woman" on the air, at one radio station I worked at. The other is from my husband who dubbed me 'his kat'; he is a big cat lover.

Now it is what all of my patients call me too. While I am a RDI® Certified Consultant, I came in to the field of autism through a different route. For the first 12 years of my career, I was in broadcasting: TV and radio, the talent if you will, from radio morning shows to reporter to show host, to music and promotions director. I loved radio and TV. Ten years ago when my precious son was 2, he was diagnosed with moderate to severe autism. I left broadcasting behind with no regrets and stayed home with him, becoming involved with his interventions and getting trained to be one of his therapists.

After many years, I needed to go back to work to help fund his treatments so I began as an ABA lead therapist under a wonderful consultant. During this time, I started hearing about RDI and how it addressed social and emotional domain issues. I decided I had to check it out and signed up for the beginning professional training workshop. Within the first day, I realized that RDI was addressing the core social emotional deficits of autism in a systematic way and it was just incredible. That, plus Dr. Gutstein's heart for our children and their futures and his relentless passion to keep working to help them made my decision immediate. I decided to go through the certification process and become a consultant. I'm honored to work with families like Lorie and Maddy.

Returning a child to their family is why I became involved with RDI. To me, robbing families of their precious children was the most horrific aspect of autism. The children lost their family and the family lost a child. Now this was certainly not true for every child. But for many families, the emotional separation begins at diagnosis and is never repaired. Often, families are told to go on with their lives, live for their other children. Our family never believed this was right but we had heard this upon diagnosis. So I knew through personal experience families were being told that this was the only thing to be done. When I heard Dr. Gutstein speak at my first training, I knew he was different. He wanted parents to be the most important part of their child's life and he believed that there was a better life for them. I knew I wanted to be a part of that passion.

This chapter is not about me and what I have done with this family. This chapter is completely about this mother and father and how they have worked to continue to bring their daughter into an understanding relationship. I just helped nurture their awesome ability to parent. If anything, we can learn from their commitment to family and their strong philosophy about not leaving any one family member behind.

Lorie is a woman who walks in a room and it lights up. She is gracious and her personality is contagious. You just want to know her. Her smile, her presence, her energy and up-front passion for her child are incredible. She came to our consultation organized and taking notes. She had seen a presentation I had given and was certain RDI would help her child.

A New Time
Lorie Talks

It was the fall of 1997 and life was perfect! I had a great job with lots of responsibility, a wonderful husband - my college sweetheart, a cat, and a house in a great neighborhood perfect for raising a family. I wanted it all!

When I found out I was expecting a little girl, I thanked God for answering my prayers. I longed to have that very special relationship mothers and daughters share. I dreamed of hair bows, frilly dresses, dance recitals and cheerleading practices. I wanted to be the June Cleaver type of mom; one to whom my daughter could tell all her secrets and all her heartaches, the mom she would come to for advice or a shoulder to cry on. Our perfect family was on its way.

When Maddy was born, I was thrilled! Our precious angel was such a perfect child; so smart and so beautiful that people would often stop to tell us how stunning she was. Maddy was such a happy baby and such a joy to be around. By seven months of age, she was saying "Mama", "Dada" and "zebra."

She was exploring her world with an excitement and intelligence beyond her age. But, things would soon change. Around the time Maddy turned two and shortly before our second child, Matthew, was born, I knew something wasn't right. Maddy was not combining words, was obsessing over strange objects and her behavior was growing more erratic every week. She would often stare off into space; her eyes glazed over and would refuse to look at us seeming not to notice us at all. She would erupt into screaming fits for no reason.

I recall taking her to a friend's birthday party and when we arrived, Maddy retreated into her own little world. She would not even attempt to interact with the other children. After a short while, Maddy began to scream and cry. I had no idea what had happened to set her off, nor could she tell me.

We visited countless doctors who told us everything from, "Don't worry, kids develop at different rates," to "it could be a language disorder" to "your daughter has sensory issues." Martin and I felt more helpless after each visit. No one was giving us any advice on how we could help our baby to get better. We scheduled an appointment with a pediatric neurologist. Surely he would be able to help us! After several visits, the doctor told us Maddy might have autism. He told us that it was life-long, permanent and irreversible. He said we could expect small steps of progress, to call him if anything changed, but there was nothing more he could do for us. When I got in the car, I cried.

I never expected to hear the word autism! It hit me like a punch to the stomach, disintegrating my perfect world and throwing me into what I now refer to as the autism coma, an endless mind-numbing chasm of disbelief and desperation. I spent many waking hours thinking about autism, reading everything I could get my hands on and surfing the Internet until the wee hours of the morning in hopes of finding a cure. The prognosis was not good and treatments were very limited.

Everything I read said the same thing - lifelong, permanent, irreversible damage. I refused to accept that. There had to be something we could do. I wanted so badly to help Maddy that it consumed my whole being. At night,

I lay in bed and grieved as though my daughter had died along with my dreams. My feelings even a couple of years after diagnosis were still raw.

In between work, family responsibilities and researching autism, I would worry about what the future held for my precious baby and for our family. At first my worries for Maddy were simpler; would other kids tease her, would she be able to keep up with her classmates, would this obsessive behavior ever stop? Maddy had difficulty doing the simple things that other kids did with such ease. She couldn't swing, run or jump. She obsessed over flowers and would spend hours, if allowed, picking them and then pulling all the petals off. But she was still so young, I argued. She's not that far behind the other kids.

As time went on and her condition failed to improve, my worries grew. I worried about whether or not she would ever be toilet trained, if she would ever learn to read and if she would ever know what love and friendship felt like. Who would love her and take care of her when we were gone? I worried about the financial stress of her care and treatment on our family. I worried about poor Matthew, the forgotten child, as Martin and I often referred to him. He never got the amount of attention that his sister did. He was so easy-going and required so little from us. On the other hand, his sister was the attention black-hole; we had to keep an eye on her every minute. She was constantly getting into things; dumping things out of the pantry, opening nail polish, trying to touch the hot pans on the stove. I wondered if Matthew would be okay. Were we damaging him for life? Would he resent his sister? Would he be embarrassed by her? And, I worried about my marriage. Would it survive the stress of all this pressure? I gave so much of myself to autism that I had almost nothing left to give to my husband and son.

I had always dreamed that my children would have the close relationship that I shared with my brothers and sisters. I wanted Maddy and Matthew to be able to have that same closeness: someone to confide in, someone to share secrets with, someone who knew you like no one else does, someone that could laugh about your mistakes and celebrate your successes. I wanted them to grow old together and for their children to grow old together. I wanted them to have each other and a sense of family even when Martin and I were gone. Would this ever be a possibility? I ached inside thinking that they might never have this relationship.

In Her Own World

Time was racing quickly away as Maddy continued to slip further and further into her own world. I didn't know what to do! Our interactions with her consisted largely of her shrieking while my husband, Martin and I, tried desperately to figure out what was wrong. We tried holding her, rocking her, telling her everything was alright. Nothing seemed to help. I felt desperate, but Martin remained hopeful. We began an intensive therapy schedule for Maddy. When she wasn't in school, she was with a therapist. I viewed every moment as an opportunity to try and teach her something and every moment missed was another step to nowhere. We began speech therapy, occupational therapy and applied behavior analysis in hopes of reversing our daughter's downward trend. Each of these interventions was helpful in its own way and Maddy began making small steps forward. She had learned to say "yes" and "I want" and gradually increased her vocabulary. Yet, her social interactions with the family continued to deteriorate and when the environment changed, she would shriek and cry. No more going out to dinner. Along with the shrieking, she added tantrums, hitting, pinching and scratching and her primary target was me! Maddy was no longer a joy to be around. In fact, I found myself looking forward to my time away from her at work. I hated myself and the way I was feeling!

Kat Talks

What I met Lorie she was experiencing the heartache of every mom with a child with autism. She was seeing her life with her daughter continue to diminish, shrinking to the small boundaries of their home and in fact, those boundaries were becoming intolerable. Maddy was receiving lots of therapy but Lorie wanted a relationship with her daughter. Mom was on a heart breaking daily journey of rejection by her daughter.

Lorie Talks

It was obvious that Maddy loved her daddy. She would cry for him when he left her sight and would run to him when he arrived home. His soft, calm voice was the only thing that seemed to soothe her when she got out-of-sorts. He was marvelous with her. He never got frustrated, never lost his cool and always seemed to have an abundance of patience. Martin had always been a creative problem-solver and proved to be the same with Maddy. He would ramble on forever in his calm, even tone making up crazy stories involving all the people that Maddy knew. He instinctively put on his silly dad act and would have her laughing in no time. He would make silly faces, funny noises and pretend to be the various animals that Maddy loved. I, on the other hand, could do nothing to comfort her, much less engage her. My dreams for that special mother-daughter bond were coming unraveled.

Our family life revolved around Maddy and her moods. We were constantly walking on eggshells, trying not to upset her. It left us mentally and physically exhausted with little time or energy to enjoy time together as a family or with our new baby boy. Maddy began to be aggressive with others. She would hit and scratch Matthew any chance she had. We couldn't leave her alone with him or any other baby.

We did not have a normal life. Going out to dinner or to church with Maddy was like playing Russian roulette; you never knew when she might blow up. Movies were out of the question. Maddy would be constantly out of her chair trying to eat other people's popcorn, grabbing food off the floor, or screaming at the top of her lungs. Visits to other people's homes were too stressful. I would spend the entire time chasing after Maddy to make sure she didn't break a family heirloom, or destroy a prized flower garden or invade our host's pantry and gorge on their food.

We began to stay home more and more and decline offers for outings with our friends. Others with typical children just didn't understand what it was like, and try as they might, they thankfully never will. My faith in God and my belief that He would help us through this was the only thing that kept me going. Autism not only robs the affected child of a normal life, but it robs the family as well. After a couple of years of this, I was starting to believe that this was just how our life would be, then I learned about RDI.

A friend had encouraged me to attend a parent support group. She said they were a great bunch of moms who were committed to getting their children with autism well. The first meeting I attended was about the Relationship Development Intervention® Program. I had never heard of RDI, nor did I know anyone who was doing it. The topic didn't particularly interest me, either. After all, how could I work on a relationship with Maddy, when she didn't even want to be in the same room with me? I listened as the presenter, Katherine Lee, an RDI® Consultant, explained the fundamentals of the intervention. Then, she demonstrated the activities used and showed us videotaped samples of some of her sessions. It began to catch my attention.

This was a therapy that involved me personally in my daughter's therapy and focused on the social deficits of autism. It wasn't a therapy that was administered by a team of strangers that taught my daughter how to respond to life in rote sentences. RDI seemed to be the missing piece in our program; a therapy that would start from the ground up rebuilding and removing social deficits, adding layer upon layer, one step at a time. I couldn't wait to get started! Before I left the meeting, I had scheduled a consultation for Maddy with Kat.

Kat Talks

Lori contacted me right away to get a time for me to see Maddy. If it would have been possible, she would have started the next day. We scheduled the three part assessment and had our pre-assessment consultation within the next few weeks.

I met 6 year old Maddy at our first assessment. She had beautiful bows in her hair. Maddy was darling, but she was incredibly frustrated. She angered easily, often hitting herself when she really got mad. Her mom continued to try to engage her in games such as pulling her around on a carpet or playing on the beanbags, to distract her from her frustration. Sometimes, she was successful but only if she did exactly what Maddy demanded. Any variation brought frustration and sometimes even doing what Maddy wanted brought the same frustration. I knew I had super mom on my hands because Lorie just hung in there, staying positive in her attempts to engage Maddy.

Even through the frustration, I saw little smiles every once in a while when we tickled, or pulled Maddy on the magic carpet. The little girl she was meant to be was in there, we just had hard work in front of us to pull her out. Despite these difficulties, the assessment was quite successful and we were ready to get started.

A few weeks later, we met and went over Maddy's treatment program. We discussed in detail our plans and I began training Lorie to be an RDI® mom. Every mom that comes to me is a sharp lady. I totally respect each one. But every one of them agrees; learning to be an RDI® coach takes time and mentoring. This is no easy chore for the 30 and 40-something women who are in charge of many aspects of their lives.

Permission to Enjoy My Child

At first, RDI with my daughter was a struggle. Maddy would not even stay in the room with me for more than a couple of minutes without trying to escape. Years of always telling her what to do had conditioned her to think of our time together as one big demand. Frequently, our RDI® time together ended with Maddy hitting, scratching and throwing a tantrum. How could my baby girl not want to spend time with her mommy? I recall the disappointment I felt after my first RDI® session. Maddy and I were going to spend some quality time together just enjoying each other's company. Sounds simple enough, laying on the bed was something Maddy enjoyed, so I thought I'd join her. Each time I climbed onto the bed, Maddy would screech at me and make a bee-line for the door.

I was feeling so incompetent, but determined not to give up on our relationship. After years of failed attempts at establishing a relationship with my daughter and listening to other experts tell me how to interact with Maddy, I did not trust myself or my judgment regarding her any more. I deferred to others who I thought were more knowledgeable about my child.

How Does It Work?
Kat

We started with simple activities, making adjustments all along the way for Maddy, so that she could begin to feel more competent. We took advantage of every opportunity. For instance, putting on masks and popping out from behind a shower curtain while she rested in the bath water. More significantly, I had mom just lie next to Maddy and gaze at her, while blowing gently in her face. A wonderful relationship developed between them as they made this a part of their daily life. We called it 'just being'. But I had to watch out for Lorie too. The beginning of RDI can be a fragile time for moms and dads. They are hard on themselves and sometimes want some one else to do it because they feel so badly about themselves as parents. But that is just the autism and years of what it brings talking. So I knew that Lorie was not only capable, she was the most competent person to be leading her child to relationships.

One thing that was imperative was that Lorie was open with me about her feelings. If she was feeling rejected or like she was a failure, she told me. Just as importantly, I did not judge her; I knew she could do it. Living with autism had beaten her down. Her openness allowed me to help her.

I meet regularly with moms and dads in person and by phone, mostly every two weeks, some times every week if needed. Mostly, I just make sure parents know that I'm available. We review tapes and we continue training. Sometimes I see the children in person, though we find that tape review is our most effective tool and I have a policy to never talk in front of the children. We don't know what negative memories they might encode from our conversations or what they might misunderstand.

Mostly though, in the early stages as we are working together, I want the parents to feel encouraged and to recognize their own strengths as parents. In Lorie's case, we met in person at least once a month, but by phone once to twice a month as well. Lorie also sent me tapes of Maddy and her family at minimum every two weeks, sometimes more often. I would review and e-mail notes to her. Lorie and Martin were faithful from the beginning about getting the tape to me and scheduling times to meet. It is critical for parents to get feedback, both to train and to encourage.

I provided creative strategies for her mom to engage Maddy in social interaction. We focused on keeping it simple and short, then building on that foundation. Activities were brief and structured; jumping together, putting on masks, and blowing on Maddy's face. A relationship cannot be rushed; they needed to take their time.

One of the first things I had to help Lorie do was to just be with her child. She had never just lain quietly on the bed with Maddy and gazed at her, shared sweet looks. We laughed that when autism arrives in the home, it seems the last thing any one wants you to do is slow down! You go in to super sonic speed. Now, I told Lorie, it was time to put on the brakes. She had the permission she needed to just enjoy her child. Lorie and Maddy both deserved to have this time together.

Lorie has told me time and again she feels guilty when work gets in the way of RDI. I tell her this is a process and some days are going to go better than others. In fact, some weeks are going to go better than others. The point is to stay on the journey and hang in there. Lorie had already crossed the hurtle of wanting to spend time with her child, she just had to find the time.

Lorie

Over the next few weeks, Maddy and my time together began to change. Instead of drilling and demanding, Maddy and I were laughing, smiling and snuggling. We spent many sessions just gazing into each others' eyes, smiling, laughing and being silly. This was fun! For the first time since Maddy's diagnosis, I was having fun with her and not feeling guilty about wasting time. The RDI® Program had given me permission to simply enjoy being with my baby and the icing on the cake was the fact that she was learning at the same time! I knew that RDI was having a positive impact on Maddy, but finding the time for it was a juggling act.

With a very demanding full-time job, a husband that traveled frequently and a very active 4 year old son, I couldn't see how I was going to continue working RDI® sessions into my schedule. When I called Kat, she listened to my concerns and understood. She too was a mom with two kids - one on the spectrum, a husband and a full-time job. She understood exactly what I was going through.

Together we analyzed my daily routine. With her trained eye, Kat saw opportunities that I could not. She took routine activities and turned them into RDI® activities. Ten minutes here, fifteen there and quickly we had worked in an hour of RDI. Soon dressing, bathing and cleaning were fun RDI® activities. I began to look at everything as an opportunity for relationship development.

Trusting My Instincts, Again

The more time I spent doing RDI, the more natural it became. I integrated the sessions into my regular household activities, reducing the stress of trying to get it all done in a limited amount of time. Instead of Maddy controlling our time together, I was taking charge and acting as her guide and, she was a willing apprentice. Bath time became a time for sharing smiles and silly faces and preparing meals and doing laundry became times we worked on turn-taking and complementary activities like stirring and pouring.

I began looking forward to spending time with her again. One particular Sunday afternoon, Maddy and I baked cookies. I remember taking the first batch out of the oven and after they cooled, handing one to Maddy. She took a bite then raised the cookie up to give me a taste while smiling the entire time. It was an amazing moment. She was sharing her cookie and her joy with me! She was feeling more successful in our relationship and so was I. Her trust in me had been restored and I was beginning to trust my own instincts again. Maddy had begun looking to me for encouragement and comfort. She now takes the initiative to interact with me and others.

Not only was RDI having a positive impact on Maddy and our relationship, but it was also having a positive effect on our entire family. We worried less about Maddy and her future and began enjoying life again. Martin and I began spending more us time together. We began scheduling date nights and time away from the kids. We began experiencing happiness again, laughing together again and looking forward to the future again. The heavy weight of stress I carried every day began to peel away, making me feel lighter and lighter. I no longer felt as though I had a perpetual rain cloud over my head.

As Maddy and I spent more time together enjoying each other's company, we began to strengthen our mother-daughter bond. Maddy began requesting my attention over Daddy's. Instead of acting oblivious to my arrival home from work, Maddy started rushing to the door to greet me, seeking my attention and affection. Mine was the hand she would take when we would go for walks. I was the one she wanted to say her prayers and tuck her in at night.

Kat

One of the first things I noticed when I met Maddy was that she was constantly asking for her daddy. Mom shared with me that this request was continual and really quite heart breaking for her. She wanted Maddy to want to be with her, to ask for her. I felt that Lorie was one of the most courageous people I had met. Even though she knew her daughter was not going to want to be with her, that she would continually ask for daddy, she went into the RDI® session regardless and maintained a positive, happy attitude with her daughter, no matter what happened. Then one day, Lorie arrived to say, "Maddy wants me over daddy!" She was so happy!

I remember the day Maddy's mom came for our meeting and said with joy, "RDI has given me back my daughter." Wow! There was no question their relationship had changed. She was looking forward to her time with Maddy and in that meeting we planned more activities they could do together. As always, she had her video and I saw Maddy and Lorie just relaxing and sharing gazes with each other. Again, they looked like just any mother and daughter enjoying time together. Exciting changes were definitely taking place.

The RDI Family

Lorie

Seeing my success with Maddy, Martin joined in and turned bath time into show time. He encouraged Maddy to interact and share her laughter with him while he donned crazy masks and made funny noises. Dancing to R & B and disco music on the kitchen floor became the highlight of their father-daughter time together. Once again Martin's creativity paid off. He had an endless supply of novel ways to do the same activity. He knew just how much newness was enough and took Maddy to that edge, helping her to expand her ability to accept change and variety.

Martin began serving several roles. He was the main person behind the camera, making sure video angles were good so I could see what was happening between Maddy and me. He was also critical in making sure Matthew had his share of attention. While I was spending time with Maddy, Martin was with Matthew playing their own games or doing chores.

We began incorporating more and more RDI® activities into our family life. Soon, even four year old Matthew was an RDI® pro. He would encourage his sister to find a hidden object by using only facial expressions and practice playing hide and seek. After every session, he would proudly tell us how he helped his sister learn something new.

Through RDI, we discovered Maddy loved to cook and it became our favorite family activity. Together we whipped up batches of cookies, brownies, smoothies and even meatballs. Preparing a meal was no longer a tiresome task; it was a family adventure!

Swimming has always been a favorite activity for everyone in the family, except Maddy. She was afraid to step foot in the water and had even refused to come out of the house when we went to a friend's to swim. Knowing how important this activity was to the family, Kat suggested we incorporate swimming into our RDI® program. Kat helped us develop a plan that encouraged Maddy to gradually get closer to the water, eventually sitting on the side of the pool with her feet dangling in. She would just sit there getting used to the pool and the noise, before we tried to get her to swim. We decided to take it one step at a time.

A couple of weeks later, we went back to our friend's home to swim. To my surprise, Maddy walked right out with us and got in the pool without hesitation. She jumped and splashed and had such a wonderful time she didn't want to leave.

Kat

Our long term plan was to keep her swimming year around so we would not lose ground. Eventually, we designed fun pool games for her, so she felt competent in the pool and was ready to play with us while. But improvements in swimming were not all the changes we were seeing.

Lorie

Within six months of beginning RDI, Maddy has developed a greater sense of mindfulness. She became more aware of herself, her surroundings and others. She has begun demonstrating flexible thinking*, allowing herself to experience the fun of doing things a little differently instead of relying on learned procedures. During a recent visit to a friend's home, Maddy spotted some candy in the cabinet that she wanted, but knew she could not have. Instead of throwing a tantrum which was her previous method of operation, Maddy plotted a way to get what she wanted.

While I was distracted, she told my friend, Jamie, that she needed to use the restroom. Since Maddy had only been to their house once before, Jamie accompanied her. Maddy told Jamie to, "Go play." Thinking she needed some privacy, Jamie closed the bathroom door. No sooner had the door shut; Maddy ran to the kitchen and had almost gotten the candy out of the cabinet before Jamie realized she'd been had. It may have been the first time in history that a mother was proud of her child for having lied. But, I knew that lying required thinking and that it could not be learned from rote teaching.

Friends and family began commenting about how much Maddy had changed since they last saw her. They wanted to know what had we done differently to produce such a rapid change. When they talked to her, there was an understanding look in her eyes instead of a blank stare. She would smile and greet our friends and call them by name and instead of avoiding them, she would repeatedly approach them for interaction. She would even miss them when they were gone.

I remember vividly a recent visit to our friend's home. We were standing in the living room chatting when Uncle Glenn and one of his three boys entered the room. Maddy noted their arrival and surveyed the room. Then, she looked at us and said, "Where's Zach?" This was the first time she had verbalized that she knew something was different; someone was missing from the group. I was thrilled and so were our friends.

This is one of the best parts; when people "not in the know" tell you they see a difference. I think somewhere in the back of our minds, we parents have been through so much, and we wonder if we are imagining the changes. It might not be rational, but it makes total sense to me. When others comment about change, happiness overflows.

Another day, we went for a walk with our neighbor and her two daughters. Maddy was excited to see them. As we walked along, Maddy reached out and took one of the girl's hands and they continued the walk, hand-in-hand. My eyes filled with tears of joy. Most parents wouldn't even notice such a simple gesture, but to me it was a glimpse of the friendships to come for Maddy.

One evening, Martin had an errand to run and left the house after dinner. When Maddy discovered him gone, instead of becoming hysterical, she said, "Miss Daddy." I nearly fell out of my chair! She had told me how she was feeling and I was able to comfort her, knowing exactly what was wrong.

At our six month re-assessment, I was totally amazed at the changes in my daughter. She was much less fearful and anxious when being challenged with new activities. She eagerly looked for me when I hid behind a tower of bean bags. Prior to starting RDI, at her pre-assessment, this activity caused her such anxiety and confusion that she had a total meltdown; she had no idea where I was or how to find me. This time she interacted with me and Kat and even demonstrated complex turn-taking between the three of us, which she initiated on her own. She looked to me for guidance when she was uncertain about what she should do.

I realize that we still have a long road to travel with Maddy; many days have been and will continue to be rough. It's like being on a continual roller coaster; one that not only goes up and down, but backward as well as forward. I have learned to document everything - the good, the bad and the ugly - in a journal. On those particularly challenging days, I will look back through my notes and remember just how far we've come. And, some day, I plan to share the details of this journey with Maddy.

I remember an e-mail Kat sent to me during one particularly difficult week: "Hi- just a word of encouragement during this difficult time. You are doing a great job. Keep lying on the bed with her and relaxing and just being. Don't feel like you are wasting time...just gazing and sharing and blowing on her face will comfort her and you at the same time."

My Dreams and My Daughter
Lorie

Maddy continues to make daily progress both cognitively and socially. She is experiencing joy and sharing emotions for the first time in the four years since autism stole her smile. She laughs with joy when I make silly faces or kiss her noisily on the cheeks. The tantrums, although much improved, still surface occasionally, but now Maddy can tell me she's mad. Life at home has become so much easier and more enjoyable. There is now a spark in Maddy's eye and emotion in her gaze. It is the first time since she was an infant that we have had an emotional bond and have been able to really share special moments together.

Finally, Maddy and I are experiencing the relationship that I had always dreamed of and I am feeling competent as a mother. This is what being a mom is about! Children grow up so quickly, and we need to be able to enjoy every minute of their childhood. I am enjoying my time with my daughter again and truly have hope for her future. I don't know what the future holds for Maddy but I know she will always be Mommy's little girl! I have my life, my dreams and my daughter back!

A recent note from Lorie:

We are at Maddy's seventh birthday party; a swim party luau no less. Everyone is having a great time, including Maddy and me. Maddy is in the pool, swimming with her family and friends. I am relaxed, enjoying conversation with the other parents (not chasing my child around frantically). When it comes time for the birthday cake, we light the big number 7 candle on her cake and everyone begins to sing. Maddy's eyes are glued to the cake and a huge smile dances across her face. As the song ends, she leans toward the cake and blows. The candle goes out; my heart leaps for joy. This is the first time she has ever shown an interest in her birthday party, ever blown out a birthday candle. This is the first of many firsts to come…

Kat Reflects

I want to write a word about mothers and daughters. I have a lovely 15 year old daughter. All of our time together, despite the pain of her brother having autism (and maybe in part because of it) has been precious to me. When I see a mom and daughter affected by autism, I can't help but want for them the relationship I have with my own children. That is one of the things the mom's communicate to me; they so desperately want that relationship and I want them to have it. I want them to have what they were meant to have as mother and daughter.

Recognition

I recall taking my son for a speech evaluation. Maybe for the first time, I realized something really was wrong with him. The speech therapist acted weird with me. My baby didn't want to do anything, he just ran around laughing. He wouldn't sit for her. I said, "He is a happy boy." She replied "Yes, he has his joy,"as if that was the only thing he had. I said nothing. Inside I said, "What does she mean by that?" I had that creeping, haunting feeling. We ended cordially, with her promise of results in a month or so. I took him to the car and put him in the car seat. I got in the drivers side and burst into tears.

He didn't even notice. I looked at him, "What is wrong with you?" I cried. He just kept playing. Then internally, "It's okay…there is nothing wrong with him…or if it is it is no big deal. It will be okay…you are over reacting," and I held that thought for several weeks, until diagnosis.

The realization that something is wrong does not come on at once. It is creeping, subtle, almost haunting and there is a part of you that thinks you are imagining a problem that doesn't exist. Perhaps you are still tired from having a newborn or maybe you are adjusting to the stress of motherhood; how can you know after all, especially with a first child? You are new to being a mommy. I remember right before our diagnosis that I told a good friend, "I don't want to claim ownership to pain that isn't mine to have. Other people have really bad things happen to their children and I don't want to claim their pain for something minor." I was soon to find out that the pain I was feeling then was nothing compared to what was coming.

Autism is not easily recognized by pediatricians, causing us dismay, because we are just sure something is not right, but what? We are often told to start with a hearing test and speech evaluation. Eventually, hopefully, we get to some one who can tell us what is wrong. But of course, the blow of a diagnosis still knocks us out.

As I got to know Maddy's story, I relived my own. First, the devastation of the diagnosis, then wanting to save your child - it consumes your entire being. All you eat, drink and breathe is finding a way to help your child. As with any horrific diagnosis, no one can understand completely unless they have walked those painful steps. I remembered a play I saw once in which one of the characters was in such emotional pain he said, "I feel as if all my skin has been peeled off." This was the pain I felt, this was the pain Lorie felt.

Another thing that goes out the window with autism is balance. Everything becomes about the chronically ill child. Marriages suffer. Relationships with other siblings suffer and the worrying is terrible. One of the goals of RDI is to bring things back to a balance and help the family start functioning together, not separately. This involves open, honest conversations about relationships; who is doing what and what needs to be addressed in order to get balance established.

After the balance goes, we tend to start gazing heavily at the future. We stop enjoying today and worry about ten or tewnty years from now. Will she get married? Will she have a family? The list of worries is long and full. I try to get families focused on today. No one knows what the future holds for any of us. Appreciating today, caring today for our loved ones and holding moments dear is what we have to do right now. Thoughts of despair about the future hold no value. They paralyze us with fear or cause us to work so fast we burn out. So we begin on getting focused on the now and what we need to do today.

Relentless

I remember my own start with RDI. I had worked as one of my son's ABA therapists for years. We spent a ton of time together, both working and doing fun activities. But, when I started really addressing his social/emotional development, he resisted. I remember trying to play on his trampoline with him one day. He said, "Mommy, will you leave?" I went inside to my husband and said, "He doesn't want to play with me. What am I going to do?" I was upset. My dear husband and my best friend, said, "Well, I think you are going to be relentless. You are going to go back out there and play with him no matter what happens." And, I did. I knew just how Lorie felt and I knew I had to keep her relentless.

Incompetence

It never ceases to amaze me how these super moms feel so incompetent in their mothering and their ability to create a relationship with their child. It never ceases to amaze me because, I admire and respect them so much for all they are doing for their children and, without exception, they are the best people to lead their children. I always tell moms, "No matter what you have heard, no matter what some one has told you, you are the best person to help your child. You know your child better than any one else, better than a teacher, better than a therapist, better than a doctor, better than me, better than anyone. You are the one when it comes to your child."

I have to tell them this truth because everyone associated with autism, even well meaning professionals, have communicated otherwise to them at one time or another. And, as a mom with a child with autism, I know that even the smallest error on my part can make me feel like I am the worst coach for my son.

Every Good Relationship Takes Time

Unless they have many children before their child with ASD, parents really don't know what it is like to be a typical parent. They don't know what typical looks like. One thing I try to do, is show them they do know what to do and that they have not changed, only their circumstance. They are still the brilliant, impressive dynamic people they have always been.

When both parents have to work two full-time jobs to make ends meet, finding time is easier said than done. And, the time spent must be quality time, spent enjoying and sharing, not something that comes easily when your child is hurt. You learn to move very fast and you forget how to slow down. Finding balance is definitely a challenge.

Many times, when a family starts an RDI® Program, the child is running the home, not the parents. I immediately start to try to turn that around, giving the parents tools to take back the home and establish some order. A relationship is not just about the time spent in structured activities, but ongoing; before school, after school, during breakfast, during dinner, waking up and going to sleep. All of those are moments make up a relationship and when the child is completely in control of all of those, chaos is king. Getting the day under control can bring great joy to a relationship. And, I saw this with Maddy and her mom.

Kat Learns

I learn something new from every family. From Lorie, I have learned how to be positive even when things are difficult. Even when she shared her fears and her concerns, she stayed positive. She was interested in practical ways to address problems and even though I know at times she was in a lot of emotional pain, she put that aside to focus on how to fix the problem. Her face would light up with interest as we would trouble shoot a problem and come up with strategies. What a joy to work with her!

Some professionals look at children with ASD as only being able to do so much, go so far. Over and over again, parents tell me how they have been given no hope for their child. When faced with some problem or issue, professionals say to them, "Well, the child can't do this," or "Well, we just have to accept that." I think the reason children can't is because we have not figured out how to help them. There is so much inside these children; we must challenge ourselves to keep improving, keep studying and increase our passion for helping them live their lives fully.

Maddy's Meatballs

1 pound lean, organic ground beef

1 small organic onion, chopped

1 organic egg

1 vine-ripened organic tomato, chopped

1 organic bell pepper, chopped

Salt, pepper, garlic salt

1 jar pasta sauce (Maddy likes *Newman's Own* brand)

Roll into 1 inch balls. Pan fry, turning frequently until browned on all sides. Cover with pasta sauce and simmer until cooked through. Serve over spaghetti noodles al denté.

Enjoy!

✎ **Katherine "Kat" Lee is an RDI® Consultant in the Dallas/Fort Worth, Texas area. She has been a RDI® Certified Consultant for two years and lives in North Texas with her husband of 18 years and their two children. As the mother of a child diagnosed with ASD, Katherine not only consults in RDI, she lives it day to day. You can contact Katherine at kat1216@aol.com.**

8

The Same Destination

by Brad and Claudia Andreessen
with Hannah Gutstein

Brad

Claudia and I were married in 1994 and were very excited to start our life together. We knew from the beginning that our life was not going to be a cookie-cutter relationship. Claudia and I were in an inter-cultural marriage. She is from Mexico and I am from the Midwest United States. Languages, cultures and lifestyles are very different between us, and yet we have found several common grounds in which to base our lives. In the beginning this was an adjustment, but when it came time to have children, we agreed upon how to raise them before they were even born.

On July 10, 1997, Nicholas, our son, was born. I remember being the typical excited first time father and Claudia being, well, a mother for the first time. The labor was a 16 hour adventure, but the end result made it all worth it. Nicholas was everything I imagined him to be, perfect, in every way. There were no clues that 20 months after the birth of our first child, a path we would never have imagined presented itself.

As we made our way home, all I could think about was how delicate our newborn was. We took extra care in holding him, putting him in the child restraint and driving home for the first time as a family.

The first couple of months were normal. We went through all the processes; feeding, watching him turn over for the first time, enjoying making Nicholas grin and crawl. We really did not see anything different in his behavior, because we had nothing to compare it to.

About 6 months after Nicholas was born, Claudia and I were blessed with another piece of great news. We were going to become parents again. Even though we seemed like experts the second time around, there was still something very new about the birth of our second child. Once again everything went according to plan and on November 1, 1998, we were blessed with a girl. The joy we shared was the same as when Nicholas was born, but had a different connotation to it because this was our first girl; one boy and one girl, just like we had it drawn up. We decided to name her Claudia, after her mother. Of course with us, there had to be some distinction between my daughter and my wife, so we nicknamed her "Cachita."

By this time, Nicholas was over a year old and was walking and attempting to talk. So even though our two children were both very young, they were in two very different stages of life.

I do not know exactly when or where, but our lives started to change from what we had planned. All I remember is Claudia mentioning to me that her sister was a little concerned about how slow Nicholas' reaction time seemed to be. Rosita, Claudia's sister, has a wonderful little boy who is approximately 8 months older than Nicholas, so she in fact could tell some of the differences in the two. Claudia became a little concerned about this, and as the days passed she began to notice some of the things her sister was telling her. I have to admit, I shrugged it off at the beginning. But as time passed and more and more observations were made, it became clear that something was not right. The first thing we actually talked about was a hearing problem.

We decided to get Nicholas' hearing checked. It was a simple thing to do and if it explained some of the things we saw, we could address them properly. So we took Nicholas to a hearing doctor in Monterrey, Mexico. He got through his hearing test fine and we waited for the results. I remember thinking at the time how devastating a hearing loss for Nicholas would be to me, and I became emotionally torn. On one hand, if the test came out positive, we could address the problem and take steps towards a resolution. On the other hand, I wanted the test to come out negative so we could rule out a potentially devastating result for me at the time. In the back of my mind, I always thought if it did come out alright, there must be something else.

After a couple of days we finally got the results we were waiting for-Nicholas' hearing was normal. Relief, but a little nervousness ensued. I was happy for the good results, but it was time to do something else to find the cause of his delays.

The hearing doctor suggested a neurologist in Laredo for us to see. He explained that this was the normal course of action whenever a hearing test came back with results like Nicholas'. So, on his recommendation, we went to go see the neurologist. I was not sure at the time what a neurologist was or did, but knew it had something to do with the activity of the brain. It was hard for me before this appointment because the uncertainty of what to expect was overwhelming.

I was working late the day we had our appointment with this new doctor. The day began like any other. The sun was shining, the temperature was comfortable, and it seemed like any other day. I remember our appointment was in the middle of the afternoon, because I had gone to work first and was going to meet the family at the doctor's office. We went into the doctor's office and I was pleasantly surprised by how nice he was to us. I was used to going to the doctor for cuts and bruises, and my expectations for this doctor had been much different. It was almost awkward to a point. But as considerate as he was to us, he was even friendlier to Nicholas. The doctor ran Nicholas through a series of games and procedures that did not seem to take long at all. To me they seemed like typical toddler games and the responses Nicholas gave were what I considered very normal. When they were finished, he set Nicholas up with some toys and told us that he wanted to speak with us privately.

He was very calm, and again very friendly, but with a little more firmness in his face. We all sat down and he explained a little of what he was looking for in his playtime with Nicholas. He confirmed to us that his delays were apparent and promptly acquainted us with the term "PDD," or Pervasive Development Disorder. At the time, I had no idea what this meant and more importantly how it related to our child. I still, to this day, am not sure of the words or terms he used. At the time, I just knew there was something wrong with our child. It did not click for me on any level, until part way through the conversation when he brought up the word autism. I had been exposed to autism through movies and articles, but it still did not make much sense. How could a child of mine have something like that? During the course of the conversation our emotions started to take over, and the more Claudia and I heard about the condition the more emotional we got.

Once we came to terms with what we were dealing with, the neurologist offered us the names of two good specialists that he recommended for further testing and an official diagnosis. The first was a doctor in Monterrey, Mexico, and the other - The Connections Center in Houston, Texas. We knew we were going to have a decision to make and that it would be a long term commitment. It was not something to take lightly. We had to consider that we were not going to be able to communicate with the specialist on an ongoing basis and would probably have to make several trips back and forth, but these were things we would have to address later.

We left the neurologist with more answers, but all that seemed to do was draw up more questions of how we were going to proceed. I actually had a sense of relief right after the doctor's office; some may call this initial denial. I decided to go back to work even after the trauma of the news we had just heard. I believe I made it back to work and within 20 minutes, I awakened to what had happened. I asked myself what I was doing there and why I wasn't with my family. Needless to say, I managed to finish up some small details and went home.

As soon as I got home, Claudia and I, although we were shocked, knew we had decisions to make. After a long period of discussing all the positives and negatives of each doctor, we decided to look more closely at the Houston option. We used the internet and researched more about autism and PDD. We then went to see how the Connections Center dealt with the two.

This was our first introduction to RDI. We called to inquire about making an appointment, but found out it would be months before a space was open. Claudia did not let that stop her. We made the appointment and in the meantime, she was determined to use her time wisely and find out as much as she could about the condition and about RDI. This was in 1999 and RDI was just in its initial stages. The more we heard about it, the more intrigued we became. At this same time, we also investigated other methods such as ABA, just so we could make an educated decision of where to proceed. It was a gut wrenching time to say the least. We were not sure which way to go, we were uneducated about what we were looking for, and we were still dealing with the realization our son and our lives were going to be changed forever.

The more we read and talked about the Connections Center, the more comfortable we became with the program. Then one day, something great happened! The Connections Center called and said there was a cancellation and asked if we could come within one week's time. There really wasn't much of a discussion on our part because we knew the sooner we could get a grasp on the situation, the sooner we could get started on what needed to be done.

My work was very supportive about our situation and I was able to get time off on short notice. Claudia had been staying home since the birth of our children, so we were on our way.

I remember pulling into the parking garage and thinking how comfortable I felt during such a stressful time. I really could not explain it. It was almost like I felt something special was going to happen, and while I felt nervous and anxious in the beginning, there was sense of calmness that came over me when we arrived. Maybe it was the fact we were close to getting some answers, or maybe it was the fact that we were just advancing in the whole process that made me feel this way.

We walked into the office and it was like any other office. It was simple, yet inviting and this made me feel even more at ease. There is just something about how an outside environment can affect your perceptions, and the look of the office did just that. This was the first time I met Dr. Sheely and she was everything I thought she was going to be. Sometimes you imagine what a person is going to be like and she was absolutely what I had envisioned. I knew she was going to give us some answers about our child.

Just like the neurologist before, she was amazing with our child. She knew exactly how to act in front of him, how to talk to him, and how to interpret his personality. It was like she had known Nicholas for years. Again, we set up a series of conditions and play, many of which are the basis of what most people see when they first have their child go through the evaluation process, or what they now call the RDA™ (Relationship Development Assessment™). I was merely the camera operator while Dr. Sheely and Claudia actually did the administration of the exercises. At first I thought how simplistic the exercises were and wondered what could be interpreted from them. I must say that I was pleasantly surprised at how effective they both were at working with Nicholas and how he responded to them. But I still wondered how this was all going to be useful.

The next day, we came back without Nicholas. I knew that it was then that we would get some answers to our questions. I began imagining some of the scenarios that were about to be presented. But, as Dr. Sheely started talking, I was shocked by how complimentary she was toward our son and to us as parents. She did acknowledge that, yes, Nicholas was on the autism spectrum, but told us all the positive things she saw in her evaluations. Because, this predicated everything else we were going to talk about that morning, it set a very positive tone for what we were going to discuss regarding the future. Although Nicholas was on the spectrum, it was very good to hear how strongly she felt that, with some help, he would be able to lead a very productive life. We had a feeling that we had not felt since we first started going through this process - hope.

Hope is an incredible thing. It is the one inalienable condition of the mind that tells you no matter how bad things get, there is always something positive that might happen in the future. This is what I felt that morning. I felt for the first time that there was something positive that could happen. It was going to take a lot of work on everyone's part, but it was a journey we were now able to accept with open arms. Other than hope, the relief we felt was simply indescribable. We knew we were on our way.

Soon it was May, 1999, a couple of weeks after our initial RDI® evaluation. Nicholas was a little over 20 months and Claudia and I had been married for about 5 years. I have to admit, I have never seen her as determined as she was with Nicholas. She jumped in with both feet and everything from then on revolved around our son. I was in full agreement with this because; we felt the first 6 months were going to be important.

At the time, the structured lab work was critical. We rearranged our daily schedules and even took our guest room and made it into our lab room. We wanted to make the room look as blank as possible in order to help lessen distractions and expedite the progress in lab time. Every day, for an hour in the morning and an hour in the afternoon, Claudia and Nicholas spent time in the lab room. I was working, so this all fell to Claudia, who had to do this while juggling our other child, Cachita, who was only an infant.

As the days and weeks passed, progress was made, slowly. After the first couple of months, the schedule we were trying to keep became harder and harder and we simply were not seeing the results we thought we were going to see. We hit a wall. But, as we continued to work, this wall began to crumble and we soon found ourselves back on track. Call it perseverance, but there was not one time we thought about revaluating the path we had chosen.

We continued to go up to the Connections Center every couple of months so they could evaluate our progress and, to our surprise, at every visit they felt we were doing well. Maybe one of the reasons we did not see the progress was because we were so wrapped up and so close to the task at hand. In essence, these trips back to Houston were as much about giving Claudia and me reassurance, as they were about evaluating Nicholas' progress.

There was actually one time, during one of our visits, where we were able to sit down with Dr. Sheely to do nothing but discuss how our lives and how we as parents had been and would be affected. Part of the RDI success, from what I have learned, depends a lot on how parents are able to join their ideas and personalities. We talked about our history together and even our history before we met. It gave both of us an interesting view of our lives together, and what we could do to help harness our strengths into one cohesive path. It was quite a self realization for us.

Soon it was June, 1999, and we were pulling along, day by day, week by week. As we became more and more involved in the program, we could not help but think how much easier and better it would be if we lived in Houston. It started weighing on our minds more and more, until we felt we had to move. I decided to speak with my employer and once again I could not have found a more supportive group than the one I had. Our company actually had affiliates in Houston; so almost immediately everyone began pulling together to see if there was a possibility I could find a job. It was only after weeks and weeks of investigating that I found out, financially, it was not going to work. At first it was tough to take, but I also knew that I still had a family to provide for.

It was then that, just when I had nowhere to turn, I received a call from a company in Houston interested in bringing me on board. From then on, things began happening very quickly. I flew up to interview, and a couple of days later an offer was made that I was able to accept. In August, 1999 I started my new job in Houston.

With this new job, came other obstacles. Everyone likes to believe that when something happens to your child, everything else in life can be put on hold. Unfortunately, this is never the case. We were 4 months into remediation, and I had a new job in a new city, we had a house to sell, and we had to again adjust our lives in order for everything to work. Although some people questioned our decision, we could only think of how much better living in Houston would be in the long run. It was a gamble we knew we needed to take. I moved to Houston and went into temporary housing, while Claudia stayed home with the kids in Laredo.

We knew keeping things as consistent as possible would make the move easier. For the next five months, I visited the family every couple of weeks. It was the single hardest thing I have had to do. I was away from my family during one of the most important times in our young family life. At the same time, Claudia was left alone with our two children, trying to give a sense of normalcy to their lives.

Claudia and I spoke almost every night; I could hear both accomplishment and despair in her voice. It was as much a test of our faith as anything else. I would call Claudia a spiritual person, but for me, spirituality was not a priority. What I can say is that those five months gave me a whole new perspective on how I view us and our faith. I would say that there is a reason for everything that happens, and for me faith during this time was my reason and I am forever grateful.

I was also able to have a new view of the progress our son was making whenever I came home to visit. Earlier in the year, I questioned the progress or lack thereof that was being made. Because I was able to distance myself, I could see the impact I had been missing. I think this helped both of us keep moving in the right direction.

It wasn't until five months after I moved to Houston, that we were able to sell our house, move to our new city and restore the family life we had been missing. It was almost like a rebirth, something very new. We had to adjust to each other again, and all the time I had missed in those five months of our children's lives. I needed to somehow make that up to them; and I did through love and just being there for them.

Almost immediately, we tried to make ourselves a life in our new environment. There was a new sense of urgency with everything, including RDI with Nicholas. That provided the second wind we needed to get our lives organized again.

Getting acclimated to the new city was very tough and stressful, for both the children and us. We had just moved to the fourth largest city in the United States and staking our place opened up several new challenges. Nicholas was getting to an age where he was becoming more independent, as well as, coming to a time in his life where he needed to share time with peers his own age. Claudia also needed something outside of Nicholas' life, in order to enhance her own. Throughout the process with Nicholas, we needed to remember we had another child that was getting older and needed more attention every day. Little Claudia was now a little over a year old and was beginning to become her own person.

We decided to place him in a school, not for educational aspects, but more importantly for emotional aspects. Living in a city, such as Houston, we found there were many types of schools to choose from - Montessori schools, mother's day out and other private schools. After a lot of debating, we felt that Montessori school was the way to go. We did not have much information to go on, other than that Montessori schools were known to have smaller classrooms and more one-on-one engagements. It sounded like the perfect way for Nicholas to begin. Unfortunately, it was also the most expensive.

A couple of months passed, and for the most part we didn't have any problems with the Montessori school, but the payments were becoming more and more of an issue. It was something that my wife and I could not continue to do, so it was time to look elsewhere. We had just joined our local Catholic Church and we learned they offered a mothers day out program. This became the logical solution, because we felt that we had found a place we could trust, as well as, a place we could afford. It was also a good choice, because they offered classes for our daughter as well, which was important. We wanted to keep the children together, as much as possible, so that Nicholas would feel a sense of security.

Another couple of months passed, and while money was no longer an issue, for the first time we encountered a problem with Nicholas and autism. It was just one day, but it is a day that my wife and I will never forget. She was dropping the children off in the morning, as usual, but was asked to go to the administration office. The administrator told her that they had decided that the church's mothers day out could not continue to keep Nicholas enrolled, because he was demanding too much attention from the teachers. It was deemed that the teachers "did not have the proper tools to handle Nicholas and his level of autism." At first I was stunned by the news. All sorts of questions came to our minds. How could our own church turn away one of their own because of something like this? If we cannot seek help from them, who do we turn to?

Never in Nicholas' young life had we experienced this type of situation before, and to have it come from our own church was additionally depressing. It was the first time in our lives that we felt like we were back at square one with his development. We went through the proper channels and even wrote a letter to the church office trying to explain the feeling of despair we had as a result of what mother's day out was doing to us. We received concern and sympathy over our situation, but in reality there was nothing that they were going to do to help. All we could do as parents was look for another solution. Even though we thought we had lost our church, we knew that we still had our faith and this would direct us to a better future and in the end it did.

We found another mother's day out, in another church. We enrolled both children, but we did one thing differently. We decided not to disclose Nicholas' condition. Based on what we had just gone through, we did not want any preconceived notions or anxiety from the school. We needed Nicholas to thrive in a new environment, but if we compromised that environment in the beginning, we felt we would get the same results as the last time. As months passed, Nicholas really adapted to his new class and from all the accounts from his teachers, he was doing very well inside the classroom. It was only when he was enrolled in his second year that we decided to disclose his condition. We debated about this for a long time, but felt the time was right to let the school know. We were happy when they did not shut their eyes to Nicholas, but embraced him as a wonderful child with a great upside. Another successful year passed. Looking back, the problems we had, gave us an opportunity to provide our son with a much better situation. Silver linings can be few and far between, but this was one we felt our faith had delivered to our doorstep.

Transition is a part of life. While we had a couple of very good years at mother's day out, we knew it was time for Nicholas to move out of that environment and settle in to a public school. Many more students and a busier environment, along with a tougher curriculum, were now areas of concern for us. The one thing we had going for us, was that we bought our home in a school system that we felt could give Nicholas the tools to make the transition and to thrive as a result of it.

Changes for Nicholas were happening outside and now inside of the home. We were slowing down a lab based environment at home and incorporating RDI into our everyday lifestyle. I must admit, this transition was probably more difficult on us as parents, than it was on Nicholas. Lifestyle meant that it was up to us to capture those little everyday moments and utilize them in a structured way. While it sounds easy on paper, it was a huge challenge.

As we go along, we know there will be many challenges that lie ahead. Now we are dealing with more complex issues, and we will have to change our lives again. But, as parents, we relish the experience and embrace it and look forward to the future. It is a terrific way to wake up in the morning, knowing and never taking for granted what is most precious to you.

As parents, Claudia and I have struggled and viewed things differently, but that is not bad, because our destinations are the same. This allows us to stay focused on what we need to do in difficult situations without giving up who we are as individuals. We believe if two people can do this, then everything else will take care of itself.

Claudia
School

One of the good things that we have learned when dealing with schools is that we see things differently. With Nicholas, because we have always carefully monitored things, our eyes are open to how receptive people are going to be, or not.

When we had our first experience with mother's day out, I didn't know as much. I was a novice, but I knew that my work with him was much more important than anything he was getting there. I think that experience was good for me, because the next time I went more slowly and found out that the word autism really scares some people. At that point, school was mostly so that I could have a break, but I also didn't want school to be a bad experience. My daughter, Cachita, was a baby and she was a handful and I wanted to take care of her; at that time, the mother's day out program provided that for me.

The more I know about autism, the more that I know that people's ideas are not always the right ones. Some people when they heard the term autism, wouldn't give Nicholas a chance. That first time, it wasn't pretty or nice to hear, but as Brad said, we got over it and moved on.

As Brad mentioned, during our second mother's day out and the first year of school, we didn't mention that Nicholas was autistic. Instead, I just told them what he struggled with and how I worked with him at home. By that time, we had already been working with him for awhile so he wasn't quite as random or disorganized. He was already attending and he wasn't all over the place. All the work that we had done was really starting to show. But it was frustrating that people didn't know, and I had to be careful of what to say and how to say it, so they wouldn't undo everything that I was doing at home.

The biggest challenge in elementary school has been letting him go and relying on the tools that we have given him, hoping for the best. It was a big test because public school wasn't going to be a small class with two teachers, and there was a big building to navigate. The first year of elementary school, I went on a tour with him around the school. We were anxious about how he was going to respond.

It took him about a semester to adapt, and the teacher said he was doing okay. The teacher was very structured and always did what she said she would do, so that really helped. He had no problems following the rules, but my major concern was how he was going to keep up with the other kids during recess and at the cafeteria, because it is not a structured environment.

I have never actually followed him around and the only way I really find out about his day is indirectly. Even now he doesn't immediately share with me what he did at school that day. I will say to him, "Oh, so I heard that you were talking about butterflies today," and that will spark a conversation. Or I will say something completely wrong, on purpose, to start a conversation. I do it that way so that he doesn't feel like he has to share things with me. Nicholas also usually needs a break and some down time after school, so this isn't usually a good time to find things out.

Instead, we always have conversations at dinner time. This is something that we have done consistently from the beginning. At dinner, everyone starts talking about how their day was, even Brad and I. We take turns saying what our favorite thing about the day was, or if we didn't have a favorite thing, we share our most miserable part of the day. We are really honest. Now, Nicholas will start our dinner time conversation. Usually he will share just the exciting things that have happened to him, he rarely shares things that are hard or difficult.

It also really helps that Cachita is at the same school as him, but in a different grade. This is great, because Cachita will say something about school and Nicholas will elaborate. Now we are at the point where Brad and I want to talk about ourselves a little bit and get them to listen to us! Don't get me wrong, there are times where they don't want to share and neither do we and that is fine. We are pretty lenient in terms of having a bad day.

We have had some challenges with school, especially when Nicholas was out of kindergarten and starting first grade. Things were more complex and there was more of an emphasis on academic stuff, more work and less play, which is good and bad for Nicholas. For instance, he is able to do anything in math and science, probably faster then other kids. But he really struggles with reading comprehension. The school is only concerned with how fast he can read and I really don't care about that. What I do care about is if he understands what he is reading, and this is something I stress to his teachers. I want him to take everything slowly so that the words will make sense for him.

Another challenge with the school is that it is all about acquiring content. At parent teacher conferences I stress that I have a bigger goal for him. It is really a give and take with schools, because their curriculum is not about learning to learn, it is more about memorizing. I find myself working at home with him and re-teaching him everything. Sometimes we can't do it all in one sitting and we take a break. We try and finish by the next day, but if we can't, I email the teacher and tell her that we aren't done. I don't get stressed out by that stuff. At home I really push for what I want him to be learning.

Right now, he really wants to fit in at school. This week the Astros have been really big, but yesterday he didn't have an Astros shirt and he wore his cap instead. Today he told me that he didn't want anyone to see that he wasn't wearing an Astros shirt, so he kept his jacket on. Last year he didn't care what everyone was saying, but now he cares. I know some of that has to do with him following the rules, but I know it is also because he notices what his peers are doing, and this is the important thing to me.

RDI from the Beginning

It is really neat when I think about our family and RDI. We have really grown with the different emphases that they have made over the years. I remember how we were first introduced to RDI, out of the blue. The neurologist that diagnosed Nicholas just happened to mention Dr. Sheely and the other doctor in Monterrey. It was completely random and we actually had more information on the other psychologist in Monterrey. All I had was Dr. Sheely's name and when I called, I was told that Dr. Sheely wanted to start out with a phone consultation.

When we had the phone consultation, as a teacher, I was very structured. I had all of the points that I wanted to communicate in front of me. I think Dr. Sheely just let me talk for the first 40 minutes. I had so much anxiety and I was feeling so helpless. I spit everything out, non-stop. After a while, she told me how observant and intuitive I was. She said, "I know how you feel and the news you have received is devastating and there is nothing that I can say to make you feel better, however we can sit down and make a plan." There was nothing superficial in what she said. I looked over and told my mom that I just knew she was going to be able to help me. Then I told Brad that we were going to the Connections Center. At that time, it was just a feeling of personal connection.

At that point, there was no written information; everything was still just in Dr. Gutstein's and Dr. Sheely's heads. So I didn't have any theory or proof to rely on. I just went with a hunch and kept coming back every two months, after the initial consultation. I kept a journal and when we would see Dr. Sheely I would write down whatever she was doing with Nicholas, even the pace (how slow or fast) and I would try and replicate it at home. Honestly, it didn't seem to make sense, but it was working! Nicholas was relating to me. I stuck with it even though I didn't really have an understanding of the theory behind it. I didn't have the big picture. But I kept with it because I was seeing results and it didn't feel awkward.

Since then we haven't used anyone else because Nicholas doesn't have any co-occurring conditions (like sensory issues or ADD). So I really haven't had to depend on any other clinicians. It is just RDI, which means we have really seen it evolve from the beginning.

When we started RDI, it was just focused on activities. Then when we moved to Houston, RDI became about lifestyle changes and less emphasis was put on lab time. At that time, I had already been doing lifestyle, although it wasn't classified as that; I had found that the more experiences Nicholas had, the easier things were. So when lifestyle came about, I was already doing a lot of it. I remember Dr. Gutstein kept asking me what was working at home and I would always tell him that I looked for any opportunity with Nicholas. What he realized was that I was doing all of these little RDI things during the day. So for instance if he was playing with blocks, I would take the game he was playing and introduce a variation.

During those first six months, I was really able to focus on Nicholas and give him my full attention. I didn't have to worry about anything else, even though I was frustrated that Brad was not there to physically support me and help me take care of little Claudia. But during those six months, I was really able to push everything else away and I had a goal. There was a lot of anxiety, because I didn't know what I was doing, but I knew that I wanted to do the best job for Nicholas.

I remember we didn't cry when we received the diagnosis. We were numb. I remember Brad getting into the car, and he asked me if I was okay and I said that I was. I cried months later, but I think that is why he felt like he should go back to work. I don't think we realized how big autism was and how many implications the diagnosis had. I never saw Brad really get upset; he was pretty steady.

During the time we were still living apart, we were visiting with my family. We were talking about our kids and our goals; with my sisters and my mom and my brothers and all of our spouses. When it was our turn, Brad all of a sudden started crying and I asked him if he was okay, and he said, "I know Nicholas will be okay." But he just kept crying. I realized that I was so involved with my own feelings that I hadn't even considered that Brad's heart was breaking too. In my mind he was out of the picture. But in that moment, I realized that we were both grieving and struggling separately.

The move to Houston is where I really noticed a big difference in Nicholas. The change was that I didn't really have to prepare him at all! Prior to this, I had to prepare him for even minor changes. The move was a huge change and I didn't even have to explain it that much. He adapted to the new apartment quickly and I remember feeling surprised that there was less tantrumming and more going with the flow. Nicholas also attended more; he would not run off when he was with me. I didn't have to hold his hand all the time, and even when the kids were out in the playground, I could yell for him and he would run back. Even though he wasn't participating fully, he was not completely out on his own.

Doing Stuff With Dad

At first, when Brad had tried to join in on RDI, I was so much more experienced that I made him feel really incompetent. This caused a major strain on our relationship. I felt like I was doing everything and he wasn't doing anything. And, he probably felt like I made him feel worthless. We struggled especially when I started training to become a clinician. I would go home and he would be with the kids, and he wouldn't slow things down and whenever I would show him anything he would say, "Don't try to teach me!" It was tough and it continues to be tough. I still don't feel like we are really a team. That was one of the downfalls at the beginning of RDI; couples should start at the same time and support each other. We are still trying to repair that.

When the RDI Program began to focus more on lifestyle concepts, we realized it was a good time for Brad to get involved. This was also when Nicholas was starting elementary school and I had started working. Brad really took over and one of the things that I noticed was that he was doing less planned things and more projects. For example, Brad will want to put up shelves and he will get Nicholas to help him. He will say, "Mommy wants this shelf over here and I need your help." His whole intention will be to work on planning, and they will sit down and make a list. They will figure out exactly what to do together and eventually put the shelf up. Nicholas is so excited to do things with Brad and different opportunities and learning experiences are happening, because I am not the primary one coaching Nicholas.

They will also come into projects with their own ideas. I remember when they decided to organize the garage and Nicholas had the idea of using the leaf blower to sweep the garage instead of a broom. So they did that.

They also built a enclosure outside for the dog. It took them several days and they planned all the steps from the beginning and did everything by themselves. I am not involved in any of these projects. I realized that I was constantly looking over Brad's shoulder and he was feeling a lot of pressure. So now, I literally leave the house with Cachita, and he has the responsibility for doing RDI with Nicholas.

It has been a very slow process for him, but it all resulted because I was forced to pull away for work. When I travel for my job he stays with the kids and does everything! At those times I really think he gets a sense of competence. They have a nice dynamic and he is a lot looser with them and lets them do things together.

Last week when I was gone, one of my neighbors was going to take Cachita to her dance class. The kids were outside on bikes and Brad told Nicholas and Cachita to take her dance bag to Ms. Maria. The kids did it all by themselves! They were so excited and they got a real sense of responsibility and independence, which I probably would have messed up if I had been there. The kids really strive for these moments with Brad. They love doing projects with him.

Returning to Work

The whole transition of me working has not been easy. I always have subconscious guilt that I am missing out not being at school with the kids and I am losing opportunities, but other times it feels good because the children are on their own, at school, or alone with the Brad. The kids weren't relying on me and seeking me for help, they are asking each other, the school and Brad. Slowly, I feel like I don't need to be there all of the time.

Also really neat things have started happening because of my travel. For instance Nicholas and Cachita have started emailing me. It is just, "Hi Mommy. How are you? What are you doing?" But it is not something that would have happened if I hadn't been away. Nicholas has also started trying to trick me over the phone. He will call me and say, "I am Cachita. I am wearing pink." I don't think two years ago he even realized that someone on the other end of the phone couldn't see him. Before, on the phone, he would say things like, "Hi Mommy…it is hot," and he wouldn't explain what he was talking about.

It has also been difficult for me as a consultant, because whenever I see something and learn something new it is inevitable that I think about my own child. This means that I want to try everything out on Nicholas, and the more knowledge I have, the more this knowledge stresses me out. But, this is also when Brad really balances me out and tells me to take some time out. I am learning to control my anxiety. I would see opportunities for RDI and he wouldn't see them. But if I point them out, I have destroyed the moment for them. I have learned to be quiet. It is more productive for Brad to discover how to do RDI too, and he has to make mistakes and walk it on his own. I can't push him to do it. It wasn't working like that. He had to go on his own pace. It has been really hard to relinquish control, but I am slowly learning to back off. So far I think it is playing out well. Right now, Brad has the kids all to himself from 4-7 p.m., twice a week. Until I get home, he has time to be with the kids and he can feel comfortable. I guess he just needed the space.

Now, I have been really able to enjoy Cachita. We were there for her baby milestones, but we didn't have time to treasure them. I feel immense guilt for that time, and have only now allowed myself to sit down and enjoy them. Now we literally have girls time and boys time and I am so grateful to be able to be with her, on our own.

Dr. Sheely and Dr. Gutstein have had weekly online chats for two years. Brad would never get on them. But, just recently he has started joining Dr. Sheely's chats, as soon as I stopped pushing him. So now 3-4 times a month he joins. In the beginning he didn't say anything, but now he is slowly starting to participate. I think his feeling of incompetence was so big because he was married to a consultant and because of the way we started. But, now he is feeling more confident because he is taking the lead and I am backing off. He knows he can do it, in his own particular style and way.

Last month we had our updated assessment and it was really great that he heard from other people that his relationship and work with Nicholas are valuable. I have also learned that with Nicholas I have to be a mom, and with Brad I have to be a wife and I can't be a consultant and that is hard. I have to just enjoy being in the moment because we are there, not because I have to try to find opportunities. Nicholas doesn't need that much slowing down anymore, but during the day there are so many things that he participates in and I just enjoy the moment with him instead of trying to teach him something all of the time. There is still that pressure I put on Brad, he doesn't communicate it, but I can feel it. We are working on it, together.

Nicholas and Friends

Cachita and Nicholas are a year apart and shortly after we started doing RDI she was walking. I immediately included her in a lot of the activities. Like when we would roll the ball, I would roll it to Nicholas and then to Cachita. Nicholas began to get really familiar with her. I started noticing that she would seek him out and mess up his block tower and he would be okay with it. As he was becoming more aware, he was okay with his sister joining him.

A year after coming to Houston, we moved from an apartment to a house. I remember that they were already playing chase games, when I wasn't with them they were seeking each other out and making up their own games. At first it was initiated by Cachita, but Nicholas would follow her lead and play with her. He was about five when he started doing that. When they started at mother's day out together (the successful one), I didn't have to sit down with them and structure a game. It wasn't equal yet, Cachita was still putting in most of the effort, but they were still sort of playing together.

I remember when I observed him at mother's day out and he would be in the crowd but on his own. Then when he was in kindergarten he would play with other kids, but then go off by himself and then join again when he was ready. I think when it got too complicated he would back off or look for another child who wasn't really involved. That happened last year too. He clicked with the slower paced kids. There was a kid that had a walker and Nicholas really sought him out and they would play in the sand instead of keeping up with the other ones. Unfortunately, that family moved. I was really hoping that would blossom into a friendship.

Last year we had a very outgoing child in his class who is also our neighbor. That has really helped Nicholas feel comfortable at school. Tanner (the neighbor) is an only child and will seek out Nicholas and Cachita at home, and now Nicholas plays at recess with him every day.

The next big change, I am thinking about is next year when all of the kids at school start to make friends and pair with each other. Nicholas is not there yet, but I think that he has a lot of tools. Hopefully he will find someone that is closer to him. These are all just hopes for the future. The good thing that I see is that he can accept other kid's changes into games. Like instead of tagging they will decide that they want to freeze and he is able to go with the flow, but also present his own ideas. Before he didn't have any voice and would tune out when it was too hard.

Now he has something to say and gives his own contribution. That is part of the evolution of him identifying with himself. I see it with Cachita too. The other day there were camping inside the house. They got all of the pillows and blankets and they built a huge tent in our family room. I could hear Nicholas say "let's use this one" and Cachita would say "yes" or "no" and it was really back and forth and I was not interfering with their game. They built a big tent and played for a long time and they wanted to make it dark so that they could bring in flash lights; in the middle of the day it wasn't an easy thing to do. A year before I would have heard a break down, because when Nicholas was frustrated before he would hit Cachita, or he would only want to do things his way, and Cachita would walk away. I don't think their games would have lasted more than an hour. Now their games are lasting longer and I know this is only because there is some back and forth happening between them.

This is also starting to happen between Nicholas and other kids as well. It is interesting because I see something that is happening in my house and then I see how Nicholas will take it into the outside world with the neighbors. The last place is school, because that is the most chaotic place.

Not Having that Initial Anxiety

I was never anxious about Nicholas not being able to talk. I just knew that it was going to come. I was more concerned about getting his attention, which first came in Spanish. His first word was "Agua." I got him attuned to me and his speech just came. Those six months without Brad were all in Spanish. Both of the kids learned their first words in Spanish. My mom was also around as well as their Spanish speaking cousins. All of the kid's videos were in Spanish, which is probably why Brad felt left out even more initially. When we moved to Houston and at mother's day out, Nicholas and Cachita would speak English with the teacher. So that was when I started including English at home because I didn't want school to be hard for them. Now, English is the main thing. However, when someone from my family comes, my kids are able to switch. Both my sister and my brother have younger kids, and if Cachita and Nicholas want to play with the kids they have to speak Spanish.

Also for the last 3 years they have gone for 2 weeks to my mom's house and they speak Spanish there. My mom says that for the first few days, when they come to visit her, they struggle, but by the third and fourth day they are speaking in Spanish. We have always received a lot of support from my parents, and even though my mom was devastated, initially, she was eager to learn and she tried to get involved. It was hard to explain to her in Spanish because I didn't really understand the concepts. When the book came out, they translated it to try and understand more. My mother became increasingly more valuable to us and even though she didn't really understand Nicholas and how to help him, her support has always come in other ways. For example, they knew we were struggling with money and they paid for a maid for me while Brad was away; so I didn't have to worry about the cleaning or anything. That was her mother's intuition. They also will come and stay for a weekend, and we will go out to eat and leave the kids with them.

I have really been able to see Nicholas' language grow. One of the nice things that I have been able to document are the progress papers that came home from mother's day out. I am keeping all of them! They would do one when the school year started and when the school year ended. For the progress report the teacher would ask Nicholas a question and document his response. I remember one of the first ones; She asked Nicholas, "What is your favorite thing to do when you get home?" Nicholas' response was, "I like to play with my sister." I remember thinking to myself that he was really coming home and that we were finally a part of his life.

The second year Nicholas said, "I like to play with my sister and my dog outside." Gradually the questions became more complex. Last year it was what he wanted to be when he grew up and Nicholas wrote, "I want to be an astronaut." He is really into planets right now. Before he never would have even thought to refer or think of himself; before he would just copy Cachita's answers. Now he has his own independent thoughts.

Hopes for the Future

I have the same hopes and dreams for Nicholas that I do for Cachita. I am sure that Nicholas will be able to make friends and have a true relationship with somebody and have kids. I always had high expectations for Nicholas; I don't know why but I am glad that I did. I have never doubted that he wouldn't be able to have a full life. I always knew that I could help him. I think he is going to be able to choose to do things and be successful with them.

I see Cachita and him as in very similar ways and see that they both have their weaknesses. We will find out if he is able to handle things that are difficult for him. Because they are always going to be there, the flexible thinking and things like that, will always be a struggle, but he will learn to manage them like everyone does. I have no doubt that he will be happy and form friendships and will find someone to love. I see that very clearly. Sometimes when I consult with other parents I think I am shooting too high. But I think back and realize that I am not. I have never thought that this was just how he was going to be. I always knew that he would keep discovering things and learning things.

I remember when Nicholas was first diagnosed; there was a point where I really broke down and I was grieving. I would cry and pray and cry and pray and ask God why my child was the way that he was. I was a really big mess. I remember one day I got a letter from a very dear aunt. She had a lot of really sweet things to say, but one line in the letter is something I have always remembered. She wrote, "Claudia, you have been chosen to see the world in a different way."

✎ **Brad and Claudia have been married for 11 years and have a 7 year old daughter, Claudia, and an 8 year old son, Nicholas. They have been involved in RDI since 1999. Claudia's background is in education and she was one of the first parents to enter the RDI® Certification Program. Claudia works at the Connections Center in Houston, Texas and can be contacted at: andreessen@rdiconnect.com.**

9

Now Get This!

by April Choulat & Sandy Scheers

Sandy

"Dear God, please help me," I think to myself. It is 2:00 a.m. in the morning and my child awoke to use the bathroom; he is now looking for a video to help lull him back to sleep. I am exhausted and starting to feel that pulsating anxiety that used to drive so many hours of our day. My body feels sore, like the kind you feel from a first workout, that I can barely walk across the apartment to his room. There has not been one night in those 7 years that I have not awoken at least half a dozen times to either check on or console my child.

Two things are true; he has my love unconditionally, and he has Autism. I arrive at his bedroom and look at him with a soothing smile that used to mean absolutely nothing to him; but now has some definition in his world. I escort him back to his bed and so many thoughts race through my mind in a matter of moments as I begin to wake up.

"Dear God," I think again, "we have come so far." It is a miracle that my son wakes himself up to go to the bathroom independently and there are many occasions now when he does go right back to sleep. Then I remember that he has some of his own thoughts now; he makes decisions based on his feelings, because he understands that he is allowed to think for himself. And, I remember that it was when he began to have his own thoughts about things that he was able to wake up and get himself to the bathroom. I don't know the scientific explanation for how the two are tied together, but it is absolute; the two began to happen at the same time. An enormous sense of relief comes over me as I realize that we are dealing with a video as directed by us (his parents) and not a television show and not (this is huge) a computer! It is a celebration of sorts; I want him to feel good about what we are going to do. We are a team for this assignment (getting back to sleep) and we will do it together.

My first day home from the hospital, I knew something was wrong. We went through the "years of tears"; the ladylike label for feeling like I was living in hell. Here was a beautiful baby with creamy white skin, hazel eyes, the thickest and longest of black eyelashes, born 7 lbs. 1 oz. and 21 inches long; and he did nothing but cry 19 out of 24 hours a day. No exaggeration; this child never slept more than 45 minutes without screaming for 3 hours straight. After a while, you begin to think it is just normal. Of course we begged our pediatricians for help and they offered only the explanation of colic; oh and yes, they thought I was a little post partum (ha!).

The crying and screaming over feeding, changing and all those infant things, morphed into tantrums over neurotypical toddler things like going on outings in the stroller to the mall, cleaning up toys together, getting into the car seat, going to the park and then worked its way into the fits of rage over older child things like playdates with the neighbor's kids or basically anything that involved interaction with another person. I know now that most of these activities were translated by my son into demands. He could smell them a mile away. I have this one vivid memory of asking Nathan to put one toy into a bucket and you would have thought I was stabbing him with knives; I mean total freak out!

I adjusted our environment to totally compensate for his deficits, because I had no clue in the world about autism and was basically a prisoner inside my own apartment. I actually created a world for Nathan where he did not need to speak at all. I became so attuned that I could read him and just knew what he wanted or needed by simply glancing at him. We did any and everything to keep him calm. We inadvertently reinforced Nathan not to think for himself.

My friends used to ask me to meet them at the mall with Nathan in his stroller. "The mall, are you crazy?" I would think to myself. "I can't take this kid to the mall; I mean it was like a scene from a horror movie." This child was miserable; there are no words to describe it. Only a parent of a child with autism will relate to this. Events like haircuts resembled a scene from *Edward Scissorhands*. I remember trying to take Nathan to the grocery store and how he would flip out when I would try to get him out of his car seat and in to the shopping cart; there went my eyeglasses under the car, scratches up and down my arms, my hair was grabbed and looked like a bird's nest and Nathan's entire body was in the pike position, so it was impossible to get him in to the shopping cart. I just gave up going out all together at one point; it was too scary.

I remember going to a park that we had started going to with Nathan at a very young age. It was more of a static outing and somewhat maneuverable. We drove the same route every time we went, we entered in through the same exact gate and pretty much did the swing for the majority of the time every time we were there. There was a huge anxiety agenda attached to the swing, because if it was unavailable or we had to wait our turn; Nathan would tantrum and cry and cry and cry. I would literally shake from head to toe when it was time to leave, wondering how was I going to get Nathan from the park to the car without a total scene and everyone staring at us. I can honestly say that the stress was so overwhelming, that I was not dealing with a full deck

Fast forward to age 2; all of this craziness was going on 24/7 and all before the age of 2! I was talking and complaining to anyone that would listen; I felt crazed. A mother in our pediatrician's office recommended we take Nathan to a treatment center since I felt that Nathan was not developing normally, an understatement to say the least.

This treatment center is best described as a government agency that provides services for kids with disabilities up until age 3; at which point the county school system would then take over. God help us! Our first session included a Speech Therapist, Occupational Therapist, Physical Therapist, Psychiatrist and some other people with lots of titles and accreditations. It was determined that Nathan needed speech, occupational and physical therapies. I can say now that it was blatantly obvious that Nathan was on the autism spectrum, but no one wanted to admit it.

We did the circuit of therapies and I look back now and think how ridiculous it was. Thank goodness we had the where-with-all to never leave Nathan alone with any of these therapists unless we went with him. I remember the therapists taking the kids back as they were crying, literally ripping them from their parent's arms, and telling the parents that, "They'll be fine, this is normal." I never understood why the parents did not go in to the therapy sessions with their own child if it made the child more comfortable.

These therapy sessions were your typical sit at a little table and look at flash cards and answer as many questions as is humanly possible in 30 minutes. I also remember the Physical Therapist /Occupational Therapist giving Nathan an impossible feat and watching him struggle through it because, "He is capable" or, "he just doesn't want to do it." Well sure, if you don't feel competent to do something, there is no motivation. At the time, Nathan just did not have the ability or motivation, without adequate scaffolding. We needed to learn to work together as a team with Nathan so that we could accomplish things.

We also took Nathan to see a neurologist who hinted at PDD/NOS, but again, would not tell us that Nathan had autism. They did an EEG and went through a plethora of process of elimination testing, starting with Fragile X.

Nathan turned 3 and off to the School Board we went. Wooooow (sarcasm intended), the famous IEP (Individualized Education Plan) that was supposed to solve all of our son's problems. The purpose of the IEP is to officially document or map out goals for each child to master, in the classroom, given specific supports and time frames. They include people with (again) lots of titles and accreditations, who understand little about the core deficits of ASD, and are there to tell the parents of the child how the child is going to be able to "transition, given physical, gestural, visual and verbal prompts." Totally unbelievable, considering this is a person who can't even orient his body towards you if you are speaking directly to him, or notice if you are crying because you've just banged your head really hard.

The one great thing we got from the IEP - a diagnosis of Autism. Finally! I remember John (my husband) saying to the meeting coordinator, "So, you're saying Nathan does not have autism?" "No," she said, "I am saying he does." I'm pretty sure we were in shock at that moment.

It was suggested that we put Nathan in a school that specialized in autism. The doctor recommended a school, and we decided to check it out. In the following weeks, we interviewed various teachers and observed different classroom settings that would be available to our son. John and I went separately (each 3 times) and compared notes at the end; we both agreed - no way on God's green earth would we expose our son to the level of stress we could see the ASD kids were experiencing.

During the two weeks that my husband and I agreed to research, observe and convene about our observations, I literally began to have nightmares; praying daily that my husband would agree not to subject Nathan to a school environment. I became physically ill at the notion of Nathan spending 6 hours per day under duress. It was obvious that there were not enough resources or low enough teacher/student ratios for these children to get the individual attention needed. Thank God we had the same thoughts; abandon the school idea for now and move on to Plan B.

After walking around our home for about a week in shock and silence, we decided to get busy! My husband is much more the scholastic type (I lovingly refer to him as the brainiac). I am the resource person, organized and very task oriented. John, in all his infinite wisdom, did what he always does when something is important: read, research and then read and research some more. He got on the internet for hours and found organizations, lists, support groups, meetings and whatever information he could get his hands on. He began to do the circuit of organized meetings, and talked to other parents (mostly mothers) of children with autism. We came to the conclusion that we needed a home program, so that we could manage Nathan's curriculum and get the one-on-one therapy that Nathan needed.

It wasn't long before John aligned himself to a mom who introduced us to a traditional therapy with a focus on language and talking. Like many parents out there, we wanted to believe that if only our son could talk, it would all be better. This particular mom invited us to her home, introduced us to her son with autism, and shared a lot of information and contacts with us so that we could start up our own home program. We followed the traditional language centric model for 3.5+ years along side our new found mom-friend. We had a consultant and two desirable therapists, after about 6 months of going through the normal interview and elimination process. For this particular protocol, the therapists began immediately reinforcing our son with gifts; he received edibles, praise (if I never hear the words "good job" again in my life, it won't be long enough), and eventually a variety of screen time activities like television, computer or video games.

The computer quickly became the focal point of reinforcement and the center of the universe for Nathan. He had actually started out at age 18 months with a key touch program of the alphabet and became more proficient as time went on. We were so excited, of course, that our 4 year old boy could actually use the www and concentrate for hours on end. Now, picture me banging the side of my head with the palm of my hand and calling myself stupid! Hind site is always 20/20. Oh, but the damage; we paid a high price. The good news is, following a relationship centric model, we have gotten ourselves out of that predicament and pretty quickly I might add.

Well, as discussed, we continued to follow the language based therapy religiously. Nathan spent upwards of 14 hours a week sitting rigidly with 2 very nice girls, with the greatest of intentions, learning how to answer questions. We couldn't possibly have known back then that we were strengthening his strengths.

I will admit, I am angry and bitter; but that is lessening as Nathan really gets better. I just can't help thinking of the days when we ran our son ragged and how he spent his entire day, hour after hour, with people who didn't understand his disorder and the torture of failure he must have felt. I get the feeling that many people think I'm being too dramatic when I describe a typical day in the life of a child with autism as torture. Imagine your life as a pie; 30% of that pie is directed by static systems. You stand in line at the bank, wait your turn and get your money. You stand in line at the water fountain, wait your turn and get your drink. Certainly we all need these rules so we can behave in a civilized manner. But then there is the other 70%; the fun stuff, the dynamic stuff; our families, our friends, vacation, love, staring into a person's eyes in silence, holding hands, eating snowflakes, singing in the rain and oh, one of my favorites (ahhhhh), dancing! Just writing about it makes me feel good.

Now imagine that your brain doesn't naturally process or take in that 70% of the pie and you spend all of your time with people who are trying to get you to learn more and more of the 30% piece and that small 30% becomes your only strength. Now put yourself in a world where everyone you encounter seems to have the complete 100% of the pie, and you don't understand at all what you are missing or how you are feeling and they have all the control over your life. Now, could that feel like anything less than torture?

I remember shortly after we began to change the direction of guiding our child from a language based therapy to a relationship development protocol;I finally knew what it must feel like from the perspective of a person with ASD, I felt it was my duty and my responsibility to educate myself and put myself (as much as was humanly possible) in my son's shoes; to be his coach.

I think the fall of his language based therapy began when we started to notice that something was missing. I like to call it the black-hole. And, then there was this very strange part of his (language based) therapy called NET (natural environment teaching) that…well, hmmm, what can I say, it was just too weird. I don't even think I can explain it, except to say it was supposed to be some sort of play between my son and his therapist. It just didn't feel right to me and opened up a dialogue between, our then consultant, which eventually led to us finding RDI.

I tried to explain to the therapist that NET didn't feel right to me; that it didn't seem like Nathan was there with the other person and that he was not in the moment. But, the therapist seemed to be satisfied by the incessant chanting, and commented that Nathan was drawing from his bank of taught responses. He didn't seem concerned at all about the 70% of the pie we talked about earlier. I just didn't get it.

I explained to my consultant that Nathan had all of this sophisticated language, but had no idea of what to do with it; except to talk, and talk and talk and talk some more. At first she tried to tell me that we had taught Nathan to talk for the wrong reasons, i.e., edibles and reinforcement. She said now we would "shape it up." However, shaping it up never lead to filling the black hole; Nathan still did not understand that talking was supposed to have many social implications and shared emotions. I would venture to say that all of the things that parents of children on the spectrum look for, will never come from only teaching children to talk.

At the same time we were trying to figure out the black-hole situation, Dr. Steven Gutstein was coming to our area to present a two-day workshop, on an intervention that was based on relationship building and emotion sharing. I actually didn't pay much attention at the time because (now get this) the charge was only $25, and I thought, how good could it be if it was so cheap? Again, I am knocking myself in the head with palm of my hand. Look at me. I live in a 1200 square foot apartment, with holes in all my socks and underwear, with the same pair of sneakers for 4½ years now, and I'm too good to attend a workshop for only $25. I hope you're laughing at me. If you have a child with a disability, you really need to have a sense of humor, it's a life saver.

Thank goodness our mom-friend, who at one time led us to our original consultant, decided to attend Dr. Gutstein's 2-Day RDI® Workshop, and came back to us with the information. We were instantly intrigued, curious and very excited. Our little group of moms, dads and therapists who shared information, became very interested in RDI as a result of that workshop and we all sort of went on a crusade (I guess that's what you'd call it) with one particular mom at the helm. We all purchased Dr. Gutstein's video and books and contacted a couple of consultants-in-training. It's interesting, but I've never enjoyed reading; can you believe it? I think it is because I'm not a person who truly knows how to relax, and you really need to be relaxed to read. But, I couldn't put the *Solving the Relationship* book down for more then one minute, until I finished the entire thing. No question, it was love at first sight.

By the grace of God, Dr. Gutstein agreed to come to our area and presented a 4-Day Parent Seminar which my husband John attended. John came back from the training with a wealth of information and began try to implement RDI in our home without a certified consultant for approximately a year. I made the mistake of wanting to marry our past home-program with our new-found RDI, in contrast to what my husband wanted to do. John wanted to make the leap over to RDI and be totally committed to it. I tried really hard to work with the team we had at the time, teach them what my husband had learned and what I had read. I also tried to adapt to an RDI® lifestyle, at the same time. It can't be done, it's not realistic. You can't put the cart before the horse.

After about a year of not making progress, Dr. Gutstein was again giving a 2-Day RDI ® Workshop in Orlando, about 4 hours from our home. I did not make the same mistake twice. I found out that a certified consultant from our state would be attending and we contacted her to see if she could head up our program. She had originally worked with our group of parents on the RDA, during the 4-Day Parent Training Seminar that my husband had attended a year earlier.

I attended the 2-day workshop in Orlando, met with the certified consultant and could see what was coming. Many parents were getting on board with RDI, across the country and around the world. I jumped at the opportunity to connect with this consultant; there was instant chemistry and I knew that RDI was the real thing and it was based on years of research. Dr. Gutstein will tell you himself, he did not invent the information, he just sort of asked himself one day, "What's missing?" Without being presumptuous, I would say that he was referring to the same black-hole I've been talking about. I was floored, to say the least; by Dr. Gutstein's knowledge when he presented the long awaited definitions and core deficits of this disorder. Most of all, here was a person who had immense respect for the people afflicted with this disorder.

I would encourage any parent to start learning about RDI, even if a consultant is not immediately available; the great thing about learning and fumbling as you follow a path is that you gather data by doing so. I believe our consultant refers to some of that as hypothesis testing. The year of what I thought was floundering, turned out to be a huge resource of information for us. There is no bad in RDI; even if you're feeling overwhelmed, stressed-out, not competent, lonely, isolated, misunderstood and exhausted. You are here.

Whenever I feel like I'm not working fast enough or hard enough, I remember that I am in good company and I thank all that is mighty that I am part of this group of parents who have found the true meaning of remediation. I have to tell you, I am so happy to be here. I now know there is hope for my son's future.

Shortly after we started working with our consultant, I finally had the opportunity to attend a 4-Day Parent Training Seminar (up until this point, I had only attended a 2-day workshop). It was one of the greatest opportunities of my life. Again the dramatics, but I mean that with all sincerity. I guess you can call me a groupie now, but we really began to change our lives, quite dramatically in many respects.

Our philosophy was sort of in contrast to the behaviorists with whom we had shared many years of work and friendship, and we knew needed to direct our teaching methods in a more dynamic way. We also did not want to put Nathan into environments any more that were too chaotic or confusing for him to navigate; for example, attending family functions or a religious holiday where the draw for most people is emotion sharing. Since Nathan does not have sophisticated social functions, it was just too stressful for him. Even during the year or so of struggle and what seemed to be little success in RDI, our son was changing and small miracles were happening. Now, that's definitely an oxymoron, since miracles are really huge!

The first six months of working with our consultant felt like hit-or-miss. The video tapes due every two weeks were like monkeys on my back, but looking back now, I know in my case it was something I had to go through. It's a learning curve for us all; you're not quite sure what you're dealing with in terms of obstacles until you sort of trip over them. Here's the thing about all of this, it is a parent-based program and you have to be committed to do the work. I know, it seemed so much easier when the therapists came in and did the lion's share; but those days are over, antiquated, capoot! And, as Dr. Gutstein says, this is the hardest work you'll probably ever do in your life. I believe your child deserves for you to give it everything you've got.

So, I fumbled awkwardly through the first 6 months and got caught up on things like repeating the same activities over and over. It's uncomfortable at first for everyone to be under the eye of the camera and you gravitate towards known activities for comfort. I think I sent our consultant video of my son in the bath about 20 times; I laugh at myself now when I think about it. I really had to talk myself into doing RDI, because I was competing with so many things. One of our biggest obstacles was the environment. We're still getting rid of things! There are just too many toys and pieces around to compete with while I was trying to get Nathan to pay attention to me.

And, then reality hits. You can't successfully help a child if you are competing with his obsessions. The more he spends time on his obsessions, the less he will be mentally engaged. Also, in our case, our son was easily and extremely distracted by any and everything. I'm telling you, if there was one marble on a table in his line of vision on the way to get dressed, he would gravitate towards it. I began to take note of all of these things, which helped me be better prepared to work with him.

The most important thing we had to do for Nathan and for us all as a family unit was to get rid of the screen time. (Blasphemy!) Even though we saw drastic changes in Nathan, just from the switch of protocols, we knew it could be so much better by getting rid of the computer, video games and drastically reducing TV time.

Some of the early signs that language was not doing much for Nathan were his problems on the playground. This is a great testing ground for what's missing. Nathan was very articulate, but he didn't know the unwritten code of the playground. You just don't get in some kid's face and tell them to do something; you sort of read the signals of who's who and what's what. There's often a pecking order, or different tribes and you have to know which ones are okay for you to join. All of this stuff happens in a matter of moments.

Nonetheless, Nathan's interest in spending time with other people was splintering and beginning to appear at appropriate times and he was orienting towards people more when he spoke to them or vice versa and making eye contact for information. I think that is a starting point for many kids. He was looking at people's faces to try and read them and he was showing signs of caring if someone was hurt. Still, it's not enough; a neuro-typical child will size you up in all of 2 seconds and be outa' there if you are even the slightest bit off. They have radar for that sort of thing.

One of the early signs, that started appearing as we got into RDI, was when Nathan began, about once every 2 – 3 weeks, to express I love you. It came in different shapes and sizes. He would also come to your aid if you were very deliberate in your exasperation; talking to yourself out loud about, "Oh, how can I do this alone?!"

Another sign was he began to problem solve on a very primitive level. This was huge because in the past he would tantrum or cry, and now, well it brings tears to my eyes, he is such a good little fixer, and he's becoming so independent. You can tell that he has taken on our perspectives when completing a task on his own, because he says to himself, "That's okay," if it's not perfect. Most important, when he needs help, he asks for it in a very typical way. This from a kid who used to scream and tantrum and panic uncontrollably if a piece of paper ripped.

We learned, during Nathan's 6 month review, that he is totally unregulated; he does not feel competent and so he displays passive floppiness (acts like deadweight). This also means that he is not in the moment and totally distracted or all over the place and appears hyper. In our case, Nathan is 7½ years old, weighs 110 lbs., is over 4½ feet tall and going in to a size 5 shoe. He is very impaired in fine and gross motor skills. He has ants in his pants for sure. He is also not regulating, because he can't coordinate his body to the environment. I think it makes him feel sort of lost and so he becomes disorganized. So, our consultant came up with a plan for us.

I started to keep a very close zone of connection to Nathan shadowing him during activities where he is unregulated and used my body rather than words to act as his coach; I began to really feel his struggle with negotiating his environment. He doesn't read cues from the environment or non-verbal communication from people. For example, instead of moving out of the way to let someone by; he will bump into them. I found when I actually put my arms around Nathan, I really get a true picture of how disoriented and unregulated he is in so many environments.

Surprisingly enough, he seemed to like it and didn't protest. He quickly learned that my protective bubble made him successful and gave him competence and it became a great tool for him. I began to realize that I had, in the past, put Nathan into many situations that he simply could not handle.

I guess it was also the week of our 6 month review that motivated us to get rid of Nathan's computer, Game Boy, Game Cube, Gaming magazines (huge obsession) and even board games and toys with little parts to them. During this time, we realized that we couldn't go to Wal-Mart, Target, Toys-R-Us, the library, bowling (arcade), Boomers, Science Museum (filled with computers), and many friend's homes that had a history of Nathan using the computer or PlayStation, for an unspecified amount of time. It was an exhausting week and a monumental week.

So, my husband and I spoke in depth with our consultant in order to solicit her opinion about getting rid of screen time. We planned our drive home from the (out of town) review during the evening hours, so that my son would fall asleep in the car. The mission was to get him home in to his bed and then remove all the techno-toys and hide them away until we could sell them on eBay. He had been without his computer and gadgets all week, since we were out of town, and talked a lot about getting back to them all, once we were home.

My husband and I stayed up practically all night and were able to hide all of the stuff. Although we had prepared prior to our trip, by removing the computer out of Nathan's room and relocating it to another room, it was still disheartening for him to awake in the morning to no computer. This was a child who spent upwards of 7 hours a day on computer or video games; now at the blink of an eye, it was gone. The following days proved very challenging and nauseating, to be quite honest. The begging with the strongest of eye contact and body language and hanging on our every word of explanation was exhausting and I felt helpless.

I have heard that the average time for a child in this situation to sort of get over it is about a month. It did not seem believable to me at the time. For 30 days we kept Daddy's office door locked while Dad used the computer for work; we prepped Nathan for about a month prior to our 6 month review that Dad's computer was simply for work and nothing fun. I also gave up my computer and our explanation to Nathan was this; our family does other family things for fun now.

Eventually, I set up my computer on the floor in my husband's office, under about 3 bed sheets with stuff scattered on top, in order to camouflage it and then slowly moved it on to a desk and kept it covered there. I only use the computer late in the evening when Nathan is fast asleep. John and I give up things along with Nathan as a family; we feel that is fair or at least comforting in some way. But here we are August 18th, just 37 days since Nathan has used a computer, and I lived to tell about it.

Every once in a while, Nathan asks about some computer related issue, but it seems to be fading from his repertoire of obsessions. We are now able to leave the office door open sometimes and Nathan simply looks at it as history has recorded; a place where Dad works. Make no mistake; it was brutal in the beginning. "Mommy," Nathan would say, "did you make a mistake, computers are only for older kids?" "Mommy, but I like computers!" "Are computers all gone?" "Is the library all gone?" "Do you go to a hotel and computers are all gone?" "But I don't like family things," (although he hasn't said that one for a few days). Nathan seems a little paranoid now that things are just going to disappear or that if something isn't available for a day or even 5 minutes from now, he worries that it will be gone forever. We are working our way through it.

As a side note, the television became much more desirable once all the gaming equipment was gone and that did lead to a problem. It crept up on us and again, an obstacle appeared. Nathan turned TV in to a static system for himself and it totally interfered with my efforts. Sometimes it feels as if everyday we take one step forward and three backwards. We attempted to implement specific times for watching television, on a very loose daily schedule and written on a clipboard with crayons. He kind of obsessed over it and then he would worry throughout the day about when it was coming.

What we've had to do is disconnect the cable from all the TV's and shut them down during Nathan's waking hours. In his room, the VCR still works and he can watch videos for 30 minutes, 2 – 3 times a day, and for sleep. Although we realize it is not productive, we allow it and we usually watch with him. We are trying to morph it in to family TV time. He begs for channels and we also allow that on a limited basis in the living room, but I definitely notice a change in his behavior when it goes past a certain amount of time. The days where he doesn't watch television seem so much better.

So, here we are, just 10 months from when we began to work with a consultant, what we consider our official start of RDI, and I am a coach to a child with a disability. It is something you simply can not plan for, believe me; I have my days where I think, "Why can't today be normal?" I see women in my neighborhood who look so put together with these darling little girls who are just so genetically neurotypical and they stand perfectly still next to their mothers, in line at retail counters and they reference about 100 times in 5 minutes. I am so envious and angry at myself for being so, but I am tired after 7 years of daily struggle. The physical and mental labor of raising a child with autism is beyond belief and it is painful to deal with an uninformed public and ignorant people who talk about these children in their presence, as if they don't count. I hate it, but just for a moment and then I remember Nathan, and how he needs me.

It's not like just wanting a great dress or a new purse that you save up for and then maybe you have to use the money to buy a new iron or toaster, it's a totally disastrous kind of disappointment. Most of us wait half our lives to meet our soul mate and have a beautiful child with that person and dream of dressing that child up all cuddly and cute and proudly rolling him through the mall. But we, parents of children on the autism spectrum, don't get to do that, at least not so far. But now there is a parent-based therapy out there that can change the face of autism; change the face of your child.

I remember back when we were knee-deep in the traditional language based therapy that our son was labeled HFA or high functioning. We thought that because he could spew out 8 – 10 word sentences, that he was "high-functioning." But he is 7½ years old now; he can not negotiate a school environment, he can not handle disappointment, he could spend upwards of 7 hours straight on a computer without even thinking of checking in with another person, he asks the same question over and over because he already knows the answer, he doesn't understand the beauty in just being with another human being and...he does not have one true friend. Maybe somewhere out there in the universe there is a planet where incessant talking and spending all your time alone is considered the norm; but here, on planet Earth, we define ourselves by the company we keep.

We are social. We want to just hang out with our buddies; make those secret encoded facial expressions that can tell a story between two dear friends, hold hands and people watch, sit on the stairs of the courthouse and eat a sandwich next to a perfect stranger and spark up a conversation, smell roses, feed the ducks, and most of all, we want the best for our children.

I am infinitely grateful for the research that has opened up the eyes of so many parents to embark on remediation of autism and for the opportunity to be part of this crusade. I will share with you a little story with a giant message. A few weeks ago, one of our home school assistants arrived in the house and poked her head into Nathan's room to check in and say hello. Nathan looked up at her and said, "Oh, did you get your hair cut?" And, she said, "No, I just did it differently because of the rain. Do you like it?" Nathan looked at her with his lips perched, head nodding up and down (as if to say yes) with eyes wide open and said, "Um hmmmmm!" How great is that? My child actually noticed that someone's hair was different than the day before and wanted to make her feel good about it when she asked him if he liked it! He is getting better every day and the work is paying off.

I always try to remember what Dr. Gutstein says, "Think of it as a marathon, not a sprint." There are no short-cuts and there are no magicians that will come to your home and unlock the secrets; but there is support and information out there. If you haven't had the opportunity to attend a parent training on RDI, sign up now; sell your jewelry, borrow the money or write a letter to your family and closest friends and ask for donations. Just get there and we'll meet you at the top!

Where There's a Will...
April's Story

"Where there is a will there is a way." If there is one adage that summarizes the plight of this family's fight against autism, this is it. Sandy and John have faced more than their share of obstacles as they journey together towards a happier, more fulfilling life for themselves and their son, Nathan. When Sandy and John initially decided to remediate Nathan's autism, the odds were stacked high against them. I hope their story can inspire other families not to give up hope.

When a family pursues consultation for Relationship Development Intervention® Program (RDI), the main issues discussed during the intervention planning period are how to progress past parent and child obstacles and how to minimize them. In this family's case, the obstacles at times were, and sometimes still are, seemingly insurmountable. Every RDI® family will face obstacles that interfere with progress at one time or another. No family should have to face every obstacle that can occur, and certainly not simultaneously.

John initially contacted me in October, 2003. Dr. Gutstein was coming to his area for a parent training and he and Sandy were excited about getting an assessment for Nathan so they could begin RDI with him as soon as possible. I met John during the assessment, just before the parent training held that fall, but it would be another year before I met Sandy. My first impression of John was that he was stressed and concerned about his son, willing to do whatever it took to get him the best services possible.

Upon first meeting Nathan, I was struck by what a happy-go-lucky boy he was! He was a big boy for his age, with pale skin and dark hair. At 5 years old, he was only 10 pounds lighter than I was! I remember how excited and happy he was, playing with his dad throughout the assessment, always with a smile on his face.

Although he was able to speak in full sentences, Nathan was less adept at nonverbal communication. Social referencing and facial gazing were poor; and his behavior was very random as he ran around the room tirelessly. Although he frequently smiled, it was difficult to tell if it was true emotion sharing at first glance; Nathan appeared happy no matter what he was doing or what was going on in his environment. His chaotic actions and distractibility made it difficult for him to sustain a connection with his dad for very long.

After the assessment and the subsequent parent training, John communicated via email with me every once in a while, but did not pursue ongoing consultation at that time. I would learn later on that many tremendous challenges disrupted the family's path to remediation that year.

The year before the parent training, in June, 2002, Sandy was diagnosed with breast cancer. At that time she began what would turn out to be 2½ years of chemotherapy, radiation and multiple biopsies and reconstructive surgeries. She was unable to attend the parent training due to the effects of the chemotherapy treatment. She was so disappointed to miss the parent training, but was so excited about RDI. She had just read the book and couldn't wait to get started. She knew being bedridden would slow down their start, and she was anxious to get started right away.

During this time she was in and out of consciousness, depending on what type of treatment was going on. But when she was cognizant, she concentrated on learning all she could about RDI, which kept her mind off the cancer. Later on Sandy told me that RDI had given her hope for her son's future, and that was what kept her fighting her way back to recovery. I was amazed at her tireless determination and unwavering hope that there was something she could do to help her child.

Prior to attending the 2-Day RDI® Workshop, Sandy and John had spent an enormous amount of time, money and energy supporting intensive early interventions for Nathan. His treatment over the last few years culminated in a financial crisis. Occupational therapy and Physical therapy were paid for by Medicaid, but his intensive behavior program was funded with personal savings and retirement accounts.

When the personal funds were exhausted, Sandy swallowed her pride. To raise funds for Nathan's therapies she wrote letters to every friend and family member she could think of, asking for help. She took desperate measures to help her son, and it paid off – she accepted $10,000 in donations which went toward paying for therapies for Nathan. When that money ran out, the only thing they could do was live on credit. All living expenses, everything from rent payments to milk, were billed to credit cards. With credit card debt already as high as a mortgage, additional financial strain was unavoidable due to Sandy's prolonged illness.

Despite these extreme health and financial crises, Sandy and John chose to home school Nathan during this time. The decision to home school Nathan was made based on their concerns that he would not benefit from a public school autism program. Sandy and John researched all possible options, and felt that there was potential for damage to occur if they allowed Nathan to stay in any environment where he was not meaningfully engaged for long periods of time. As Sandy has said to me, she feels obligated as his parent to parent him, and not to 'send him to the wolves' before he is ready. Their commitment to Nathan's well-being was so high that, even during the time in which they experienced a serious health crisis, they chose to keep him at home where they could supervise him.

Out of necessity and dedication to his family John stayed home to care for Nathan, as well as Sandy, during her recovery. What makes this decision so remarkable to me is that Sandy and John did not have access to a family support system to provide respite, so the level of emotional and psychological stress was certainly greater with Nathan in the house 24 hours a day.

John attended the parent training and passed on the information to Sandy when she was awake. He decided it was necessary for Nathan to receive as much opportunity as possible for remediation of autism in his daily life. However, Sandy's medical condition, financial hardships and a hectic family schedule prevented effective implementation of RDI® principles. For a year Sandy and John attempted to add RDI® principles to their previous therapies, with limited results. As Sandy neared the end of her battle against cancer, she and John contacted me again regarding services for Nathan.

Now that she was mostly recovered and had energy again to focus on Nathan's autism, Sandy was highly motivated to pursue RDI. November, 2004 she emailed me to find out about the possibility of assessing Nathan again. She only had one more surgery to go (the week following the assess-ment), and then she would be ready to implement the RDI® lifestyle. I couldn't believe what Sandy was telling me...she, who had been on her deathbed, was fighting for her life, so that she could get up every day and fight for her son's life. She seemed to have no doubt in her mind that it was possible for her to recover from chemotherapy and 7 surgeries, and then jump headfirst into an intensive remediation program for her son. She knew it was not a glamorous job she was signing up for – she had attempted to infuse RDI into her day without a consultant for the last year. She was ready and committed for the long haul, and was ready to do whatever it took to help her son. I said, "OK."

Only two problems stood in our way: Nathan had extreme anxiety over traveling and spending the night away from home. He was anxious about other things, too, like death (though he didn't call it that). Most likely as a result of his mother's chronic illness, Nathan tied together calendars and time, and began to ask what happens when you are 99 years old. Sandy reported that he cried for days about this. She felt that his anxiety level was too high, and while she had a plan to acclimate Nathan to build up to spending the night on a trip, she felt that a 5 day trip away from home was a good year away.

The other problem was financial. They could not afford the travel expenses associated with flying or driving the whole family out of town for the assessment. Family members had already provided a lot of assistance over the last several years and asking for additional funds was not an option. The cost of the assessment was funded by a scholarship Nathan received through a charitable organization, so at least that part was taken care of.

I decided to travel for Nathan's assessment due to the extreme circumstances. Sandy and John used points they had collected from their credit cards to pay for my hotel expenses. A month before the assessment, Sandy was excited and filled to the brim with enthusiasm. She reminded me again that RDI was her motivation for recovery, filling her with hope that she could learn to guide her little boy back to the place he 'fell off' the developmental track.

It had been a year since I had seen Nathan last. Having spent just a few days with him, the only thing I had remembered was that he was a very big boy for his age, and that he had seemed so carefree and easygoing. Upon meeting Nathan again for his second assessment, the 'happy-go-lucky' aura seemed to have faded. He did not smile as often as I remembered him smiling a year ago.

During the assessment Nathan was still disorganized and random in his behavior. Even though the assessment was conducted in his own home, Nathan demonstrated anxiety and control when presented with uncertainty. He became anxious when his mother pretended to 'lose' her voice as part of the assessment activity, and attempted to verbally control her actions. If his words didn't get the results he wanted, he attempted to leave the room altogether. In situations of uncertainty, Nathan preferred to control the outcome or avoid it; he was unable to reference his mother's facial expressions for security or reassurance.

In addition, language had become a huge obstacle. Both he and Sandy engaged in a lot of language, but very little true communication. Sandy was anxious, exhausted and highly stressed. It was clear from the assessment there was very little true experience sharing for Nathan to build upon and develop a relationship with his mother.

At this point in time, Nathan had learned some isolated skills, but he had not made progress in terms of emotional connection with his parents. I remember during this assessment asking Nathan some questions relating to emotions and his preferences. I asked him things like, "What makes you happy?" and "Who do you like to play with?" His responses were all scripted, as he pulled the answers from photo cards and stories he had memorized. Nathan attempted to answer with what he thought was correct, but he seemed totally disconnected from his sense of self, of his own likes and dislikes. His only repertoire, the only memory he had to pull from, was that of things he had learned in a rote manner. He had no concept of friendship and told me his 'friend' was a character from one of his computer games.

It really struck me at that time how impaired Nathan really was, even though he could speak in full sentences, and appeared to a lot of people to be high-functioning. I felt really sad for him at that moment, this little boy who seemed so detached from himself and the world around him.

Sandy and John admitted they attempted RDI® activities with Nathan, but played them in a repetitive manner. A slight variation of one of the assessment activities made it evident Nathan had learned the roles in a rote manner; he could not adapt his actions to accommodate a variation from the way in which he initially learned the game. He could only play the game in the same exact way he had played it countless times before.

This became an obstacle to think about when creating Nathan's intervention plan. We only seek information through social referencing when we are uncertain. By learning rules to activities in a scripted way, Nathan assumed he knew the outcome, which limited his ability to reference.

Other obstacles became apparent as I observed Nathan in his natural environment. I noticed how he randomly navigated the house, with little sense of purpose or direction. If he did engage in purposeful movement, he was usually headed for one of two things – his computer or the kitchen. Computer time took an enormous chunk out of Nathan's day. Because he was at home 24/7, there was ample opportunity for him to accumulate 10+ hours a day on the computer. He woke up at 5 a.m. and got on the computer first thing in the morning.

For exhausted parents, the computer became a much needed respite from taking care of Nathan, as well as a welcome opportunity to catch up on just a few extra minutes of sleep! For Nathan, the computer served as a comfortable static (unchanging) system, which was predictable and comforting in, what was for him, an anxiety-provoking, ever-changing world.

Unfortunately, even when the computer was off, it was still 'on' in his head. Sandy had a difficult time competing with the allure of the computer. A drastic reduction in the daily exposure to computer gave Nathan more time and motivation to participate in shared activities with his mother, and resulted in much less repetitive, rote language.

I also noticed how much Sandy overcompensated for Nathan; she anticipated his every need. If he headed to the kitchen, she poured him a drink; if he left the dinner table, she cleaned up his mess. He didn't even have to ask. It was as if Nathan was floating through space with the world catering to him. He did not demonstrate any sign of appreciation or awareness of any of the things Sandy did for him. I don't recall seeing Nathan express any sort of affection or emotional communication to his parents.

As a result, Nathan was very passive in the beginning. Sandy admits this was a huge obstacle for her; she jokingly refers to herself as an enabler, and has worked very hard over the last 6 months to avoid doing everything for Nathan so that he can develop competence. In the beginning stages Nathan was unable to solve even the simplest of problems for himself. He simply was never required to be mentally engaged. Sandy frequently says that she inadvertently taught her son not to think. What had been previously viewed as a positive (compliance) actually became an obstacle. Nathan was so submissive in the beginning it was difficult for him to take an active role and participate as an equal partner in shared activities.

It took several months of giving Nathan a simple role and allowing him the opportunity to participate in activities guided by his parents, before he began to perceive himself as competent. After a few weeks Nathan began to become more assertive – the previously docile and obedient boy became more defiant and insistent on expressing what he wanted. His use of language, which had always been repetitive and lacking emotion or true communication, began to expand in a qualitatively different way; he began to spontaneously share with his parents when he was bored, cold, happy, or crowded in. I remember how ecstatic Sandy was when Nathan spontaneously said, "I love you" for the first time. A few months after beginning RDI® lifestyle, Sandy told me how Nathan was missing his dad, who had been working long hours. Out of the blue, as Sandy and Nathan were leaving the house, Nathan held onto John, stared him in the face and said, "I love you, Dad, you should come with us; because when you love, you stay together."

As Nathan began to develop competence, so did Sandy. She had functioned for so long as if she were one of Nathan's therapists that she initially was uncertain and tentative in taking back the role of his parent. Her interactions with Nathan had previously been reactive, meaning that she had gotten into the habit of responding to him and adapting to what he wanted, even if what he wanted was not healthy or productive. She was reluctant to expect too much of him, to require him to follow her guidance. She was uncomfortable with the idea of possibly making Nathan upset. She was unsure about her own abilities to follow through and un-do a lot of bad habits. But she knew she had to regain her rightful role as Nathan's guide in this world if he was going to ever have a chance at a full life.

During the first 6 months of videotape supervision Sandy was extremely focused on her performance, and anxious about her ability to carry out RDI® principles. The big challenge was reducing the quantity of language that she used with Nathan. Her previous experiences and training in other interventions had resulted in an abnormal style of 'pseudo-conversation'. It was not truly about sharing experience and perceptions, but instead about trying to direct or elicit behaviors from Nathan. The words were getting in the way of Nathan's ability or need to seek Sandy's face for emotional communication and information.

After several months she finally internalized the concept of communicating with Nathan, instead of focusing on words. As a result of Sandy's changes in communication, Nathan began to look at her more, to study her face and think about what she was communicating to him. Now when he is uncertain, Nathan is able to reference her nonverbal communication much more readily than he could 6 months ago.

After a couple of months of focusing on competence with Nathan, he was able to solve problems much more quickly, and was very motivated to take actions to help his mother. Nathan began to offer Sandy his assistance with an enthusiastic, "I will help ya!" if she struggled to push in a chair, or open a jar of peanut butter.

Now Nathan takes no longer than a few seconds to realize if something needs to go into the refrigerator, or be thrown away. He no longer stands in a confused daze staring at a problem; instead, he is an active participant in daily activities and frequently helps Sandy solve problems as they cook dinner or make the beds together. His simple problem-solving skills are spontaneous and natural, and he rarely needs 'big fat hints' to get it.

In the last 6 months Nathan has made steady progress, as Sandy and John steadfastly tackle each obstacle one by one. Defying Sandy's prediction 6 months ago ("we're at least a year away from a 5-day trip"), Nathan traveled for his re-evaluation and did not experience travel-related anxiety. During his assessment he was notably more relaxed and attentive to Sandy when she pretended to lose her voice. Instead of controlling or attempting to escape the situation, Nathan approached her, waited for her initiation, and then finally began very simple play interactions with her. Interestingly, Nathan used much less language during this last assessment than the previous one. However, he sought facial information more, and was able to sustain a connected interaction with Sandy for longer periods of time.

This time when I asked Nathan, "What kinds of things make you happy?" and "Who do you like to play with?" he was able to name a few activities that he really did enjoy. Instead of a computer game character, he named his mom and his dad, as friends that he likes to play with. Were his responses totally age-appropriate for a 7 year old? Of course not. But they were a good sign that he is making strides in the right direction.

In the last 6 months Nathan has shifted from living in a computer-generated fantasy world and relying on rote memorized information, to forming meaningful connections between his experiences and his emotions, as well as connections between himself and others. He is learning to participate as a competent partner in shared activities, and beginning to be able to see his parents' point of view. Sandy and John are slowly but surely building the foundations that will enable Nathan to function competently at more advanced social-emotional and cognitive levels when the time comes.

Remediation is a long-term goal; slow and steady will yield a better outcome than racing to the finish line and burning out early in the game. Getting out of survival mode requires simplification; removing distractions from the environment, including computer, game magazines, and TV; avoiding stressful social situations, simplifying family schedules and planned activities.

Burned out after five years of therapies, in addition to the incredible health and financial crises that have caused additional stress, Sandy still has the tendency to put herself last. Now that Sandy is well, one of her goals is to take more time for herself. For John, the stress continues with the pressure of long work hours, but he is planning breaks in his day so that he can spend more time with Nathan.

I am so proud of Sandy for all the hard work she has done (and is still doing), persevering on days when the changes are so small that she can't see them. She came into RDI blind, so to speak, since she was unable to attend the parent training and received information second-hand. In addition, when Dr. Gutstein came to her area a second time, she cancelled the last impending surgery so that she could attend that training and get the most up-to-date information.

It is clear to me that Sandy has a very strong will to help her son. She is not willing to lower her standards for his future or for his quality of life because he has autism. Despite the obstacles that they faced, they are still making progress. And, as each obstacle becomes smaller and smaller, their goal gets closer and closer.

RDI is about becoming a parent again; autism can take away natural parenting instincts and leave parents feeling helpless, confused, ineffective, anxious, and willing to try anything and everything for a quick fix. All of these feelings Sandy and John have experienced at one time or another. Thankfully, they are now also experiencing more feelings of competence and success at parenting their child.

To all those families who feel they have too many reasons
why they can't remediate autism:
If you are willing to slow down your life…
If you are willing to set long-term goals…
If you are willing to evaluate your own obstacles,
accept that mistakes are not the end of the world
and know that with practice, it does get easier…
If you are willing to set achievable goals for your child…
If you are willing to guide your child to a better future...
If you are willing to help your child develop
competence in relationships…
Then you, too, can find a way to surpass any obstacle
that may momentarily block your path.

10

"Happy birthday Patrick. You are the bestest buddy that there ever was."

by Kim Downey, PT and Karen

Chris - Karen's Son

Karen had a typical pregnancy with Chris. In spite of this, his birth was difficult and a week late. Karen had pregnancy induced hypertension, labor was induced, and Chris had a large head requiring vacuum extraction. After everything was over, Chris cried briefly then fell asleep. This was a precursor for the future, sleeping became his coping strategy during stressful moments, including events such as receiving shots. Besides a preference for sleeping, Chris' parents found him very responsive. At five weeks he gave his first smile. Chris was a very peaceful, calm, sweet connected baby. He nursed well and was easily soothed by his parents. Karen felt that he was easy to read and that he responded well to her attempts to engage him. It felt, to Karen, that they were in synch.

When Chris was four months of age, Karen had a mild concern about his motor development. Unlike other babies his age, he still couldn't lift his head while on his stomach. Eventually, he did achieve this milestone, and Karen didn't think much more about it. During his first year, Chris achieved other motor and language developmental milestones at the late end of the normal range. He first waved goodbye at 9 months old, the same age that he spoke his first word, "mama." He crawled at 9 months of age, and walked at 13.5 months. There were no real red flags early on. Chris was just thought to be a late bloomer and Karen worked hard to help him catch up. Looking back, Karen realized that she instinctively knew she needed to provide extra support to scaffold Chris' development.

By the middle of his second year, Chris was giving his parents kisses and hugs, saying more words, and laughing, smiling and giggling. He loved being chased by his parents, and would hold his arms out to his parents and Grandma when greeting them after being separated. Chris was generally a very happy toddler, although Karen's mother-in-law noticed that he did not talk as much as her kids had, and mentioned this to Karen. The pediatrician reassured her that Chris was developing language, and that boys are often late bloomers.

At this time, Chris began displaying some unusual behaviors. He could remember and say all the words in his books, and would sit and look at his books for long periods of time. He had learned most letters of the alphabet, color names and numbers. He was interested in things that spin, such as fans, and he liked to turn the fan and lights on and off. Chris was also a toe walker.

He was also part of a playgroup at 18 months and he was happy to be with other kids, but he wasn't playing with them. Karen noticed that Chris did not seem to have the attention to do simple shared craft projects, like some of the other kids at the playgroup. She attributed this, again, to immaturity and didn't feel too worried. She was expecting that this would come in time, like all his other late milestones.

Chris' family moved when he was two years old. He seemed to handle the transition well. He was talking in sentences and would get his mom's attention by saying things like, "Look, mommy!" His language had some unusual qualities, however, including pronoun reversals, "You want go outside," instead of, "I want to go outside" and inventive wordings, "plug out" instead of "unplug." He also seemed to remember some very big words and use them, including "inclined plane" for the ramp on his toy garage.

He didn't get into mischief like other toddlers. He would sit and play with water for extended periods of time and would turn his tricycle upside down and spin the wheel. He was very interested in gadget type toys, where he could press buttons and get a predictable response over and over again.

When Chris and his mom would take walks, he always wanted to look at the drains. His gross motor skills, such as riding a tricycle, developed late but were still in the normal range. A friend noticed that Chris was still toe walking and mentioned it to Karen. Again, Karen and her husband Jim attributed this to being a late bloomer. Chris was their first child and they did not know how atypical some of these behaviors were.

Chris' family moved again when he turned 3. His sister, Catie, was born one week later. Chris seemed stunned with this combination of life changing events. He started turning lights on and off constantly and spinning toy car wheels. He became more withdrawn. His sister Catie was colicky and this upset him; he would withdraw when she cried. At other times, when his sister was calm, he enjoyed the baby. He would go up to her and give her hugs and hold her sometimes and he liked to cuddle up with her when she was laying on a bed or the floor.

Amidst all the chaos of the new baby, new home and postpartum hormones, Karen began to feel that something was not right with Chris. One day when she was planting bulbs, Chris did not engage with her or seem interested, even when she attempted to get his attention and include him. Karen began to cry, because it felt like Chris was not interested in sharing the experience with her at all. Chris just looked at her blankly. Karen remembers feeling that something was desperately wrong, and wondering why Chris didn't seem to care that she was upset. Another time, when Chris was eating blueberries, he stared at a fan, flapped his hands, and didn't seem to be there. Karen thought he was having a seizure, but testing that included an MRI showed nothing was wrong.

Karen also began noticing that Chris seemed to have a problem with attention and impulse control. He seemed more stressed and less easily soothed. He was not meeting her internal expectation of what a 3 year old should be able to do. However, he still remained a loving, connected child, who responded affectionately to his parent's affectionate gestures and turned to his parents for comfort. Everyone thought this was typical stress brought on by moving and having a new sibling, and that Chris would readjust. Karen tried to push away the nagging feeling that something was just not right and tried to cope with all the life stress.

That fall, Chris began attending a regular preschool program. Some concerns emerged, including an apparent delay in his motor skills. This was mentioned casually to Karen by the teacher. Karen also noted that Chris was sitting on his teacher's lap during circle time. As an elementary school teacher herself, Karen realized that this was a sign that Chris was having difficulty attending and participating like the other kids.

That fall, when Chris was 3 years 3 months old, the family went for an overnight visit to stay with friends who had a child the same age. Chris and the other boy did not play together the entire visit. Karen and Jim noticed that Chris did not act like the other child. A few weeks later, their sister-in-law mentioned some of the behaviors that she had noticed and told Jim that Chris might have a problem.

Karen began looking in her child development books, and remembered some of the special needs children she had worked with when she was teaching. In one awful, stunning moment Karen realized that Chris had autism. She looked up autism in the DSM IV, the logical place to look for a physician dad and a teacher mom, and confirmed for herself that it did apply to Chris. Jim was not sure that she was right. He called his mom, a teacher, and she agreed with Karen. Karen called her friend that they had visited that fall, and she too had been thinking that Chris had autism. Karen and Jim were devastated.

Karen felt certain that Chris had autism, but was hoping that she was wrong. Jim was still not as certain as Karen. Their pediatrician didn't think he was on the autism spectrum, but did refer them to a developmental pediatrician. The developmental pediatrician, after taking a detailed history but spending only a few minutes with Chris, thought he had a "pragmatic language delay" with some echolalia and scripting. He also gave Chris a diagnosis of Mild PDD so that he would "qualify for services." Karen shared her belief that this was autism, and asked him outright if this was the diagnosis. He again said "No," but did feel that Chris would "need services" and would "probably be fine by Kindergarten." He also recommended getting a preschool evaluation. They then brought him to a special education preschool. He was accepted into the special education program for full day integrated preschool.

At that time it became very obvious how socially delayed Chris was. He was not seeking out or playing with the other children in the class and did not have many age-appropriate play skills. He was not having any reciprocal conversations with adults or peers in the classroom. The preschool staff agreed that Chris was on the autism spectrum.

To help Chris, Karen and Jim set out to learn all they could about autism. Karen fell into depression, as she read more and more about how hopeless her son's future looked. For Karen, it was the darkest time in her life. It felt like there was very little hope for her son, this child that she loved with all her heart. From what she read, it seemed that a child like Chris was incapable of loving or caring about anyone. Karen began to doubt that she knew her son at all, and wondered if she had imagined all those loving, connected, moments with her child. To Karen, it felt like the happy life she envisioned-with their beautiful boy had been shattered.

Despite her depression, Karen spent extra time finding ways to connect with Catie, ever watchful for signs that she too had autism. Catie, not yet 1, continued demand attention and Karen felt sad and guilty that Catie was not getting the happy, secure parents that she needed. Jim, though feeling depressed and angry, had more hope than Karen. He had a more practical attitude, and wanted to find ways to help Chris. He managed to keep their life running as Karen fell apart. Karen and Jim remember this as the worst time in their marriage and their family life.

Many well meaning people had a lot of advice and recommendations for Karen and Jim. Professionals and friends of family members, who had never even met Chris, urged Karen and Jim to get a 40 hr/week intensive ABA program for Chris. They were told that time was running out, but that there was a good chance that Chris could recover from autism if they did this intervention. One ABA consultant told Karen over the phone that she would "Ruin his life" and "deprive him of any chance to have friends if she did not do ABA." These words haunted Karen for years. Karen and Jim began to intensively research ABA and learn all that they could about it.

They spoke to countless parents and professionals using ABA, and read the Lovaas study along with other ABA research that they found. Other parents, professionals, and a small amount of research were all pointing them to this intervention. Still, deep down, Karen and Jim did not feel that this was going to be right for Chris. They wanted to find a way to go beyond rote social skills and appropriate responses, and find a way to help Chris develop an internal motivation for social interaction. They wanted his relationships to be genuine, and ultimately they wanted him to be happy. They were not convinced that ABA was going to help Chris develop these things. The special education preschool coordinator and staff, who knew Chris well, also felt that ABA would not be right for Chris. They were concerned that he would become rigid instead of flexible, and urged them to take a different path to intervention.

Trying to stay open minded Jim and Karen sought out an intervention consultation and second diagnosis from a neuropsychologist at a well respected university that researched autism. The neuropsychologist did an extensive evaluation of Chris, and diagnosed him as a "High functioning child on the autism spectrum." The diagnostic code used was PDD-NOS. Chris' parents asked specifically about an intensive ABA program for Chris. The neuropsychologist recommended against this for Chris, and provided instead, a detailed intervention plan based on Chris' strengths and needs. Karen and Jim brought this plan back to the preschool and tried to implement the recommendations.

The neuropsychologist, who felt that Chris was high functioning, could not reassure Karen and Jim about Chris' future. She was unsure if he would ever live independently, hold a job, or have friends. She predicted that his difficulties would get "worse and worse" as his peers moved on developmentally and he remained behind. Her advice was to try to use his strengths to compensate for his weaknesses and to continue to advocate for what he needed.

Karen and Jim's greatest fear was that Chris would never have the opportunity to derive joy and fulfillment from real, reciprocal relationships. While Jim managed to maintain some sense of hope that Chris could attain some quality of life, Karen was still depressed and afraid to have any hope at all.

During his second year of preschool, the classroom was very small, and there were lots of kids who yelled and hit. Chris started yelling and hitting, as he was very sound sensitive and overwhelmed in the noisy environment. Karen and Jim asked the teachers for help, and they shared their strategies. At home, Karen used social stories, a brushing program, industrial noise reducing headphones and strategies like teaching Chris to tear paper and punch pillows when he was mad. They worked on helping him to use words to express his anger. Karen also spent a lot of time trying to simply soothe Chris, with soft words and quiet, soothing time spent doing nothing. Looking back, Karen and Jim realize that they should have removed him from that setting. But, at the time, there were no other suitable placements available and Karen and Jim were afraid that Chris would not be getting the help he needed. He was also approaching age 5, and they had heard that time was running out for making any real difference for him.

Over the 2 years in preschool, the staff was successful at improving Chris' motor skills, teaching him some social and play skills and correcting the pronoun reversal. Chris also slowly stopped his echolalia, and began a more communicative way of speaking. He remained relatively flexible for a child with ASD. Despite the hard work and nurturing on the part of Chris' parents and school staff, he still experienced anxiety with anything unfamiliar. He also had a great deal of social anxiety except with family. He was interested in peers, but he needed help to initiate and sustain interactions. The pace of pretend play moved too fast for Chris to keep up, and his imagination and thinking were clearly impaired. His interactions with peers and unfamiliar adults continued to be one-sided and non reciprocal. He also maintained the pattern of emotionally reactive behavior that began in the second year class setting.

After 2 years of intensive preschool services, Karen and Jim were not seeing the results that they were hoping for. They had hoped to see much more reciprocity, better peer relationships, better developed thinking and imagination. They had hoped to see more genuine social motivation. They had hoped to see their family life becoming better and their son becoming more integrally involved in family life. None of this had happened, despite a full arsenal of preschool services. Karen began to look for something else to help Chris.

The spring prior to Chris entering kindergarten is when Karen found out about RDI and one of the resources mentioned to her was *Solving the Relationship Puzzle*. Karen was intrigued by the title and ordered the book, eager to learn more. When the book arrived Karen began reading, and could not put it down until she had finished it. Dr. Gutstein's ideas made sense to Karen and spoke to her hopes for Chris.

Karen felt that the intervention model was well thought out, structured and fit with what she, as a teacher, knew about learning and what she, as a mom, knew about her son and his needs. She liked that it was a parent based model and that she could provide this intervention for her son directly. She realized that the public school was mandated to provide Chris with a "free, appropriate public education," but was in no way obliged to remediate Chris' autism. It was reassuring to know that she didn't have to give up and just accept what the school offered. Karen was sure that she wanted to give this a try, and encouraged Jim to read the book. He read it and agreed that he was interested in learning more about RDI.

Karen and Jim attended an introductory RDI® workshop on Long Island. Jim had an opportunity to speak with Dr. Gutstein that day and left feeling excited. Karen's initial impression from reading the book was reinforced by hearing Dr Gutstein speak. She knew that they would need to try to do this with Chris, and was very eager to begin. She started to feel a small glimmer of hope. Karen contacted the Connections Center in Houston and scheduled an RDA for later that year in November. Karen and Jim committed to try RDI for 6 months.

At the time, it felt like a leap of faith. It was a significant investment of time and money and many people had never heard of RDI. Moreover, there were no research studies at that time to confirm the effectiveness of RDI. Others had warned them of snake oil cures, scams and other hopeful but ultimately ineffective treatments for ASD. Still, they had done their homework and RDI seemed right for them to try. Six months seemed like a reasonable amount of time to test out RDI for their family.

When they arrived in Houston, Karen felt nervous during the RDA. She was worried that she would not be a good coach, or that they would be told that Chris was beyond help. Karen had also grown accustomed to professionals giving the impression that parents didn't know what they are doing. Chris' preschool staff had tried to get Karen to, "Just be mom and let the professionals take care of it." In contrast, Connections Center staff members, Ana and Melanie, were very reassuring, and shared with her that they thought the RDA went great. They helped both Chris and Karen relax and feel comfortable. Karen was especially impressed with the staff's ability to connect with Chris and help him relax, given his history of anxiety with strangers. Connections Center staff developed an intervention plan for Chris that was customized to his unique strengths, obstacles and level of relationship development. Karen and Jim left Houston with a plan, a commitment to 6 months of ongoing support, and a feeling of increased hope for Chris.

When Karen got home, she initially felt overwhelmed. It was a lot to take in and put into practice, and she wasn't confident that she would be a competent coach. She felt that it was as much a learning process for her as for Chris. The family's consultant, Dr. Sheely, was very supportive and encouraged them to begin slowly; this took some pressure off Karen.

It seemed to Karen that they got off to a slow start the first six months. The ongoing support became a critical part of the plan, as it helped Karen to make adjustments and to judge mastery. Dr. Sheely's reassurance and encouragement also helped Karen to feel more competent in her coaching abilities. Karen's teaching background and the focus on, "Are you meeting your objective?" was really empowering to her, along with the fact that she was not surrendering her child to the experts. Karen slowly started moving out of depression; she was finding ways to work effectively with her son and began to feel competent as a parent again.

Jim and Karen saw changes in Chris right away, particularly in the area of social referencing. Chris quickly learned to check in with his parents to determine his actions in uncertain situations. He also began looking for his parents' nonverbal responses for feedback on the actions he had taken. This made a huge difference in the family's quality of life. Taking Chris to a crowded store, for example, became less stressful. Before RDI he would often wander off, without looking back. After beginning RDI, Chris would stay with his parents, and check in frequently to determine the relative safety of his actions. After 6 months, Karen and Jim decided to stick with RDI.

During the second year of RDI, Chris was seeking his parents out; he wanted to interact and play. He played t-ball, and watched and imitated other kids. By the middle of the second year, Chris was more engaged with peers and teachers noted, for the first time, that he had started chit chatting with classmates. He also seemed to feel more confident and competent. He was beginning to take more responsibility for regulating interactions and his interactions became increasingly more reciprocal.

By the middle of his 3rd year of RDI, Chris had developed a genuine caring and concern for others, and became motivated to coordinate and collaborate with adult partners. He also began to show some generalization with peers, making his first, un-facilitated friendship with a child in his class and was observed by teachers participating and initiating in conversation and play, at both recess and lunch.

He also began to play with a same aged neighborhood boy, again, un-facilitated by adults. Karen watched with nervousness and excitement (from the living room window) as Chris would play basketball, go bike riding, play games and go exploring with his new neighborhood friend. At the same time, Karen observed that Chris continued to have difficulty following the fast pace of play. Chris had to work hard to maintain coordination and repair breakdowns.

Now, at the end of the 3rd year of RDI, Chris has a best friend in his class, a close friendship with his dyad partner and plays well with the boy across the street. Chris and his friends seek each other out to play, and look forward to being together. Chris is actively engaged with peers at school lunch and recess, and is eager to join in the dynamic play of the neighborhood kids. He has become increasingly self aware and gradually more flexible. He plays baseball on a little league team and enjoys participating in Cub Scouts. Chris really enjoys spending time with his family. He likes to cook, help with chores, do projects together, play with his sister and help Dad with guy stuff. He is a good apprentice and is eager to learn new things from his parents.

Karen is pleased with Chris' progress, but also feels that there is still important work to be done. Chris still has challenges, yet they are different; more subtle and complex. He continues to work on emotional regulation and increasing flexibility. He still has difficulty completely following the fast paced play of peers and the fast paced "thinking curriculum" in place at his school. He processes things slowly and needs more time than NT (neuro-typical) kids. He also has some difficulty interpreting the intent of others, but only in more subtle situations. And, as he becomes more self-aware, he struggles with feelings of competency. Karen knows that he still has many obstacles to overcome, but feels that RDI offers her an opportunity to work through these challenges.

For the first time since his diagnosis, Karen has allowed herself hope, and at times believes that Chris will be ok; he has the potential to become a responsible adult, to live independently, and to have friends. The painful memory of Chris staring blankly at his upset mother planting bulbs will not repeat itself. Chris is very in tune to his mom's feelings and regularly makes comments such as, "What's wrong?" or "Can I help you?" and "It will be ok." Chris went from being a kid who just watched other kids, to having a real best friend, whose relationship had not been facilitated by an adult. He used to hide behind his mom; now he goes out of his way to interact with others.

While it is still hard, he can join into spontaneous games with kids. He is much more independent, he is a better problem solver and he thinks to use more strategies. He has better self regulation, he is more open to trying things, and can self talk his way through disappointments. He knows his own mind, has his own opinions and is much more flexible. There has been a transformation in the family dynamic as well; from a depressed mode to a feeling of competence. Chris has become a contributing member of the family and he thinks about his family when he is not with them. There is no sense of him being an outsider.

Chris' parents' marriage is better as well. Initially, Jim felt that since Karen was teacher by profession, she could handle doing RDI. Also, he felt that he needed to see some results before becoming too invested. Last year Jim and Karen attended a parent training together; now Jim is more involved, and has good ideas of ways to address RDI® objectives with Chris.

Karen also appreciates that the RDI® Program takes into account the value of sibling relationships and they are addressing Chris' relationship with his younger sister. Attending the parent training as guests last fall, Jim and Karen realized how far Chris has come and how competent they have become as coaches. They found it very inspiring, especially Jim. Jim now gets a payoff in his relationship with his son; Chris seeks him out and wants to do guy stuff with him. There is something special about their father/son relationship that is very motivating to Jim.

When Chris was first diagnosed, just the idea that he had a form of autism was devastating and his parents hoped that it wasn't true. It doesn't bother Karen as much having that diagnosis anymore. She comments that while challenges remain significant, it no longer seems like some horrible, life limiting, end of the world condition. With continued hard work they expect that he will live independently, have friends and be happy - that he will be okay.

Patrick (My Son)

There are many parallels in Patrick's story, right down to a favorite book being Goodnight Moon, and a perseverative interest in drains during walks. I had a typical pregnancy following two miscarriages within the prior year. The AFP (alpha fetal protein) level was low, which can be a marker of Down Syndrome, but I did not have any further testing during the pregnancy. I was induced for slow progression of labor two days prior to Patrick's due date. My husband, Maurice, and I were excited, and I was relieved to be told that we had a healthy baby boy. By 1 month of age, Patrick was sleeping

7 hours a night; however, he barely napped at all, maybe twenty minutes once a day. He wasn't colicky, but it was an effort to keep him happy and he spit up a lot. I washed a few dozen cloth diapers daily, which I would use to clean him up, myself and everything else! Patrick was not very good at amusing himself, which was stressful for me. He did not do well and became fussy when cared for by others, the main exceptions being Maurice and my mom, whom he spent significant time with regularly.

Looking back, this was a difficult time; we had made many life changes within a short period. In the months surrounding Patrick's birth we moved to a new town and bought our first home, which was an hour away from our familiar supports/social contacts, Maurice switched jobs, and I stopped working as the acting Department Head of Physical Therapy at the Easter Seals Rehabilitation Center.

I do remember thinking that I was grateful that Patrick was so good about sleeping through the night, as it made getting through the days easier since I had a decent night's rest. Patrick was always very connected to us, especially me. I played lots of baby games with him in which he actively participated. He loved being read to, and from a very young baby age of just a few months, if he was supported appropriately in my arms; he would swipe his fist to turn the pages of books, if I got the pages started for him.

Once he could crawl, I would say, "Patrick go get..." such and such a book, like The Foot Book by Dr. Seuss and he would crawl over to the book shelf, knock the correct one off, then crawl and push it back to me so we could read it together! We would get a new book each week at the grocery store, and he came to know them all. I always felt that Patrick needed to know what we were going to do next, and I talked to him a lot. I recall more than once instance where strangers at the grocery store would comment, "Oh my, how he studies you; it looks like he knows what you're saying!" Oddly enough, I would think to myself, "He does!"

Patrick was a very cautious baby, and would look worried when presented with objects that typically made other babies smile, such as most stuffed animals. Although, he did like a specific wind up clown that played music and a Pooh bear, which were his favorites. When he would frown, wrinkling up his little forehead and eyebrows, my family came to refer to it affectionately as Patrick's "worried look." His gross motor skills were on the late end of average, and he began walking independently at about fourteen months of age. Although he could stand alone 1-2 months prior to that, being very cautious, he didn't seem to want to take any independent steps until he was sure he could do it. He was also wary for some time about small surface changes, such as the slight step down out of the garage to the driveway, or walking down a slight incline, for example.

We joined a playgroup when Patrick was 15 months old and it became obvious to me then, that at that age, the other kids were interacting more with each other than he was. During the weekly playgroup sessions, the other kids would play with each other on and off, parallel play, and were generally more interested in each other. Whereas Patrick had a great interest in fans and other things that spin; switches and dials that work the lights. He would be off exploring those types of things on his own, or using toys that wind up and play music and gear type toys.

My concerns, which included his bearing weight on the top of his wrists instead of his palms, along with his decreased interactions with peers, were not shared by his pediatrician. On one hand, this was mildly reassuring, because I didn't want anything to be wrong, but on the other hand, I was still worried that something just wasn't quite right.

Patrick's language development was precocious, for example, at a very early age he already knew the alphabet, numbers, shapes, letters and colors. We had those blocks with letters and pictures on them and at around 14 months of age Patrick pointed to an "S" and seemed to want to know what it was. I told him, and we continued in that fashion with other blocks and letters. Within a month, Patrick could say all the letters of the alphabet when I held up the block with that letter or pointed to it in a book. It was surprising to me at the time, but even more surprising later in retrospect when my daughter was that age, and I couldn't fathom her possibly having any idea what a letter of the alphabet was! Of course by 12 months of age, her relationship skills had already surpassed those of her three year old brother.

By two years of age, Patrick had memorized all of his books, a placemat of all the presidents, and the Pledge of Allegiance. He really seemed to enjoy memorizing things, so that's what we did. My mom would teach him the names of flowers when they would go on walks. For a while, I thought maybe he was just gifted. I was familiar with stories of folks who have high IQ's and are socially awkward. However, also around that time, Patrick began to display what I would refer to as autistic-like behaviors that I had observed in my work as a pediatric physical therapist. I used that term because this was still the mid 1990's and I hadn't yet heard of Asperger's Syndrome. I didn't think Patrick could possibly be autistic since he spoke so well and was so connected to us. He had always flapped his hands when excited, which I thought was cute, but then progressively more and more I would see him look and talk at his hand, make strange noises and jump around aimlessly.

I was really worried about him, but since he spoke well and related best to adults, his deficits were not as obvious to family and friends, and they generally didn't share my concerns. I got the feeling that they thought I was an overly anxious mom, which left me feeling frustrated, and continued the seed of doubt planted in my head about Patrick's development.

Patrick never lost skills or had a regression; his unusual behaviors were more of an addition to who he was. Looking back, he spoke well but, he wasn't really conversational. He would ask questions that he knew the answer to and wanted us to ask him, or we would ask him various questions that he would answer. For example, we began attending a "mom and me" type group just before Patrick turned two, and I would hear him ask the teacher something like, "What color is that?" They would answer him, but he would just ask again. I knew that he really wanted them to echo back his question so he could answer it. I did a HELP checklist (Hawaii Early Learning Profile) on him myself, but didn't see him as delayed enough in any area that he would have qualified for Birth to Three services. I was half hoping for confirmation of my concerns, and half hoping that nothing significant would show up. However, that changed by his 3rd birthday.

When I looked at the checklist for 3 year olds, it was obvious to me that he now looked more delayed in several areas - the expectations for 3 year olds are higher. I saw significant delays in both his fine and gross motor skills and especially in his social development. For instance, he held writing instruments with his whole fist and his arm turned inward, he couldn't jump and he didn't really interact at all with peers.

I discussed this with Maurice, and told him that I wanted to refer Patrick to the special education preschool for an assessment. At the time he thought "Patrick is just Patrick" and he wasn't as concerned as I was, particularly since Patrick had so many strengths. But, he was fine in going ahead with an assessment. I guess I was already feeling that the burden of researching/managing any special needs that Patrick had would be up to me.

I can't recall a defining moment when I realized Patrick's diagnosis, but more a series of confusions and disappointments in Patrick's response to certain situations. His sister, Shannon, was born shortly before his 2nd birthday and Patrick never really showed much of an interest in her. He wanted to know where she was, and he seemed to have a certain wariness of her, but he didn't make many, if any attempts to engage her unless he was directly prompted by us. The following year, I remember being at my grandmother's funeral and crying, and being hurt that my emotions did not seem to register at all with Patrick. He didn't appear to notice or care that I was so upset.

The fall of Patrick's 3rd birthday we referred him to the school district for an assessment. At the time, they did a screening through a playgroup situation, where parents who had concerns about their child's development could bring their child in on a specific day, and the preschool teachers would walk around, speak with the parents and take a look at the kids. During that brief visit, they didn't see any characteristics distinguished enough to warrant further assessment, and I was told to send him to a typical preschool. I left feeling very frustrated and disappointed.

I followed their recommendation and enrolled him in a local preschool program that was beginning that January. It was held at a church that had a bell in the steeple. At the time, Patrick had a fascination with church bells. He didn't mind going to the preschool building, but I sensed that was only because he wanted to see the bell at the church. We gave it a month, as I knew it would take extra time for my cautious little guy to adjust. But, the teacher said he cried practically the whole time after I dropped him off each session, and he did not interact at all with the other children.

The last day of January was the first time that month that he actually said he didn't want to go - he had gone willingly prior to that. Patrick had delayed pronoun reversals and as we ate lunch he began to cry saying, "You don't want to go to preschool. You want to stay home with Mommy and Shannon." I tried to encourage him to go for the last day, planning a treat afterwards, but he was adamant and that was the end of our typical preschool experience.

I had known in my heart all along that a typical preschool wouldn't work for Patrick. I had tried to be optimistic but I was now even more upset and frustrated that Patrick had to fail and be miserable for a month before he qualified for a special education evaluation.

It didn't make any sense to me. I felt that as a professional who had worked for a number of years in pediatrics, that I had shared valid concerns with the special education preschool staff, and had provided specific examples of behaviors and incidents that should have set off some red flags. I wasn't asking them to take my word for it, but to do an assessment and draw their own conclusions. I did refer him back to the school district after the failed preschool experience, but it wasn't until the end of that school year that the assessment was completed and Patrick was admitted to their special education program for social delays.

That fall, just shy of his 4th birthday, he began attending the program for 4 year olds. It ran for 2½ hours a day, for 2 days initially, which was later increased to 4 days at my request and with staff agreement. They did a good job of easing Patrick into the program and helping him feel comfortable. He didn't mind going that year, but he didn't really make any progress either. I saw Patrick as very high functioning and was hoping they could teach him to play with the other kids. Of course I was sorely disappointed.

Just as Patrick entered kindergarten, he was evaluated by a neuropsychologist. Unfortunately, the date of the assessment coincided with class picture day and I recall being incredibly disappointed that Patrick would not be in his class picture. There was something inside of me that recognized that even though he didn't fit in with the other kids, it was important to me to have a picture of him as part of his class. But, it didn't work out. The neuropsychologist documented some PDD-like tendencies in his report, but said that young kids can change, and that he wouldn't offer a more definitive diagnosis until Patrick was 7 years old.

Once again, I had mixed feelings; I still held out hope, because I hadn't actually received a formal diagnosis, but I felt lost or in limbo without one. Patrick had a creative teacher for kindergarten who was good at thinking up ways to engage him and get him involved in classroom activities. There was an aide in the classroom as well. Over these early years, other services were added to include PT, OT, Speech, and a social skills group run by the school psychologist.

By the time Patrick was in 1st grade, his differences were so unquestionably significant to me that I finally decided to read more specifically about Asperger's Syndrome. The term had first been mentioned to me by a special education preschool staff member when I asked about diagnostic possibilities, when Patrick was 4. Initially, I waited for the neuropsychologist's opinion. Still without a formal diagnosis, I didn't want to read about something he might not have, but the time had finally come. I read Tony Attwood's book first, as he was an internationally known clinical psychologist who specialized in the field of Asperger's Syndrome. Although I was trying to find all the ways that this diagnosis did not fit my son, I realized upon completing the book that I had dog-eared every other page, as it had applied to Patrick!

At that point I was 99% sure that he did indeed have a diagnosis on the autism spectrum, and that it was most likely Asperger's Syndrome. I had been experiencing a generalized worry, concern, and anxiety about Patrick's development since he was a toddler. It was a gradual process of realization and acceptance of the supposed, and later the official diagnosis of Asperger's Syndrome.

During further reading that year, I had also seen the book *Solving the Relationship Puzzle* referenced, initially in the O.A.S.I.S. book. I believe the title intrigued me; I was on the lookout for it and picked it up shortly thereafter at a conference. I read the whole thing on the ride home from the conference. I was very excited, because I just knew that this program would help Patrick. There were many similarities to my training in NDT (Neuro Developmental Treatment), which was founded by the Bobaths back in the 1950's. I felt that RDI addressed the cognitive social emotional aspects of neurological impairment in a way that was similar in many respects to how NDT addressed the motor aspects. I was even more excited to discover at the back of the book that the Connections Center was located in Houston, TX, where we had planned a visit to relatives in three weeks!

Maurice was still not as worried as I was, yet he trusted my judgment, because he knew he was not knowledgeable about developmental disabilities. He still doesn't consider himself to be the worrying type, unlike me who comes from a long line of worriers on the Italian side of my family! He has an overall attitude that there is a grand plan and that things will work out. Over time, he has had more of a tendency to become frustrated rather than worried, about Patrick's behaviors and delays. His concerns were always more related to Patrick's life threatening food allergies, which include all nuts. The nut allergy was yet one more commonality we would later discover between Patrick and Chris.

Dr. Sheely was able to meet with Maurice and I, during our initial Houston visit. While there, we decided that we definitely wanted to return for an RDA, which we scheduled for 3 months later. I could hardly wait; I was so eager to get started that 3 months seemed like a long time. Back then, the Connections Center employed the only RDI® Certified Consultants in the country and it was our only option. Coincidentally, Dr. Gutstein was giving a presentation in Long Island later that spring, which Maurice and I attended. Unbeknownst to us at the time, it was the same presentation attended by Karen and Jim! Hearing Dr. Gutstein speak, particularly on the research about the lack of successful outcomes for high functioning persons on the autism spectrum really hit home with me, and I wanted to do all I could to help enhance Patrick's development.

Upon our return visit to Houston the RDA went well, and we really appreciated Dr. Sheely listening to and sharing our concerns, as well as our views of Patrick's strengths. She, along with Ana Hermosilla, one of the Connections Center staff, developed a treatment plan that was specifically tailored to Patrick. Diagnostic testing was done as well, with Patrick receiving a formal diagnosis of Asperger's Syndrome several months prior to his 7th birthday. I remember it felt really good to have someone (Dr. Sheely) just listen to our story, share in our concerns and have a plan for remediation.

Even after all this, there was still a small part of me that wanted to deny that Patrick was on the autism spectrum, but my prior reading and research had prepared me and helped me to accept it. Maurice didn't have any trouble accepting the diagnosis. As mentioned earlier, he always just assumed that Patrick would "be ok," and he considered the diagnosis to be just another word that could be used to describe his son, not to define him or his potential. He was impressed with our experience at the Connections Center and he got the overall impression that they really knew what they were doing, knew what they were talking about and he trusted the plan that had been created for Patrick. I felt empowered to know what to do to help Patrick develop in the areas that he needed most, even though the responsibility felt daunting.

We began RDI at home that summer of 2002, when the RDI® Activity book (Relationship Development Intervention for Young Children) was hot off the press. It was a little slow going at first, and we did what most folks do, which is to start at the beginning and focus on one thing at a time. I found the ongoing support through videotape review and feedback to be invaluable and very motivating to know I was on the right track. We also saw results right away; Patrick was so ready for this that once we knew how to help him, we had so many more ways to engage him and have fun with him.

At first, I just focused on communication changes; changing the way I communicated with Patrick; chanting and emphasizing non verbal communication. Then we started doing some emotion sharing, followed by referencing activities from the book, one being the "Freeze Game," which Patrick enjoyed and would later request periodically for quite a number of months! We also made up some activities of our own, such as a referencing winking game that we played at the dinner table, and another one where we would make an exaggerated face (like very happy or surprised) and look at someone; that person was to make the face back. Patrick really started referencing us much more, and he seemed to look forward to doing RDI® activities (which was the focus back when we began RDI).

Before RDI, Patrick's play with his sister consisted mostly of occasional brief, scripted games that I believe were mostly of Shannon's design as she figured out ways to get Patrick to play with her for brief periods. As we continued with RDI, we saw their imaginary play expand together. We were also told that Patrick started to initiate games such as "I Spy" at the lunchroom table. He and Shannon have a close family friend, and Patrick's relationship with her expanded; from joining in only for very short bursts to playing together for extended periods. The family friend had become a Harry Potter fan, which spilled over to Patrick and Shannon, and one thing they would do was to ride around on broomsticks outside pretending they were playing quidditch.

Before RDI, Patrick didn't mind going to other kids' houses, or having other kids over to our house, but he didn't really play with them either, and he didn't talk about them when they weren't around. We saw him begin to anticipate and look forward to play dates with the family friend, and to talk about her during the week, asking if they would be able to have a play date with her after church on Sunday.

These days, Patrick is much more willing to try new things, and he really enjoys time spent with the family. He likes to go for walks, help me cook, he helps out with chores such as doing the laundry, and he really likes the idea of helping my husband fix things, if he has a simple active role. A while ago, Maurice was fixing the oven and Patrick came over, sat next to him the whole time and handed him the parts he needed. He really wants to be his dad's apprentice. Patrick and his dad have installed a chandelier, hung pictures on the wall and fixed Patrick's hover disc. Patrick often approaches us asking if we'd like to do something together.

He still has significant motor delays, which interfere with his participation and interest in team sports, but he has found other interests. This fall he began TaeKwon-Do and he will be playing the trumpet in the school band. He is joining the chess club again and wants to work on the school yearbook this year. He is also a Boy Scout, and he is in our church choir and bell choir. When creating something together with us, the relationship and interaction with the other person takes precedence over Patrick wanting to use only his own ideas. For example, when co-creating a story or skit, Patrick blends our ideas with his, modifies his idea if we comment that we don't like it, and frequently asks us what our ideas are.

Before RDI, I used to worry a lot about whether or not Patrick would be "ok" as an adult. Now, I can't see any reason why he won't be able to live on his own and have a good job and fulfilling social relationships. We recently went to a Chinese restaurant to celebrate my birthday. Patrick's fortune cookie said, "You will maintain good health and enjoy life." What could be a better fortune than that?! That is what we hope for Patrick and Shannon.. We have no amended hopes for him because of his diagnosis.

When Patrick was in second grade, the kids had to write about what they wanted to be when they grew up, and Patrick wrote that he wanted to be "a Daddy." We believe that is possible for him. Patrick, Shannon and the family friend were scheming this summer about a restaurant they want to own together when they grow up. They created a name for the restaurant, and even talked about what their personalized license plates would read when they park next to each other in front of the restaurant.

During a recent walk, Patrick asked me if I thought that the three of them would really own the restaurant together someday, or if it was probably just for pretend. I said I wasn't sure, but that you never know. He went on to say it might not be such a good idea because you have to work long hours at a restaurant and he wouldn't be able to spend much time with his family!

With my son having a diagnosis on the autism spectrum, I found myself wanting to be as educated as possible about it. RDI made such a difference with Patrick right away that I wanted to share it with other families. Those factors combined led me to pursue certification as an RDI® Consultant. I became interested and excited about it as soon as I started seeing results with Patrick. But, before working with other families I needed more time to feel comfortable and knowledgeable about RDI by working with my son first. I began the certification process about 6 months after that, and I was certified in June of 2003. Around that time Dr. Sheely and Dr. Gutstein came to our area to do a parent training.

The Dyad

That summer I attended the parent training as a professional and Karen, Chris' mom, attended as a guest parent. We were introduced, and Dr. Sheely shared with us that she thought our sons would be good dyad partners. We were both working on Co-regulation at the time, and eager to begin peer work. We began getting the boys together on a weekly basis that fall as school began.

In spite of living over an hour apart, we made finding time for the dyad a priority in our schedules. Prior to getting the boys together for the first time, we e-mailed each other to share information about the boys and the types of activities they enjoyed most. Other than our family friend, Patrick hadn't developed any real friendships with other kids, and I was hopeful that he would develop a true friendship with another boy around his own age, possibly facilitated through the dyad.

At first, it was somewhat difficult to keep Patrick and Chris in the room together for very long. We did all the work to keep them together, regulated and interacting with each other. There were breakdowns that they needed help repairing during each session. I recall a time when Chris accidentally rolled a toy car over Patrick's fingers. Patrick overreacted, which caused Chris to over-react. Patrick then over-reacted to Chris. This type of vicious cycle typically continued until an adult coach intervened to de-escalate the situation.

Even with the breakdowns happening during those early stages of the dyad, the boys would talk about each other and wanted to get together; they liked the idea of having a friend, but they had no idea of how to make it work. The dyad introduced Chris to looking at other kids in another way and having reciprocal interactions with them. Chris started chit-chatting with other kids at the class table at school, then during free choice time.

Last summer, just under a year into the dyad, the boys really seemed to cement their friendship. There was generalization, which means they carried over relationship abilities they had been practicing in a lab-type situation, to typical activities they did together such as going to the lake, on hikes and sleepovers. They would think about each other and talk about each other when apart, and began sending e-mails to each other.

They also enjoyed setting up surprises for one another. Here is an early e-mail sample: "Hi Patrick! The next time you come to my house I'm going to give you a locked box game. Your friend, Chris." Patrick's response: "I would love to do the locked box game! The next time you come to my house can you bring Bemo? I'm also going to give you a different kind of locked box game. Sincerely, Patrick"

This summer, Chris began making comments such as, "Patrick would really like this!", "Patrick is smart" and "Patrick would rather do this." It was very important to Chris that Patrick and one of his other good friends attend his birthday party this year. Patrick began making similar comments in reference to Chris.

These days, the boys spend time together for extended periods, sometimes structured, and sometimes not. Obvious breakdowns occur much less frequently. Now they are more likely to use words when initiating a repair, and with less over-reacting, like saying they are sorry, or saying they don't like it when something happens.

Looking back, we do believe that we started the dyad a little too early. Neither Patrick nor Chris was close enough to mastery of managing coordination breakdowns. In any communication exchange, there are continual breakdowns and repairs. Since the boys hadn't had enough practice with this individually, their communication breakdowns required too much intervention from the coaches, Karen and I. We probably both wondered early on if the dyad was worth it. Karen would make the long trip over, the boys would be in the room together for about fifteen minutes, ask for a snack, and that was about it! It was great for me though, to have another mom to talk about RDI with; these were the days before RDI yahoo groups and weekly RDI® chats. And even early on, the boys seemed to have positive memories of their weekly sessions together. By the next summer, when we steered away from more formal sessions and really took advantage of lifestyle opportunities, they had become real friends.

Over this past year, Chris and Patrick have really become a team. They have made things together such as pancakes, cookies, and a pasta lunch. They have helped their dads with guy stuff, such as fixing things, leaf blowing and raking together. They have fixed their little sisters snacks, and teamed up against them in games such as hide and seek. Patrick often refers to Chris when he is not around, and he thinks about things they can do when they get together. Some common comments from Patrick include statements like, "Chris really likes this song." "Maybe we can do that when Chris comes." "Me and Chris could help daddy do this."

For Patrick's birthday, Chris made him a card that celebrates how far they have come together. It reads, "Happy birthday Patrick – You are the bestest buddy that there ever was. You are super nice to me. I like to go bowling together. I like to take sleepovers together. I also like to play together. I hope you have a nice birthday! Your friend, Chris." That was really touching to me; those are the moments which make it all worth it!

✎ **Kim Downey, PT has been a RDI® Certified Consultant since June 2003. Her private practice, Special Connections L.L.C., is located in Brookfield, Connecticut. Kim can be contacted at Kimdowney@charter.net.**

11

Beginning a Joyful Journey

by Janice Guice, M.A., C.C.C.-S.L.P.

Names have been changed to protect the family's privacy.

In October, 2004, we began a journey. I use the word "journey" because I want to suggest a greater opportunity to take in the sites, to be changed by the travel and even to experience unexpected detours along the way, without fleeing for the familiar.

The power of the journey thus far, has been in what we have observed, how we have changed, the competence that has grown for everyone involved and the revelations that we did not expect to find in our travels. The vehicle we selected for our journey was the Relationship Development Intervention® Program. When I say we began, it is meant literally, in every sense of the word. It applies to all the travelers, me included. My companions for the journey were parents of a child recently diagnosed with Asperger's Syndrome.

I am trained as a speech language pathologist but my path to that title was not typical. I decided as an adult, more accurately a wife and mother of two small children, that helping children learn to communicate, in a world that's defined by and experienced through communication, was one of the most significant careers I could pursue. That decision had been impressed upon me, by my son's communication impairment that stemmed from a brain tumor located in the language center of his brain.

Following the tumor's removal, we learned that his ability to organize his ideas and express them had been impacted by the tumor and we pursued speech therapy to attempt to remediate the deficits. As a parent, I had seen that a child's inability to communicate caused behavioral problems born of extreme frustration. This kept us from enjoying his childhood in the ways that we had always dreamed we would.

As I observed the professionals that worked with him, I knew that they were changing his future and they were having fun at the same time. From blowing bubbles and racing cars to feeding stuffed animals and throwing balls, they were able to elicit labels, requests and comments from him that he had never spoken before. My son never knew that with every laugh and turn he was taking he was building the foundation of communication for a lifetime. During that time in my life, I developed an incredible passion for the power that communication gives each of us and the meaning it brings to relationships. With tremendous support from my husband, I returned to school and completed a Bachelor's and Master's in Speech Language Pathology.

While I was attending school, I was required to participate in numerous clinical rotations. In my first rotation, I was assigned a 3 year old girl who had autism. She was basically nonverbal with the exception of some echolalia, (brief phrases she had heard on television or in conversation that she memorized and repeated with no purpose) and showed little to no interest in play with her parents. She was unable to follow simple directions and comprehended only a few labels for familiar objects. I was terrified. I felt that my coursework to date had not prepared me for the issues I would face as I worked with this child. It was as if I would be groping my way through a dark room with an unknown enemy - revealing for all to see that I did not understand what I was doing.

I braced myself and forged ahead. Although, I certainly would have been lost without my supervisor's consistent guidance and her mother's patience with my learning, my work with the little girl changed the direction of my career. It never once resembled the fearful imaginings I had worried over. There in that clinic room; was a sweet, lovable child, who offered me glimpses of her world and occasionally let me join her. Yet, I was puzzled and torn over how to reach her. I was overwhelmed with care and compassion for the effects of autism in her life and the life of her family. I knew, as that semester came to a close, that I wanted to work with children and their families who faced the day to day realities that the diagnosis of autism presents its victims.

In a later clinical rotation, I worked in a preschool program for children diagnosed with autism. This time I was excited and eager to learn. The school district was spending incredible sums of money on a pilot program I had been assigned to work in. The children spent half of their school day in discrete trials training and half of their day in a typical preschool program.

As the speech language pathologist, I was directing a team of 10 paraprofessionals in executing each child's discrete trial programming: aiding them in targeting generalization of the discrete trials content in play and reciprocal communication, conducting group language lessons in the classroom portion of their day and putting out fires wherever they popped up. The paraprofessionals were resistant to play, because it was harder to take data, less predictable and often unsuccessful for the child. I now realize how incredibly incompetent they must have felt as I insisted that talking about colors or shapes while playing on the floor could be achieved without the use of an M&M or a Skittle. I left that rotation thinking that I had failed because I was sure that I had been unable to convince anyone that knowing and labeling your colors was useless in isolation of sharing about the color of objects with others. The challenges I experienced in this learning lab did not dampen my resolve. If anything my passion grew.

As I finished my training and entered the public schools to begin my career, the diagnosis of children with autism was growing everywhere. I continued to work with many children on the autism spectrum that were in self-contained classroom settings, where class size and make-up were designed to facilitate maximum learning throughout the entire day for a small group of children with specific disabilities. I also served children with autism whose disability was addressed in resource room environments where a special education teacher helped small groups of special needs children with instruction in specific subjects before they returned to the regular education class for other subjects they were able to learn along side of their typical peers. Finally, I worked with children who participated in regular education classes with paraprofessional assistance.

By this time, I had begun the search through all the known approaches to treat autism. I went to the seminars, read the books and even tackled the research in the field of communication disorders. I became an eclectic therapist. I borrowed as needed from any and every approach. As a clinician, I was fortunate in that most of my efforts helped the children make progress in their communication and even their social skills. But, that was all they made progress in –skills; scripted skills and accurate use of concepts to that one context. As I met with parents over and over again, I knew in my heart that even those children with the brightest futures, that might include college, were going to have less than what every parent desires most for their child –a future with meaningful relationships that is the heart of a successful life. Every gain I described in the Individual Education Programs (IEP) or percentage obtained that demonstrated progress was somehow empty because it lacked a genuine hope for the future.

By 2003, the growing caseloads, shortages of speech language pathologists and the never ending expansion of paperwork had resulted in 16 hour work days in the public schools. I felt the distant heat of burnout approaching rapidly and decided to leave the schools and begin my own private practice. The transition was smooth and many families that I had worked with in the schools followed me my private practice and referred their friends. My caseload was primarily children with autism. Even though I enjoyed the flexibility and luxury of controlling my own practice I was still frustrated by my failure to get at that almost intangible aspect of communication that results in relationships. That was the communication the children I served rarely or never achieved.

In May, 2004, I attended a two-day seminar presented by Dr. Gutstein about the Relationship Development Intervention® Program. I had previously read his book, *Solving the Relationship Puzzle*. I thought it had some interesting concepts in it but, I was not moved enough to adopt it as a new approach and instead I merely stored the parts I found useful in my eclectic files for future use. However, the seminar was different. In his words and the videos of various children was the aspect of communication that results in relationships. It was so evident and yet I was scared to believe it was true. Had this man merely gotten lucky and had the added fortune to catch it on video tape? I listened while Dr. Sheely met with professionals interested in becoming certified in the RDI® Program. It seemed exciting and yet I was terrified by the financial commitment that it would require. What if it was a hoax or the therapy of the month?

I mulled the seminar over in my head for a week or so and finally sat down to talk with my husband about becoming certified. I shared with him that I was not sure I could ethically or morally, continue to provide therapy in the manner I had for years knowing that there was something out there that could change the future for these children. On the one hand, had I not been where these families were, praying and hoping for a future that was bright and counting on professionals to take my son into that future? On the other hand, it wasn't a great time in our lives to be tackling a financial or time commitment of this magnitude. Following the attacks on the United States on September 11, 2001, my husband's career had taken a never imagined turn and he was rebuilding after over a year of unemployment. Within a year both of our sons would be in college and I had a private practice in its infancy. Despite these overriding issues, my husband calmly encouraged me to explore the details of RDI® certification. After review of the paperwork for certification and discussions with the staff at the Connections Center in Houston I signed on. I knew that I was headed down a path that would change me and my professional career. Now, fourteen months into the journey and almost at the completion of my certification process I am astounded at the changes, benefits and pleasure in the work and sense of hope I have for the children I work with.

My partners for this journey are Michelle and Andrew, Jeremy's parents. Jeremy is their beautiful, bright-eyed little 6 year old boy who was diagnosed with Asperger's Syndrome about one month before his fifth birthday. They also have 4 year old twins, Sarah and Michael and their newest addition, William, who is 9 months old.

Michelle is a 30-something housewife who arrives at every session and phone call full of energy and enthusiasm. She is communicative in every way, from the light in her eyes and smile on her face, to her descriptions that paint detailed pictures in the listener's mind. She has always loved children. In college she worked as a nanny. Later, her career led her to work with children on the autism spectrum as an ABA therapist, prior to having her own children. She began that work at the New England Center for Children in Boston, Massachusetts. When Michelle and Andrew relocated to the Miami area she continued her work as a home therapist. Michelle would describe herself as a child at heart. It is easy to see her love for the playful parts of childhood and that she prioritizes that aspect of life, with her four children, above most things.

Andrew, is an accountant, working in corporate America. He is articulate and yet reserved in how frequently he communicates or the quantity of words he uses. I have learned that when Andrew talks, I need to listen with care. When he shares, it has been carefully thought out and is more often than not profoundly important and full of insight. He always has a gentle smile and a twinkle in his eyes. He shared that his own family background and birth order - "I was the classical middle child" - led to a great deal of independence even as a teen. It is very easy to see that he is comfortable in his skin and does not require a great deal of interaction with others to enjoy the life he has created for himself and his family. He is a person who prefers a small number of good friends, rather than general acceptance by a larger group of acquaintances.

At first, they considered Jeremy brilliant. He was a sponge and learned easily. Michelle and Andrew shared that pride with family and friends. Jeremy was very verbal early in his development. Michelle recalled that at nine months, Jeremy would drop something and say "ought-oh." He would also label things and say "mama" and "dada." By 12 months of age he was using two word utterances such as "want juice" or "Daddy home." This early development was noted by Jeremy's pediatrician. Andrew and Michelle attributed his verbal skills to Michelle's own communication style, as well as, her play and modeling with him.

However, by the age of 2 Michelle was concerned that there was something very different about Jeremy. The first sign that raised flags for her was Jeremy's tendency to get stuck on something. This pattern was often stimulated by television shows. Hours after watching a program he was able to repeat entire episodes using appropriate character voices, even accents and reciting every word. Michelle noted that Jeremy's repetition of scripts could occur in isolation of anyone's involvement. He found pleasure in these episodes without any connection to his family or their responses. A great deal of his play was independent. Michelle was frustrated by her continued presence on the floor trying to engage Jeremy in play and his ability to carry on without her. Michelle's friends were envious of Jeremy's ability to play independently and expressed their desire for their children to be more like him. The irony was that Michelle's love of child's play made her sad that her son did not need her to enjoy and expand his play like her friends' children did.

Because of their concern about Jeremy's increasing tendency to prefer isolation in the scripts of movies and television programs, they limited his access to media. Instead, they focused on reading books together and play. Jeremy translated his obsession with the scripts of movies and programs to reciting the books that were read. By the age of 3 it appeared that Jeremy could read because his ability to recite the text from the books was so accurate. When older children in the neighborhood would visit and try to read the books to Jeremy he would finish the sentences well ahead of the children. Michelle realized that he had merely memorized the book and done so with ease.

Jeremy also rejected his parent's efforts to play even the simplest games. Jeremy would become frustrated and refuse to participate. Michelle changed the focus. In order to make their time productive, now that Jeremy was not watching TV, Michelle would complete preschool worksheets with him. Relying on her ABA training, she would give him fruit snack rewards for completion of a line or a page.

During this same time in their life, Michelle made efforts to participate in play groups with Jeremy. She realized that Jeremy rarely stayed and participated with either the children or the mothers. He would retreat to another room or when he did stay and play he would spend all of his time in isolated play or taking toys away from others. When Michelle would discuss her concern with the pediatrician, the doctor would always state that parallel play was developmentally appropriate given Jeremy's age. But, Michelle knew in her heart, that it somehow was very different from how the other children in the play group were playing.

In retrospect, Michelle and Andrew now realize that Jeremy was experiencing sensory problems throughout these years. On the morning of his 2nd birthday, Michelle, Andrew and Andrew's parents joined Jeremy in his room after he had awakened to sing "Happy Birthday" to him. Instead of lighting up with excitement, Jeremy collapsed into fitful tears that took

10 minutes to resolve. He still hates to hear the "Happy Birthday" song and resists participating in birthday parties for himself, siblings and family friends in an effort to avoid this event. Michelle was very concerned about his reaction.

As a 3 year old preschool student, Jeremy's skills were noticeably different to Michelle. When it came time for the class fieldtrip to the pumpkin patch, Michelle was ready to join Jeremy for the fun. It included a hayride and a variety of relay races and games. Jeremy's classmates and their mothers were enjoying the fun and Michelle found herself off on the fringe trying to help him recover from a meltdown. Michelle wondered why she always found herself on the outside of social settings handling Jeremy's struggles and why other children were able to handle the situations, but not Jeremy. His teachers expressed concerns, but attributed his struggles to sensory problems and did all they could to help.

Jeremy's weaknesses were very noticeable when there were class performances or in daily show and tell. He resisted any participation in these opportunities. Michelle watched as other children squirmed and begged to participate, while Jeremy played with the carpet or his shoe.

One memory of show and tell that stands out for Michelle happened when Jeremy's grandmother was visiting from England. Both Michelle and her mother-in-law were helping in his classroom. As the morning came to a close the preschool teacher said, "We really want to thank our special guests that were here today, right Jeremy?" Jeremy did not respond and the teacher repeated it to help Jeremy focus on a response to indicate his mother and grandmother's presence. A number of his peers tapped him on the shoulder and said, "Your mom and your grandma," as they pointed to both visitors. Within a moment or two Jeremy recognized what was being discussed. Michelle's eyes filled with tears as she contemplated the distance that Jeremy maintained from his world. This incident confirmed that it was time to seek professional help.

Michelle knew in her heart that something was wrong and as she added up the pieces she was fearful of what it might be. Andrew was not as convinced. He had spent time with a number of Michelle's autistic students and could see a clear distinction between their behaviors and Jeremy's. Although he recognized that Jeremy demonstrated behaviors, which if not completely different to his peers, were certainly uncommon, Andrew was concerned that Michelle was overly focused on the similarities to autism because of her background. He was hesitant that one who had been trained to see autism would only see autism. Despite his uncertainty he supported Michelle's efforts to seek professional help.

Michelle began her search with their pediatrician. The doctor responded by minimizing her concerns. She always provided Michelle with some reason Jeremy's behaviors were not a real problem and told Michelle that she was being overly paranoid. The doctor repeated that as long as he was interacting with other kids it was OK. Yes, sporadically Jeremy did successfully complete a few cycles of reciprocal play or conversation with a peer. But, he did not demonstrate those successes as frequently or as naturally as other children. Repeatedly, Michelle would leave the doctor's office feeling only a small sense of relief from the doctor's response and acutely aware that the underlying concern was still alive and well in her gut.

Having met with little support from the medical profession, Michelle turned to the school system with her concerns. After an extensive evaluation by the preschool team at their local school system, it was determined that there was nothing more concerning about Jeremy's development than mild sensory issues. They provided the family access to an occupational therapist, who supervised home programs with Jeremy. Additionally, Michelle recalled that they eventually questioned her need for a diagnosis; stating that it would not change what she was doing for him and a diagnosis would not change her son. Their response baffled her, because she felt that a diagnosis would lead to a specific treatment approach and a resulting plan would be developed that would help her son.

The next stop was a pediatric neurologist at a major children's hospital in New England. After the doctor completed her evaluation and physical examination of Jeremy, she assured Michelle that nothing was wrong. From research on the internet Michelle had found descriptions of children with Asperger's Syndrome and her concern was growing that this was what the diagnosis would be. In response to Michelle's direct question, "Does Jeremy have AS?" the doctor responded abruptly that he did not and it was time for her to see other patients who really needed her help. The doctor added that if Jeremy had AS he would be sitting there talking only about the weather. Michelle reminded the doctor that he only talked about television shows or books. The neurologist told Michelle that she was being a paranoid parent and there was nothing wrong. Michelle knew that other parents might have left that appointment elated that there had been no diagnosis, but she felt ill. She could find no one; not the pediatrician who knew Jeremy well, not the schools or the specialists who could see what she knew was there.

After a move to the Atlanta area, during an unrelated visit to their new pediatrician for one of Jeremy's siblings, the pediatrician responded to Michelle's concerns about Jeremy's atypical behaviors. After having the parents and his new preschool teacher complete a series of inventories, the pediatrician referred Jeremy to a developmental pediatrician for evaluation and determination of a potential diagnosis. Almost simultaneously with the developmental pediatrician's diagnosis of Asperger's Syndrome, a clinical psychologist who they had also sought out for an evaluation and assistance, provided the same diagnosis.

At the prompting of the clinical psychologist, they removed Jeremy from a private preschool program; where Jeremy's struggles, were viewed merely as a behavior problem. This led the family to have Jeremy evaluated by the public school system. They also determined a diagnosis of Asperger's syndrome. Within an 8 week window they had the answer to the initial question that they had been asking for years and it had been confirmed by three professionals.

Their first response to the news on February 13, 2004 that Jeremy had Asperger's Syndrome was relief; it finally had a name. Michelle knew where her battle would be and she could work to help her son. She was also relieved because it confirmed that nothing was wrong with her as a mother for insisting that something was wrong with her son. Their feeling of relief lasted a mere 25 minutes, the duration of the drive home.

Once at home, with the family together, their grief set in. Despite her insistence that something had been wrong, Michelle realized that she had held to the repeated assurances that Jeremy was fine. As the reality of the news set in, she knew she was grieving the loss of a typical childhood for Jeremy. She knew this had daily and more importantly, lifelong implications for Jeremy and the entire family. One of her greatest fears for Jeremy was what his future would hold. For now, she would be there to help and protect him, but what about years down the road when he would not have her or Andrew to help him? Michelle's focus was on the tomorrows of Jeremy's life.

For Andrew, the gift he had been given in his son was no less incredible following the diagnosis. Interestingly, Andrew's attention was drawn to Jeremy's todays. He felt that if they were facing a lifelong challenge, it did not make sense to think only about trying to correct things in the future; especially if things could not be corrected, only improved. With the general uncertainties of life impacting everyone involved, not only the person diagnosed with Asperger's, it would be important to ensure that Jeremy had time to enjoy today. He felt it was not appropriate to expend all their resources so that Jeremy would have a better chance of enjoying tomorrow, the challenges of which are indeterminable. When Andrew talked about Jeremy's diagnosis and disability there was a perceivable peace and comfort that was clearly not resignation. Talking later about their difference in perspectives, Andrew stated his gratitude for the balance that he and Michelle were able to bring to Jeremy's development. From Andrew comes the need to enjoy today and from Michelle the forethought and realism to prepare for tomorrow.

The initial response of family and friends to the diagnosis was much the same as it had been when Michelle had raised concerns about Jeremy's atypical behaviors. They rationalized it away, offering excuses for his behavior. Jeremy was bright, maybe even gifted and being a little different was part of the territory. Out of their love for Jeremy, these family members and friends tried to reassure Michelle and Andrew. They offered their support as they were able. Many of the family members sought to understand the disorder more thoroughly, reading and searching the internet for up to date information. Jeremy's grandmother in England began to attend classes and trainings offered in the community schools about autism and Asperger's syndrome. Michelle's family here in the states provided support and assistance wherever it was needed.

As a professional who had experienced a terrifying diagnosis for my own child, I have always dreaded the moments where I sat with a team of other professionals to share the results of a comprehensive evaluation that indicated a child had autism or any one of its associated disabilities. My own experience had caused me to develop clear guidelines in my mind about how a diagnosis should be shared, but as a speech language pathologist I was rarely the lead member of the team and I often watched in horror as the news was provided in any number of ways that reflected little or no concern for the family's need to process and understand the information that was given to them and their instinctive need to protect themselves from the news. Sometimes I was not on the team that had shared the news, but I was the professional who was trying to help the family begin to pick up the shattered dreams and reconstruct a future for their child.

Despite all the angst over diagnoses, I have never considered the diagnosis of autism to be a death sentence. I knew, because of my training and experience that my perspective of the future was clearer than the parents and there was much that could be achieved. Yet, it would likely not resemble the image those parents had previously held for their child's future. I have always held a quiet place in my heart that was filled with compassion for how hard raising a child on the spectrum might be and the impact it would likely have on every member of that family.

Now I have a different response to sharing a diagnosis. I know that there is something better to offer each of these precious children. It is a thrilling opportunity to sit with a family of a newly diagnosed child with ASD, who has come straight to RDI and know that their future is going to look different because of what I have learned. Now I can share a hope that I would have felt deceitful sharing before. Even as I began my own journey with RDI and Jeremy's family, I felt every bit of that hope for this special little boy.

Like many families who receive a significant diagnosis for their child, the energy quickly shifted to treatment. Michelle was eager to begin treatment immediately, due to her gut-wrenching frustration that those 3 years had been lost while they were seeking a diagnosis. She began work with a clinical psychologist in order to develop a Floortime approach. Other suggestions by the developmental pediatrician included hippotherapy and occupational therapy. In the end, Jeremy participated in occupational therapy and a sensory camp of outdoor adventures for children on the spectrum. He excelled in the outdoor setting that allowed for gross motor activities and the excitement of such things as hiking and rock climbing. The picture of him scaling his first rock has a place of pride on the family refrigerator. He also attended a social skills group briefly.

Following the diagnosis, the school worked with Michelle and Andrew to develop an IEP and mutually agreed on placement in a developmentally delayed kindergarten housed in his neighborhood school, for the remaining 6 weeks of school. In this new setting, Jeremy began to thrive. Teachers and staff understood his needs and helped create an environment that encouraged his success.

As they prepared for the coming school year, the school district offered a placement for Jeremy in a team taught kindergarten class. It was to be staffed by both a regular education and a special education teacher, as well as, a paraprofessional from each department. It was an optimal setting that allowed him to work with staff that understood his needs, but also have ongoing participation with typical peers that exceeded lunch and recess. Michelle and Andrew were pleased with the beginning of Jeremy's treatment path.

When they describe their start through the maze of treatment choices I was struck by the calmness they shared. I found their approach atypical compared to many families. I had struggled for years with the incredible amounts of energy and time that so many families with autistic children invest in every type of treatment. My response was not a judgment, just a painful awareness that no family can sustain that pressure and level of demand forever without increasing the likelihood of dire consequences to siblings or marriages, or both. It seemed to me that a combined 40 to 60 hours of school, treatment and therapies was not developmentally appropriate for any child, regardless of the disability.

I remember my peers and the parents sitting around me at the 2-Day RDI® Introductory Workshop were most impressed that the children in Dr. Gutstein's research had changed diagnostic categories on the ADOS. But, I was riveted by the difference in the number of weekly hours the families using RDI were investing, compared to the non-RDI group. While working with Jeremy and his family, I have seen the incredible impact of that difference. RDI considers the child's needs in context of the entire family unit and a lifestyle approach can happen anywhere at anytime. Simplifying daily life is crucial and Michelle and Andrew have adopted this comprehensive approach. They made a rapid change in his environment.

The circumstances that brought me together with Jeremy's family are an "it's a small world" story. The clinical psychologist that the family had been working with had attended the RDI® 2-Day Workshop with me. She shared the RDI® brochure with Michelle and Andrew. Michelle was very excited and went home to research the approach more. She spoke with the staff at the Connections Center and signed up, but she was discouraged by the length of the waiting list. She checked back with the psychologist to see if she had decided to pursue certification in RDI. Her answer disappointed Michelle but the psychologist referred her to me knowing that I was beginning the supervision phase of my certification and was seeking a family to work with as a case study. Michelle and Andrew were thrilled that someone locally would be able to speed up their start in RDI.

After some initial phone calls, I met with Michelle to review the theory and what would be involved in completing the case study. She shared it with Andrew and he was excited about the common sense of the RDI® approach. Our early discussions were somewhat interview-like and I chuckle now that Michelle and Andrew had the impression that they had to convince me to take them as my case study. In my mind I was hoping that they would agree to do it. They offered me a clean slate. I would not have to redefine my role with them like I would with the other families I was currently working with as their speech language pathologist. I would not have to struggle with a family that was resistant to pouring their energy into one approach. We agreed to proceed with the case study. Michelle has since shared that her reaction to the news of starting RDI was one of true belief that it was going to help them re-enter the world of the son that they had lost the moment that the diagnosis had been given. They were thrilled.

As they made the decision to pursue RDI, they had to address fears and uncertainties. Michelle was more than 7 months pregnant and they would soon have four children under the age of 5.5 years. The pregnancy and recovery from the delivery was a challenge in itself, not to mention meeting the daily needs of four young children. How would they insert focused time with Jeremy for RDI in an already exhausting schedule? I am not sure that any of us knew what making it work in their home would be like. But in the end they were willing to try. As with all things, and four children, the expense was also a concern. They decided it would be worth the sacrifice if the gains were real.

The use of lifestyle activities in RDI seemed to align itself with typical development and their family structure, "We are a team and we help each other." It was easily accessible for them and did not require elaborate materials. Laundry, groceries and garbage and all their components were at their fingertips. Michelle found RDI attractive because of the amount of play it involved and because it was fun! She loved playing with their kids and this would allow for a special bond for them to share with Jeremy.

After deciding to take the leap of faith, we started into treatment. Jeremy's parents experienced challenges that I think are common to all parents beginning this journey. One of the challenges was the vocabulary. Understanding the definition of so many new terms was not hard, but changing their thinking and their actions to embrace the new terms required a lot of effort. Creating safe and yet dynamic systems characterized by sharing and Declarative communication is much more difficult than reciting each definition or even the connection to the theory. It meant that somehow they would need to ensure that Jeremy always felt successful while they were inviting him to interact with them in new and unpredictable exchanges.

Another challenge they faced was seeing the big picture amidst the intricate details. To their credit, they were willing to trust me and accept uncertainty when they could not piece it all together. They were able to be patient for the details of the picture hoping that it would begin to sharpen with time.

Michelle's background aided her ability to analyze her own work with Jeremy, but it was an obstacle in her parenting style and in her initial work on RDI. She was used to a stimulus-response-reward method for teaching and that made RDI, particularly Declarative communication, seem even more foreign. To communicate in a Declarative manner would mean eliminating questions that required a specific response from Jeremy. What was more, she would have to provide comments that were meant to communicate her response and observations about the experience they were sharing. That might mean that Jeremy would not respond.

Like a clinical rotation in many professions, Andrew and Michelle also experienced the difficulty of transitioning from sessions where they worked along side of a teacher to working alone at home. Inherent in that were self-doubt and awareness that they had to forge ahead when they were unsure. They discovered that what felt like relative failure led to valuable video reviews and discussions, allowing them to grow in their own analysis of what Jeremy needed from them to be successful.

Andrew had to overcome aspects of his own personality and interpersonal style. His comfort with investing in only a few close relationships or even in solitary pursuits makes sharing a deliberate choice for Andrew. He recently shared that his emotional range is narrow compared to others and it is hard for him to increase his expressiveness to help Jeremy attend to and learn about sharing emotions.

All of these new challenges were embedded in what they initially found to be the most fear inducing aspect of RDI –incompetence by video. As they were stretching beyond their comfort zones in a steep learning curve, they also faced personal reviews of their efforts captured on video. Even worse, it would be viewed and analyzed by someone else, during a point in the process where they were experiencing the most change in their lives with Jeremy. Although Michelle did not demonstrate a lack of confidence, she described that the camera heightened that feeling initially. Today they would tell you that the camera is their most valuable learning tool and better yet, it is a permanent record of the successes they share along the way. Most importantly, in moments of doubt it provides reason for hope. Michelle views the camera as her helper and a third set of eyes.

Adopting an RDI® lifestyle required changing life at home for everyone. This was not an easy task for a family of six that includes 4 young children. Finding dedicated time for Jeremy was hard. Andrew's work caused him to travel frequently, often leaving Michelle to problem solve how to tackle RDI and manage the other children, too. This new adventure also left the twins feeling left out. Michelle and Andrew struggled through how to best meet this challenge. With creative use of extended family and baby-sitters they have carved out daily time to work with Jeremy, as well as, imbedding RDI throughout the day. The twins, Sarah and Michael also enjoy the RDI® activities with mom or dad on a regular basis; so that they do not feel overlooked in the process. Michelle and Andrew have found that opportunities to plan and practice new RDI® activities with Sarah and Michael are a valuable way to learn how to help Jeremy see the important moments of sharing experiences. Every game and chore shared together with Mom and Dad is time where their relationship grows closer.

Every obstacle this dynamic couple experienced during the beginning stages of RDI, was countered with a powerful benefit that I believe helped them remain focused and encouraged. Andrew and Michelle have shared that because RDI places parents as the primary interventionists, it could have been intimidating. But, because I was also on a learning curve, we were successful in establishing an environment in which it was safe to ask questions and make plenty of mistakes. Along with Jeremy's parents, I hope that I will always be successful in making that environment available for all those who are new to the process.

My intuition told me that Michelle and Andrew are parents who truly parent and are not just caretakers of their children. From the beginning, they wanted the role of mentor to a group of delightful apprentices. No one knows Jeremy like they do and no one has the vested interest in his future that they have. I have watched as they have grown more powerful in their understanding of how to create opportunities that will allow Jeremy success in entering the dynamic process of building relationships. In contrast to that powerful growth in understanding, their empathy for what he faces has been transformed into a life of giving compassion.

Andrew has described his appreciation for RDI as a business partner relationship between the parents and consultant. He once said, "It is so much more rewarding than checking your child at the door and returning none-the-wiser after the mandatory hour." It has fostered independence and growing competence for Jeremy's parents while managing all of Jeremy's needs no matter where they are and what they are facing. Yet, there is always the resource of a consultant available to help them plan, maintain forward progress and problem solve. For me, as their consultant, they have allowed: hands on learning of the theories, strategies I have learned in the coursework, reading and professional internet chats that consultant in trainings are required to complete through the Connections Center. The greatest benefit I have experienced in our business partner relationship is my growing confidence that RDI works. Whenever you venture into new territory, employing a cutting edge approach, there is a quiet nagging voice that questions, "Can it be true and will it work?" As this initial stage of my RDI® training process nears its end, that voice has been silenced.

One of the most motivating benefits of doing RDI, is that Michelle and Andrew have experienced the same growth that they see Jeremy experiencing. Michelle calls it, "Being more connected." As Jeremy smiles at them, responds with a relevant comment or bounces with excitement anticipating more fun while they play, Michelle and Andrew know that they have also grown in their ability to create opportunities where Jeremy can experience competence as a member of a positive relationship. In those moments their lives are not merely parallel events, but shared experiences. They have also begun to see his connectedness and willingness to enter into activities spilling over to his interactions with his siblings and extended family.

RDI has also changed their communication as a couple and as parents with all of their children. They are now a team that has the power to effect change, instead of two people reduced to being victims of a disability. From planning the schedule or new activities to develop with Jeremy, to reviewing video tapes; they have the opportunity to encourage one another, learn from one another's strengths, laugh at mistakes and celebrate the successes. I have to wonder how many married couples have even one common goal that unites them to share so richly as a team.

The easiest advantage of doing RDI is that Jeremy finds it fun! From balloons to bean bags to shaving cream, the times that are shared doing RDI® activities are filled with pleasure. As a mother myself, I have often thought that if I had approached chores and household responsibilities more as a shared activity, I might have met with less resistance and whining. As Jeremy puts away laundry, loads the washer with dirty clothes and feeds the dogs, these actions are valuable to all of them because they are sharing in them together.

There are also special focused activities that Jeremy is able to do with his Dad. So many fathers can relate to what Andrew has faced in the demands of his work and travel. It is hard to turn off the noise that lingers from the workday and prioritize time to play with your children, even when they do not have autism. As I review tapes, it is so evident that Jeremy loves his time with Dad during lab-time and sharing in family responsibilities.

Overcoming obstacles and understanding the rewards of their choice to do RDI did not occur in a linear path from A to Z for this family. They experienced many personal bumps in the road and intersections that could have prevented them from starting. One that was already mentioned, the pregnancy, was there at the first session as we completed the RDA™ (Relationship Development Assessment™). Michelle was agile and in great health but at 7 months pregnant rolling around on the floor is hard. She also felt the emotional challenge that another child was coming into the family and wondered how she would integrate everyone's needs into her day. The issue of the pregnancy quickly became the issue of a newborn and lack of sleep for Michelle and Andrew. William was up every 2 hours at night for the first 2 months. They were left to face each day in a severe state of sleep deprivation. To add to the lack of sleep, the other children no longer napped so there was no opportunity for recovery sleep during that time. I confess that this would have been a show-stopper for me. Instead, when the battle against fatigue permitted, they focused on the short-term nature of this obstacle and remained committed.

As we began the process, Andrew was starting a new job. Travel had been a major demand in his previous job. The new job would still be demanding, but it would require less overnight travel. Andrew was eager to settle into his new responsibilities and earn the trust of those he worked with. That meant long days and a never ending commute associated with the traffic in the metropolitan area we live in. This challenge would have caused many families to give up or least postpone the start. Jeremy's family persevered.

The twins' jealousy over all the attention Jeremy was receiving was another hurdle to overcome. The pull of determining how to best meet everyone's needs requires a great deal of patience and creativity. Sarah and Michael were frustrated that they were left out of play with mom and dad and did not understand why Jeremy had been elevated to such a special position. They resented his gain and their subsequent loss. Any caring parent would be tempted to seek some other way to help one child if it was negatively impacting other children. The guilt could have caused Jeremy's parents to participate half-heartedly in their time with RDI or give up completely. They found a way to share themselves with everyone and kept working at RDI. In achieving this, they have shared that they will never underestimate the love that Sarah and Michael have displayed for Jeremy.

Like most families that have small children, the winter months were full of illness. The entire family battled through every cold and flu bug that circulated and sometimes by the time the first ones had recovered and the last ones were nearing the end, the bug would start over again. Despite this challenge the video tapes kept coming with completed journal reviews and Michelle begged for make-up sessions and attended our sessions whenever they were healthy. One day Jeremy will comprehend the extent of the determination that his mother unfalteringly demonstrated through these challenging times to help him reach his potential.

In our early months of RDI there were also more acute medical concerns for Jeremy, Michael and William. Prior to starting RDI they had decided to have surgery on Jeremy's Achilles tendons. He had been a toe-walker and they had been faithful with the use of AFO braces to try and improve the flexing of his ankle to a natural position for walking. The braces had not proved to be successful. While still completing the RDA, Jeremy had surgery to lengthen his tendons and spent the first 6 weeks of our assessment and treatment in casts to his knees, restricting the type of play that we could use in working on RDI. I would have been tempted to at least postpone the start of treatment, for no other reason than making my life easier, not to mention Jeremy's own emotional response to the changes that casts and subsequent return to the AFO braces meant to an active 6 year old boy. But Michelle and Andrew persevered.

Just as life was returning to normal from Jeremy's surgery and their very sick winter months it was time to have Michael's adenoids and tonsils removed and tubes placed in his ears. The removal of the adenoids and tonsils were painful and required a two week recovery. Michelle never missed a beat.

As these physical needs mounted Michelle was feeling overwhelmed and after some discussion Andrew and Michelle began to search for help with the other children. This decision impacted everyone in a positive way. The babysitter allowed them to execute planned RDI® activities daily and gave Sarah and Michael some much needed individual attention that centered on fun and play.

The medical issues continued. At the age of 4 months, Michelle and Andrew noticed that William's head was flat. The pediatrician referred them to a neurosurgeon at the area children's hospital located in the city. More medical appointments, more concerns. They were told that William had positional plagiocephaly, a condition that occurs from placing infants on their backs for sleep and rest as a means of protection against the risk of SIDS. This required that William be fitted for and wear a helmet to ensure that the bones in his head could develop normally. This process required a build up of time wearing the helmet, adding another important obligation. Yet another reason to give up or at least postpone, but their commitment has continued to grow.

Throughout the case study period, it has been evident that Jeremy's difficulty in attending was impacting his success. Treatment of attention can be an emotionally charged issue for every family. After an official diagnosis of ADHD as a co-morbid condition with the AS, medication for anxiety was attempted. The result was a significant negative change in Jeremy's personality and the doctor and parents agreed that it was not working. This first failed attempt made trying medication again frightening for both parents and difficult for them to agree what the best thing to do was. Even as I write this chapter, Jeremy has started an increasing dose of medication for attention, but it is too early to see if it will improve his ability to attend.

As the professional guiding Michelle and Andrew, I often felt that I was juggling many balls to overcome the obstacles we faced. Some of them I was quite familiar with from my professional training and yet others were foreign and felt clumsy in my hands. After all, my degrees were not in psychology. It seemed that one of my greatest roles was to facilitate the parents' understanding of what the real obstacles were. Neither of them was prone to whining or complaining, but it is true that sometimes when you are in the midst of a circumstance you can become distracted and lose the ability to be objective about the real issue. Sometimes that meant a great deal of listening on my part and even granting them permission to be frustrated by the obstacle. Sometimes it meant helping them to reframe the obstacle and gain power over it.

The hardest and most terrifying juggling act was finding that narrow space in order to facilitate the family's move to a new level; nudging and pushing them to grow and change, without raising their stress level or causing them to feel incompetent and give up. Although this balance was hard to find with both of them, the challenge was very evident in working with Andrew. The obstacle here lived with me, not him. I had spent years interacting with mothers who either attended school conferences or were responsible for transporting the child to and from therapy. I had often observed that fathers cared deeply and wanted to contribute to the long term goals for their children, but that they often deferred to the child's mother to handle the details and track the progress. To coach and teach a father directly was a novel experience. It took me longer to understand Andrew's learning style and to clearly see where that narrow space resided. As our rapport grew, I finally tackled it head on. I asked him what he needed and how best to help him. I also gave him permission to tell me when I was falling short.

If you ask Andrew and Michelle what changes they have seen in 10 months of RDI, they respond that there are many, both in Jeremy and in their family. Jeremy is more affectionate. He is by nature a sweet child, but prior to RDI would have to be asked for a hug. Now he crosses the room to give his parents a hug without prompting and steps off the bus looking for Michelle and ready to hug her. He often initiates with a high-five or a "booyaah" while sharing a comfortable embrace.

He initiates play with other children more often. Examples include when he started a game with a child at the pool this summer that lasted for an extended period of time, and when he recently introduced himself to an unknown child in the checkout lane at a store and asked the child what his name was. Jeremy's school staff has also commented that his facial gaze has become more natural and requires less prompting. Michelle's family, who sees Jeremy regularly, comments that he is more a part of their world and engages with them more often and in a meaningful manner.

There have also been changes in the family dynamic. The twins are more overtly protective of Jeremy and make adjustments for him. Another significant change for the household has been a focus on Declarative communication. Michelle and Andrew have worked diligently to completely alter their communication style with Jeremy. This has changed the communication that they use with everyone and the types of communication everyone responds with. Declarative communication has replaced negative imperatives that were used when they were rushed or frustrated with the children.

They have noticed that the children are more responsive when approached through Declarative communication. Andrew described the change in this way, "This has been a particular challenge for me, in that my entire existence has been based on an Imperative* approach. What is appealing is the fact that the responses generated by Declarative language are generally much warmer, much more descriptive and promote far stronger and sustained dialogue."

The positives that Michelle and Andrew are learning with Jeremy are working with the other children. As the changes have increased their awareness of connecting with Jeremy, they have become more sensitive to the emotional needs of the twins. Another by-product is an increase in their own closeness; they have to communicate more about what their focus is and where they will invest their time. Decisions are not overlooked and are more purposeful as they work together. Now they share a common goal and although both Andrew and Michelle bring different styles and strengths to RDI, they are sharing in a hope that they will be able to enhance Jeremy's future. They are also able to accept constructive criticism, which reduces stress over how to encourage change in any aspect of their lives.

Jeremy's relationship with both parents is evolving into an emotionally sustained connection, not merely assigned roles of protectors, managers or caregivers. I have found in the journey that his successes evoke various responses from tears, to goose bumps, to adrenaline rushes that help me push forward on this not yet traveled path.

Now 10 months into the process and having tackled both some usual and unusual obstacles along the way, Andrew and Michelle have advice to share with other parents.

1. *Anticipate that the change is hard.*

Michelle: I don't want to say that and scare people away, but it was tough. I would liken it to having a baby. When you add any new component to your life you have to rework how it is going to fit into your life. It is a change and change can be hard. It will be bumpy and you won't be perfect, but that is OK. You may have to step back and take stock and see what is going on in your life, like we had to. There are only 24 hours in a day and we needed to get rid of some things so that we could accomplish something bigger.

Andrew: Remember this is a marathon and not a sprint. Find as much joy in the small achievements as you do in the major milestones. The positive energy can only be good, both for your mental state and the quality of life for your child.

2. *Accept that it will feel foreign for a while but that feeling is temporary.*

Michelle: At first RDI is not natural. You will watch the tapes of yourself and think, "that was ridiculous," and you will feel awkward. It's like a new pair of jeans; they don't feel comfortable at first, but you keep wearing them and washing them and they begin to mold and fit.

Andrew: The concepts behind RDI (at least at my low level of comprehension) have a rational feel to them that give you comfort in knowing that your choice to pursue this course has been a wise one. Nonetheless, when completing the activities with your child they can feel extremely abstract. Remind yourself of the broader framework and this will help you get through. See the forest from the trees.

3. *Find your own relationship with your child.*

Michelle: No therapist will take your child into a room and come back to share a narrative on how they did that day. This is different because parents are given the tools and therefore we can find our own style and way with our child. You feel empowered as a parent, that everyday you are helping your child. You don't have to wait until the next therapy appointment.

Andrew: Once you receive your diagnosis, you will look upon your child with a greater appreciation of who they are. Don't dwell on how this could have happened to you. This is still the child that you love, they now have a new skill set of which you have no way of determining the ultimate impact; either wonderful or demanding upon your child's life. Instead of seeing this as a fight to ensure that your child is the same as everyone else in later life, remember that it is a way of allowing you to impact your child's condition in a positive way; by minimizing the demanding aspects and allowing you to savor the amazing moments.

4. *Make it family friendly.*

Michelle: We are taking our child back to the stages that they missed when they were younger. Typical development means that what I am doing with my child is what any parent should do. Instead of using a token board or Oreos, I am using the relationship as the motivation to encourage my child to share life with me.

Andrew: With other siblings, a marriage and jobs, the treatment for one sibling cannot exhaust all of your time. RDI is a realistic approach to treatment that allows you to focus, when necessary, on the child in need. Make RDI a lifestyle element rather than a perpetual abstract chore. It is both practical and effective in our ever more demanding lives.

5. *Make a commitment.*

Michelle: You have to embrace it and commit to it. You must have a vision for the long haul. As Dr. Gutstein says, "We are going to go slow so we can go fast. There are no magic pills."

Andrew: You need to believe in what you are trying to achieve. Focus on helping a child to enjoy the value of enhanced social interaction, without making them feel stigmatized by their differences. This is about playing the cards you are dealt, not about trying to change your hand.

Jeremy's Future

Michelle: My future hope for Jeremy is that he will reach his potential. It would be my greatest accomplishment to see that come true. I want it to include a handful of friends and something to do on Friday night. The phone does not have to ring off the hook, as it may for his siblings, but I hope he will have a few good friendships. He doesn't have to be the star quarterback or Mr. Popular of the whole school, but just have a couple of people that mean something to him and he enjoys. Down the road I would love to see Jeremy have a job, a career, something that he has chosen. Maybe that means college or maybe just a job or both, but something that he is happy doing and he feels competent while doing it. I, like any mother, want Jeremy to experience his life without anxiety and with confidence when engaging socially. As long as he is happy about being Jeremy and doesn't have anxiety that leads to depression, I will feel like I have done him a service.

Andrew: The aim is to help Jeremy enjoy life, however that enjoyment manifests itself. Jeremy clearly has an appreciation of our family and my hope is that he will have the opportunity to incorporate that appreciation into his own family in the future. We must help him reach his potential and not just our perception of what that potential should be.

My greatest hope for Jeremy and his family is that in the years to come we will all smile and laugh as we look back. That day by day every dream and hope they have for Jeremy will become a reality. Fourteen months into this, it is easier for me to envision that we will eventually arrive at a place where every child with autism can share in meaningful relationships; that every child will have the opportunity to experience the world with a blending of emotion, purposeful thought and a full range of typical responses to what they experience. Until we get there, I invite you to begin the journey.

✎ **Janice Guice is a RDI® Certified Consultant and a nationally certified Speech Language Pathologist with a background working in both public schools and private practice. She founded her private practice, Essential Communication, Inc. in 2003. Janice resides in Alpharetta, Georgia with her husband and business manager, Doug. They enjoy frequent visits with their college age sons, Matt and Andy. Janice completed her RDI® certification in October 2005 and is passionate about the incredible impact it is having in the lives of families that are adopting a RDI® lifestyle under her direction. You can contact Janice at jpguice@essential-communication.com.**

Glossary

RDI and RDI-Related Terms

Appraisal

Appraisal is the act of evaluating the adaptational significance of our environment on a moment-to-moment basis. It is the essential process needed for the functioning of what Peter Mundy refers to as the "Supervisory Attentional System." It entails actively searching for opportunities for growth and goal attainment. Appraisal functions by integrating the realities of environmental demands, constraints and resources, with personal interests. Appraisal serves to make problem-solving both intentional and meaningful. Meanings are determined by the emotional content of the appraisal process.

Appraisal is only possible when we learn that there are multiple ways we can organize meaning from any particular event or setting. Even for the toddler, Appraisal does not include evaluating only peripheral events. It also includes just-preceding events, past events and expected outcomes. It also includes affect that is being carried forward (mood), as well as the history of experiences with affect regulation in this kind of situation and in general. Appraisal also includes the expectations of the child concerning caregiver responsiveness built over the course of their interactive history. Children with ASD show a very limited capability for Appraisal.

Apprenticeship

Apprenticeship is the act of one person deliberately assuming a novice position alongside a more experienced, competent person. Through observation and active participation in a junior role, the apprentice gradually learns to view their environment through the "eyes" of the master and develops their own mastery. Apprenticeship should not be confused with compliance. While compliance may be a necessary pre-requisite, it is not sufficient to establish a master-apprentice relationship. The apprentice must understand the value of observing the unique perspective of the master and must voluntarily submit to participating in a "novice" role under the master's guidance.

Asperger's Syndrome

Asperger's Syndrome is a form of Autism Spectrum Disorder in which the child demonstrates early language and an IQ measured in the average range or above. Numerous studies have failed to distinguish individuals originally diagnosed as children with Asperger's Syndrome from those originally diagnosed with Autism, when they reach adult years. Therefore there is a current debate about whether Asperger's should be recognized as a separate diagnostic entity.

Auditory Processing Deficit

An auditory processing deficit is a general term that describes a range of disorders that might interfere with the brain's ability to meaningfully interpret auditory information.

Autism Spectrum Disorder

An increasingly popular term used to describe individuals who demonstrate a common pattern of deficits while also exhibiting many heterogeneous strengths and weaknesses. Individuals diagnosed with Autism, Asperger's Syndrome and Pervasive Developmental Disorder, as well as many individuals diagnosed with Non Verbal Learning Disorder are viewed as part of the Autism Spectrum.

Autobiographic Memory (see Episodic Memory)

Autobiographical Memory is a representation we form of an event in our lives, strongly anchored by an emotional appraisal of that episode, that we use to form a sense of ourselves and to anticipate our future. The key is that it is organized around an emotional experience. Autobiographic Memory is personal representational memory. We extract meaning not from detail, or procedure, but from the subjective meaning of an event.

It requires the coordination of the pre-frontal cortex, the brain's executive, with the limbic system, the center for meaning and understanding of novelty. Autobiographic memory is very different than just remembering details of a past episode. It is extracting something that is personally important, different, changed, or something that stands out because it has personal meaning to an individual.

Without Autobiographic Memory you don't develop a sense of self. You also don't develop the ability to anticipate and think in a hypothetical sense about what might happen in your future. You don't learn to dream, create goals, plans, and really tie the past in with the future. People with ASD show a severe deficit in Autobiographic memory.

Bandwidth (see Communication Bandwidth)

Bandwidth refers to the transmission capacity of a communication pathway. In RDI, bandwidth refers to the extent the person can integrate multiple channels of information to determine the meaning of information and communication. From a neurological perspective, broad bandwidth processing refers to our ability to integrate many different brain processing centers working collaboratively to determine complex levels of meaning. The "mind" as a brain structure develops as a response to increasing need to integrate the simultaneous integration of multiple channels of information into more efficient but complex "schemas", while filtering un-related, non-critical information in an efficient manner.

Certified Consultant /RDI® Certified Consultant

The RDI® Certified Consultant is a professional who undergoes extensive training and regular re-certification which qualifies them to act as a consultant to families seeking to implement the RDI® Program. Training includes seminars, reading, clinical supervision and case presentation. Typically consultants complete their initial training in 1 1/2 years and then must undergo a yearly re-certification process to maintain their status.

Classifying

The conceptual act of determining the membership of any element in a larger category, based upon one of more properties of the element. Any element can be cross-classified in several categories, classified on a hierarchical basis, classified on a "relative fit" basis and also classified on a temporary basis.

Coach

The term used for the adult who is guiding the ASD apprentice.

Compensating

Compensations are short-term modifications made to temporarily bridge the gap between the individuals' current state of functioning and the demands and requirements of the environments that they must function within. Compensations become detrimental when they substitute for remediation and become solutions in themselves. Compensations should be limited to only those that are absolutely necessary and should always be implemented along with a phasing-out plan.

Co-occurring Disorders

Co-occurring Disorders are physical, psychological and behavioral disorders that may accompany the presentation of an autism spectrum disorder.

While they may complicate the treatment and even the diagnosis of ASD, they are distinct entities and not part of the ASD condition itself. They are included in a balanced treatment plan and may require treatments developed specifically for the condition.

Examples of co-occurring disorders are the following: Speech impediments, seizures, severe emotional Dysregulation, ADHD, immune system problems, allergies, depression, obsessive-compulsive disorder, generalized anxiety disorder, GI problems, learning disabilities, Sensory-Integration problems, Visual-Motor problems, and Auditory processing difficulties.

Communication Bandwidth

Successful human communication requires processing information along a "wide bandwidth." We interpret the meaning of any communication by many factors presented simultaneously, including prosody, facial expression, gestures, posture, physical space, context and prior relationship with the communication partner.

Neurotypical children go through a gradual bandwidth expansion beginning at birth as they become highly competent in the "broader" bandwidth communication processes – facial expression, prosody and gesture – prior to developing speech. They learn quite early to combine these channels to determine the meaning of communication. Children with ASD develop a very narrow bandwidth communication process. Even those with significant language delays develop speech, a very "narrow" band of information instead of the "non-verbal" channels of communication. Unfortunately most autism interventions reinforce narrow bandwidth processing by focusing only on the non-prosodic "speech" channel.

Core Deficits

Characteristics which are universal to all those on the spectrum (regardless of whether one is considered "low" or "high" functioning), unique, (distinguishing them from any other condition) and chronic (aspects which are present at diagnosis and remain through life).

Co-regulation

Dynamic systems require participants to engage in ongoing sampling of how they are doing in the system. "Do you understand me? Am I too fast? Am I redundant?" Along with this ongoing monitoring of the optimal functioning of the system, members must make constant adaptations, based on their evaluations, to make sure they remain at an optimum level.

This process of Co-regulation is explored at length by psychologist Alan Fogel in his book, *Developing through Relationships*. Fogel explains co-regulating as a dynamic balancing act where individuals create a smooth social experience (the dance) by continuously making mutual adjustments to each other. Co-regulation is marked by its unpredictability (not scripted nor controlled by any one person) and inter-dependency (each person's moves are critically dependent on the other's, moment by moment). People with ASD do not show understanding of the need for Co-regulation.

Declarative Communication

Declarative communication is the action of representing what the mind produces. It is the product of the highest level of mental functioning we can both share. Declarative communication is always "broad band" in nature. This means that it involves several, integrated modalities of receiving and communicating information including prosody, gestures, facial expression, context and speech.

Dr. Luigi Camaioni cogently describes the critical nature of understanding the intentions of communication, rather than the specific communicative behavior. He distinguishes between Imperative forms of communication that are about "means-ends" relationships and Declarative communication intentions, whose goal is to share a common experience. The most notable structural difference between the imperative and the declarative is the moving of the person from the "means" location to the "goal" location inside the sequence. Declarative communication offers the opportunity to share experience. When a person is using declarative communication, the goal is to share emotional reactions, intended actions, changes and variations, memories, predictions, plans, ideas, perspectives, thoughts, and predictions with another person. The non-verbal communication that goes along with Declarative communication is information rich and carries much meaning.

The person who uses Declarative communication is inviting the other person's insights, and adding them to what they already know. Responses to Declarative communication are not rote, and cannot be scripted by the person who initiates. In contrast to typical children, those with ASD use very little Declarative communication.

Dynamic Systems

A basic premise of dynamic-systems theory is that behavior (and its development) is the outcome of the functioning of a complex system, which includes its psychological, biological, and physical components. Development is seen as an emergent property of the whole system and can only be understood in terms of the complex interactions among its components. It is not reducible to any single element, structure, or cause.

Dynamic systems are inherently variable. Most of this variation, however, tends to return the system to the current "attractor" configuration. Each pattern has movement and variability yet converges toward a repeatable and recognizable stability. Both stability and change are co-regulated by the same set of system components. Innovation leading to the emergence of new stable patterns is an inherent feature of any dynamic system assuming that variation occurs across the range of system activity. Some variations will return the system to a stable configuration, while other variations will shift the system to another and perhaps entirely new stable pattern.

Dynamic Systems provide ongoing cognitive challenge because they allow for continual input of new and potentially discrepant information. The typical 12 month-old actually prefers such encounters because he has become competent in managing the tension inherent in such challenges and has already learned that the "edge" of his competence is the most rewarding place to be.

Dynamic encounters offer a potentially large payoff, but also the potential for strong feelings of incompetence if the child is unable to successfully regulate the anxiety that accompanies repeated exposure to episodes of "not yet knowing." RDI is based on the theory that ASD children develop an aversion to Dynamic Systems and never develop competence to participate in them.

Elaborating

Elaborating is the act of gradually adding complexity to activities, so that they come to correspond more-and-more to "real world" conditions. Elaborating involves systematically modifying activity elements, role complexity, distractions, increased and different partners, requirements for co-regulation and repair, simultaneous goals, requirements to divide and flexibly shift attention, degree of uncertainty, breakdowns in regulation and various elements of "noise."

Encode

Encoding refers to the act of deliberately selecting aspects of an episode that we wish to preserve for later reflection.

Episodic Memory (see Autobiographic Memory)

Episodic Memory is a representation we form of an event in our lives, strongly anchored by an emotional appraisal of that episode, that we use to form a sense of ourselves and to anticipate our future. Episodic Memory is very different than just remembering details of a past episode. For example, Bob might well remember the procedural details of a past success when he remembers an event (semantic memory). And he knows the feeling of being at the edge of a cliff (negative limbic memory). But he hasn't encoded the emotions and meaning of past successes for himself, so he can use them to plan his future (episodic memory). It is an active analytic process in which the child learns to focus on and select critical moments from their current experience to preserve for later utilization.

Episodic Memory begins to be observed between 18 and 24 months of age in typical children. It allows for using recollection of past experience to anticipate, plan and project into the future. As Endel Tulving states, "It allows people to update information critical to dealing with meaningful changes in their world." Personal Episodic Memory is the critical foundation for the development of a personal identity and self concept. Numerous studies have demonstrated that ASD individuals have a severe deficit in Personal Episodic Memory.

Evaluating

Determining the quality of a response based upon its relationship to a subjectively determined goal or objective. The term is used both in the context of evaluating the meaning and value of external events as well as evaluating personal actions taken in relation to some goal or reference point.

Executive Functioning

The ability to reflect on past experiences and anticipate potential future scenarios to make decisions in the present that lead to attainment of desired goals. In its most complete form, we consider this synonymous with Episodic Memory.

Flexible Thinking

Flexible thinking involves altering problem solutions and ways of perceiving a problem, based on ongoing monitoring of current effectiveness. Tools used in flexible thinking include improvising when necessary tools are not available, quick strategy shifting as needed, "good-enough" task solutions and rejecting formerly adequate ways of thinking for "better fitting" strategies and concepts. People with ASD are severely deficient in flexible thinking.

Framing (also Framework)

When adults "frame" an activity for a child, they purposefully modify it to optimize the activity's potential as a vehicle to provide the child with challenging Mindfulness. Framing involves analyzing how any activity can serve as a vehicle for mental engagement for a particular child. Framing involves initially setting limits and boundaries for an activity, so that we can then add novelty and variation.

Framing is helpful to the child to see an underlying constancy amidst the ongoing change. It is the concept of "same but different" that is at the heart of dynamic systems. When we engage in framing we are choosing to spotlight the underlying constancy that will survive while we do introduce ongoing variations. It involves simplifying the activity into a "prototype" by removing or modifying elements that might serve to unnecessarily absorb needed attention and mental resources from the primary task of mental engagement.

Friendship

Friendship is an inherently dyadic rather than group-level construct. Friends perceive and respond to one another as unique and irreplaceable. Children begin to have the capacity for genuine friendship by the end of the third year of life. However, the friendship of a three-year-old is far different than that of two teenagers.

Friendship quality can be evaluated by seven different resources (Parker & Asher, 1993; Howes & Matheson, 1992; Gottman, 1983): 1) Finding common ground: extending and elaborating each other's activities 2) Communication for coordination of action, perspective and affect 3) Mutual help, guidance & caring 4) Conflict Resolution 5) Reliability and emotional security 6) Validation of worth, identity, beliefs and feelings and 7) Intimate exchange.

Guided Participation

This is a term used by psychologist Barbara Rogoff to describe the way that parents interact with their children to facilitate the development of real-world thinking and problem solving. Guided participation focuses on the side-by-side arrangements in which children participate in the values, skills and practices of their communities without intentional instruction.

When we study societies and cultures all over the world, it's very clear that the way in which children become competent in dynamic systems is not through direct instruction. In every culture, parents are the reference points for helping their children to interpret and gain meaning from otherwise confusing experiences.

Parents gradually require the child to take more and more responsibility, in effect, becoming junior partners and holding up 50 percent of the co-regulatory work. Parents learn to pace their efforts, based on their child's competence. They learn to modify the speed of their teaching style, their pacing, the degree of challenging demands they place and the number of obstacles in the child's path, so that the child can experience a sense of competency and mastery while still remaining challenged.

Hypothesizing

Engaging in "what if?" thinking. The process of mentally simulating the potential relationship of actions, events, individuals, objects and relationships.

Imperatives

Imperatives refer to the use of communication in an instrumental "means-to-an-end" fashion. When we communicate in an imperative manner we are not interested in sharing experiences with others. Rather we are driven by the motivation to obtain something we want or need.

Intersubjectivity

Intersubjectivity is a scientific term representing the developmental process of linking mental states between people. The roots of intersubjectivity can be observed as early as three months of age, when typical infants intentionally use a social smile to emotionally link with adults. Primary intersubjectivity refers to the way that infants, in their first year of life relate directly to others through emotion sharing and coordinated movement.

Secondary intersubjectivity, which begins to be observed towards the close of the first year, involves a "triangulating" relationship between two persons and an external stimulus. The experience of triangulation opens the door to understanding other's minds, relative thinking, and the development of a conscious self, as the young child experiences the distinction between their unique perceptual stance towards a stimulus and that of their partner.

Intersubjectivity gradually becomes a multi-modal, complex and integrated process, where children discover that they can create self-other linkages on many different levels, such as coordinating actions and perceptions, understanding others intentions and perspectives, integrating imaginative ideas, sharing opinions and beliefs and forming relationships that extend over long periods of time and have a shared past, present and future.

Joint Attention

Joint attention is the act of sharing our reactions to a common perceptual event with another person. Typical infants discover that they can follow an adult's gaze and link their perceptions to those of the adult at around 9 months of age. By 12 months of age, infants are experimenting with their capacity to guide the adult's attention to a common location and then share their joint reactions.

Through Joint Attention infants are able to observe the ways in which more competent individuals appraise their environments and selectively choose what is meaningful to attend to. The infant also learns to compare his or her own unique reactions to that event and thus develops the concept that there are multiple ways to perceive the same situation. Children with ASD develop a very limited capacity for initiating Joint Attention.

Labeling

Labeling can be thought of as putting an emotional and cognitive frame around an episode to make it even more meaningful and powerful. It is the way we organize the memory into an integrated indexing system. Then we can categorize our memories in many different ways (e.g. scary things, silly things, yucky things, sad things, things that are hard to do, things that used to be hard but now are easy, etc.). Here are some examples of short, distinctive labels: "we did it," "the world's record," "the laundry crunch", "the junky monkey," "faster mover," "The thing," "Boom," "Oh NO," "yuck," "monster crush." We can also use other ways to enhance the memory of episodes, like photos, chants, drawings, facial expressions, songs, etc.

Lab Time - See RDI® Lifestyle.

Master-Apprentice Relationship - See Apprenticeship.

Mind

Our minds are not a specific physical structure or location in the brain. Rather the mind is an incredible upgrade to the brain's operating system that begins to come into play in typically developing children by the age of 24 months. The upgrade is necessary due to the "broadband" processing that the brain is attempting in highly dynamic environments. The mind is needed to successfully adapt to complex dynamic environments requiring rapid flexible responses to constantly changing conditions.

Our minds serve as an integrative processing center, allowing many different neural pathways to collaborate as needed in a flexible, adaptive manner. The mind is constantly evaluating and shifting mental resources (attention) among many different long and short-term goals, as opportunities present themselves. Similarly, our minds' seek out new opportunities for responding to the environment in more efficient, flexible ways. The mind also serves as a safe laboratory and engineering facility, testing theories, evaluating new information, rehearsing responses and planning for potential problems, without actually taking any physical action.

Mindfulness

Dr. Peter Hobson provides the best description I have read of Mindfulness and its lack of development in people with ASD. "A typical child, who is not yet two, has achieved 'mental space.' She can move in that space and relate to her own attitudes and actions. She can hold symbols in mind and think with them. She can hold other selves in mind and relate to the desires, feelings and intentions of others. She can begin to adopt alternative perspectives, to choose among alternative course of action. She can represent events that have happened in the past or that might happen in the future...The child discovers that he is a mental being with the capacity to think."

Monitoring

Tracking events outside of your current central area of focus. Periodically shifting attention to briefly observe and evaluate the occurrence or non-occurrence of a selected personal, interpersonal, or environmental event.

Non-linear Thinking

By the close of their second year, typically developing children have learned that small variations can produce big changes. They have become adept at managing unusual or unexpected relationships between events, objects, persons and concepts and related these to new mental discoveries. For the first time they become aware and begin to utilize the non-linear "flow" of consciousness, which changes constantly and unexpectedly in surprising and often exciting ways.

Previewing

Previewing is the part of episodic memory which we use to anticipate our futures. Some researchers refer to this aspect as prospective memory. When we preview we are using our episodic memories to create a link between our past experience and potential futures. Storing and reviewing episodic memories is only useful if it aides in productive previews. Previewing is a critical part of executive functioning. Self-regulation also requires the ability to preview a desired state or to anticipate what might happen. As well, the more we practice episodic memory and previewing the more we build the ability to delay gratification in many different situations when we need to do so.

Productive Uncertainty

Productive Uncertainty is a state experienced by neurotypical children, when faced with cognitive challenge. Over the course of the first two years NT children learn to maintain Productive Uncertainty in the face of greater and greater challenge. An adult guide's increasing variation around initial regulatory patterns gradually increases the child's state of arousal and sets the stage for Productive Uncertainty by providing experiences of competence in mastering greater and greater deviations from the initial regulatory pattern.

Productive Uncertainty involves learning to modulate higher and higher levels of tension produced by discrepancies between what is already known and what is presented in a novel situation.

Prompt Dependent

Prompt dependence refers to the end state of creating a learning environment where the ASD person learns to wait for an external prompt or cue prior to responding. The person becomes dependent upon some external agent to determine their actions.

Prosody

Prosody is the non-speech aspect of vocal communication that significantly alters the meaning of speech and provides information about how to interpret any message. Prosodic elements include stressing a syllable or word, intonation, volume, pauses and selective alterations in rapidity of speech. Prosodic elements of communication emerge prior to 9 months of age in typical infants. They are lacking or severely impaired in ASD individuals.

Quality of Life

Quality of Life is defined as the opportunity for independent living, full, rewarding employment, mature friendship, reciprocal family relations and marriage. Research studies of adults with ASD, even those with high academic achievement, intelligence and language abilities have consistently found the prognosis for quality of life to be extremely poor. To date, no treatment method, including intensive early behavioral intervention, has demonstrated any ability to improve the quality of life of individuals with ASD.

Relationship Development Assessment™ (RDA™)

A comprehensive treatment planning evaluation conducted by RDI® Certified Consultants. The goal of the RDA™ is to customize a remedial plan that fits the needs of each child and family member.

Relationship Development Intervention® (RDI®) Program

RDI is the product of an ongoing program development and research program begun in 1996. The mission of the RDI® Program is to produce proven, clinically powerful methods to remediate the core deficits of Autism Spectrum Disorders. The goal of RDI is to provide individuals with ASD the cognitive, emotional, communicative and social tools needed to obtain a quality of life which their disorder typically deprives them of.

RDI® Certification Process - See Certified Consultant /RDI® Certified Consultant.

RDI® Lifestyle

In RDI version 2.0 we differentiated between "lifestyle" time spent with the child in normal everyday activities and "lab" time spent in a more minimal stimulation "lab" setting. In our current version of RDI (beginning with version 4.0), we no longer make this distinction.

RDR Cycle

The "Regulation-Dysregulation-New Regulation" cycle refers to a basic RDI® therapeutic principle of successfully introducing cognitive challenges that require the child to form new organizational schemes and problem-solving methods in a safe manner. R-D-R begins with establishing an initial co-regulated state where parent and child establish a simple regulatory "dance" within a suitable activity. Once this is established, parents carefully increase variability and deviation from the original pattern, making sure that the child can still perceive the original patterns amidst the ongoing variations and remain an active participant.

When the child has mastered sufficient variation, the parental guide introduces a cognitive challenge; a variation which no longer supports the original pattern and requires mental reorganization. Through the adult's scaffolding, the child responds to this break in pattern with Productive Uncertainty and mentally engages with the challenge until a new regulatory pattern is formed.

Reflecting

The act of reviewing personal experience with the intent of extracting meaning that can be used for future actions.

Referencing (see Social Referencing)

This is the action of using another person as a "reference point" for your subsequent actions. Referencing occurs only following the subjective experience of uncertainty. The individual references by responding to the state of uncertainty by attempting to ascertain some element of the subjective state of another person or persons.

Regulation

Regulatory systems contain continual fluctuations within a specific range from a central point. Simple regulatory patterns teach the child to perceive predictability through pattern repetition amidst small, but constant variations of the pattern's presentation, rather than static, rigidly repeating sequence. Most ASD individuals learn to replace regulatory patterns with exactly repeating sequences, which are valuable only in static systems.

Relative Thinking

Relative Thinking can be defined as the ability to obtain meaning and solve problems based upon the unique relational configuration of information in a system coupled with the subjective goals of the individual engaged in solving a problem. People with ASD are severely handicapped in relative information processing. Relative Thinking can be outlined in the following manner:

- The degree to which any piece of information in a system is meaningful based upon the primary function of the system (i.e. what someone is wearing at a fashion show vs. at a doctor's office).
- Appraisal of the degree of completeness or adequacy that determines whether a task was completed in a "good enough" or "best fit" fashion.
- The degree to which problems can be solved only by viewing actions in relation to other simultaneous actions (e.g. are we walking side-by- side?).
- Alternately the solution can only be reached by understanding how specific attributes of one system element or member relate to another system element or member. For example, what is the right distance to stand apart from one another when we are throwing a ball?
- The degree to which an action is meaningful based upon an event that has preceded it or an event that will occur at some future time.

Remediation

Remediation is a gradual, systematic process of correcting a deficit, to the point where it no longer constitutes an obstacle to reaching ones potential. Remediation is a developmental process. It involves addressing early areas that, due to the neurological disorder, were never mastered. It involves searching for the period in development where the child "hit a wall" and was not able to progress further and building competence from that point.

Repair

The concept of repair involves the child learning at a young age that communication and interaction in dynamic systems will inevitably break down despite our best efforts at regulation. Infants learn to monitor breakdowns and make repair attempts as early as 18 months of age. ASD individuals do not appear to understand that communication must be monitored for potential breakdowns. Therefore they do not develop repair skills.

Representing

We engage in representing when we act towards a symbolic "representation" as if it were the actual object, person or event. Pretend play is a form of representation. Writing, photographs, maps and charts are examples of other representational events.

Rote Skills

When we learn to enact a skill in a mindless, automatic manner, we are said to have learned a "rote" skill.

Scaffolding

Scaffolding is a term originally used by the Russian psychologist Lev Vygotsky who is now recognized as one of the fathers of modern Developmental Psychology. According to Vygotsky adults serve as "scaffolds" to the young child, so he or she can experience success in striving to experience a "preview" of competence that is slightly above his or her current level.

Scaffolding leads to increased mastery motivation, self efficacy and perseverance and resilience. The more competent partner balances the weaknesses of the less able child with setting challenging goals, in order to assist the child to achieve beyond his/her current level of mastery. The child participates in "real-world" activities with the adult guide providing just enough support for the child to achieve competence in their role. Support is gradually withdrawn as the child gains mastery.

Self-efficacy

This is a generalized self-perception that is a hallmark of competent, successful individuals. The individual, through their prior experience believes that they have the capacity to persevere through difficulty and function in a resilient manner, eventually achieving their goals.

Self-regulation

According to Piaget (1967), self-regulation is the capacity to modify behavior based upon previous experience and the anticipation of the effects of the subsequently acquired behavior. It implies inhibition of the ineffective behavior, selection of the new correct behavior and the initiation and maintenance of the planned and organized production of effective behavior.

Many developmental psychologists such as Alan Sroufe believe that cognitive growth evolves from the child's learning to maintain organized and focused behavior (self regulation) in the face of increasing levels of tension resulting from incongruity and ambiguity. Self-regulation evolves from the child's success in early parent-child co-regulation episodes, where parents are able to gradually increase tension, while also gradually relying on the child to take on more and more of the responsibility for maintaining their emotional equilibrium.

If people don't develop self-regulation within the first couple of years of life, they must be regulated by others. As humans get bigger, this gets harder and harder to do. People who don't self-regulate are dependent upon externally regulating communications (the results of the monitoring actions of others in the social environment) and thus will receive a much higher frequency of controlling communications than people who do effectively self monitor.

We also know that controlling communications are much less effective at producing self regulating behavior than self monitoring communications. What this means is that we spend a lot more time worrying, watching, prompting, directing, coercing and yelling at people who don't self regulate. Unfortunately none of these actions makes them any better at doing it resulting in a great amount of frustration and wasted energy.

Children with ASD show significant impairment in self-regulation. Some critical areas of self regulation include attention regulation, behavioral planning, goal selection, self motivation, anxiety management, prioritization, self instruction and self monitoring.

Self-regulating Communication

A critical feature of Declarative communication is that it is a pre-cursor to developing productive self-regulating communication. Beginning shortly after the age of 2, declarative forms of language divide into two tracks; one track continues to develop more sophisticated ways to share aspects of ourselves with others. The second declarative track emerges as a tool for engaging with ourselves. During their third year, neurotypical children learn to narrate their own actions, to plan, to reflect on what they're doing.

All of these are essential developing a sense of self and also the ability to manage our behavior and emotional state. Without this self dialogue, we are left with choosing between other people controlling us, or becoming constant victims of our unmanageable impulses. ASD children do not appear to use self-regulating communication.

Social Referencing

Social Referencing demonstrates a new capacity emerging around 12 months of age in typical infants which affords the infant the ability to conceive of people and objects as linked together and thus to utilize another person's reaction to an object, event or setting as an emotional "reference point" for determining his subsequent behavior.

Social Referencing allows infants to analyze the way in which objects and actions impact others' emotions, and in turn observe how these emotions give rise to subsequent action. This information is then used to guide infants' own dealings with the world. The time savings with regard to learning are nearly inestimable. Without Social Referencing, social information will simply fly past as scattered and relatively uninterpreted change in the sensory array, and infants would only acquire information through laborious, direct, personal experience with each and every new object or person. ASD children appear to never discover Social Referencing.

By 18 months, a typical infant will look at his or her parent or older sibling when uncertain, and know how to proceed based on whether he or she is looking worried or confident, smiling or frowning. As children develop, they discover that they can reference less observable aspects of other's functioning.

Other people's intentions become a critical reference point starting at 14 months of age. Gradually referencing comes to include the entire range of internal intentions, emotions, ideas and future dreams. While we begin by learning to reference other's emotional reactions, we also gradually learn to reference our own emotional reactions. Then we learn to integrate the two.

Social Referencing is the foundation of taking responsibility for the ways our behavior impacts other's feelings. It becomes an integral part of learning to have compassion and empathy for others. It also becomes critical for self-regulation as we must have some basis for monitoring our internal states and evaluating our actions towards a goal if we are to effectively modify our actions to be more successful.

Social Skills

Social Skills refer to scripted and rote actions we learn to take that are appropriate in highly specific environments and events. Social skills are not adaptable and are most useful in situations (such as checking out at the grocery) where a learned phrase or scripted interaction sequence is likely to be successful. Individuals with ASD are capable of learning social skills but not the more difficult co-regulatory abilities that are the basis of all social competence.

Spotlighting

Spotlighting is the act of communicating to effectively encode an episodic memory. Spotlighting is achieved by any type of contrast or noticeable change in an established rhythm. The adult guide creates clear boundaries around a critical moment in an activity, causing that moment to stand out from its temporal neighbors. Spotlighting is critical for the development of episodic memories. Spotlighting is all about contrast. Spotlighting involves making sure that some piece of information stands out from the rest. Gradually children learn to take on the spotlighting process for themselves by actively analyzing events to select their most meaningfully moments.

Supervision Family

Each RDI® consultant-in-training is required to be supervised by a senior consultant for a minimum of 6 months with one family. The family that is chosen for this supervision period is referred to as a "supervision family."

Synthesizing

We engage in synthesis when we try to "extract" the critical essence of a meaningful array of information. Synthesis is a subjective process of determining how to summarize our experience in a manner that is most meaningful to us.

Tension

The particular use of the word tension is based on Dr. Alan Sroufe's concept of the ability to manage tension effectively forming the basis for future mental growth. Tension is present when some object or event acts in a manner that is not consistent with our expectations. See Productive Uncertainty to understand the critical importance of tension in RDI.

Underconnectivity

This is the term used by Dr. Nancy Minshew and her colleagues at Carnegie Mellon Institute, to describe the unique neurological deficits suffered by individuals on the autism spectrum. Autism entails under-functioning integrative neural circuitry. This results in preservation and possibly enhancement of the function of individual cortical centers, but at the same time entails poorer integration of information at higher levels of processing that require more coordination among cortical centers.

Underconnectivity explains the difficulty people with ASD have with novel cognitive tasks wherever inter-regional coordination is critical. A novel task requires the underpinning brain regions to dynamically configure themselves into an appropriate network, and the poorer connectivity in autism impairs this dynamic ability.

Zone of Connection

The Zone of Connection refers to the degree of physical connection needed for the child to maintain a constant state of co-regulated engagement. Prior to discovering Social Referencing, ASD children lose their perception of emotional connection when they are not in direct physical contact with their partner. As the child progresses, we seek to increase the Zone of Connection so that the child can maintain their perception of being in a relationship over further distances and time periods.

Zone of Proximal Development

This is the idea, introduced by Russian psychologist Lev Vygotsky that children learn through their interactions with more experienced adults and peers, who assist them in engaging in thinking beyond the "zone" in which they would be able to perform without assistance. During social interaction with children, adults temporarily enhance the child's performance beyond the level at which the child is capable of functioning alone. Adults supply supportive "frames" by which the infant can organize existing, but incomplete, behavior patterns into functional systems